YOU

HOW TO
COMPLAIN

YOU & YOURS

HOW·TO COMPLAIN

Practical advice on how to get a fair deal

DAVID BERRY

BBC BOOKS

Acknowledgements

*Chris Longley, Bridget Jeffery, Suzanne Webber,
Guy Dehn, Glenn del Medico, Rose Anne Varley, Ken Vass
and all the* You and Yours *team*

Published by BBC Books,
a division of BBC Enterprises Limited,
Woodlands, 80 Wood Lane, London W12 0TT

First published 1990
© David Berry 1990

ISBN 0 563 21440 6

Photoset in 10½ on 12½ pt Perpetua by
Ace Filmsetting Ltd, Frome, Somerset
Printed in Great Britain by
Richard Clay Ltd, Bungay, Suffolk

CONTENTS

INTRODUCTION

by the You and Yours *presenters*
John Howard and John Waite

JOHN HOWARD I bought a record player recently, had it a couple of months then it started going wrong, and do you know I was not all that sure whether I was entitled to my money back.

JOHN WAITE You didn't know about the Sale of Goods Act? And you're a trained lawyer, aren't you? I don't know, the kind of people they get presenting radio programmes these days . . .

HOWARD Of course I knew about it. But I couldn't remember the qualifications that applied when you had used an item before it went wrong. We did an item on this in the programme a few years ago but you can't remember every single part of every single *You and Yours*. I bet you can't remember, John, every single bit of information you've presented on *Face the Facts*.

WAITE That's true. But if we can't remember these things, John, what hope do the listeners have? I mean, *You and Yours* has been going, what, 15 years now?

HOWARD Twenty years, actually. And with roughly five items a programme, five programmes a week, that's a lot of information we have broadcast over the years. It could make several books.

WAITE So, why a book on complaining?

HOWARD Well, complaining covers all the areas *You and Yours* has focused on over the years, and it is also the thing most listeners, at least the ones who write to me, seem not to know that much about.

WAITE But most ways of complaining are pretty obvious, aren't they? I mean, you just go back to the shop and ask for your money back . . .

HOWARD That's true in most situations where you buy something from a shop. But what about when you buy something on mail order or when you buy a holiday? What about problems with your bank or insurance company?

WAITE Yes, you're right, of course. And complaints about your doctor, solicitor, surveyor, your children's school, the environment . . . they're more tricky.

HOWARD They certainly are, especially with all the legislation that has recently gone through Parliament. We have tried to cover all those things as well. And more. The A–Z of complaining. This book could save you pounds and pounds . . .

WAITE And hours and hours of listening as well. John, you sound like an advertising agent.

HOWARD Well, I'm excited about this book – and all the *You and Yours* team are as well. I hope our listeners and the readers of this book will be too.

WAITE I'll certainly go along with that.

NOTE TO READERS

There are many organisations listed in the various chapters of this book: their addresses are at the end, listed alphabetically.

For the sake of convenience, the male pronouns 'he' and 'him' have been used throughout when individuals are being referred to. We are sorry about this and certainly mean no offence to our female readers. It is just too convoluted to keep writing 'he or she'.

We have also referred to all Acts of Parliament with the year written before the Act, for example, the 1979 Sale of Goods Act. In law, the date comes after the Act but we feel it is easier to read our way around.

Finally **Scottish** and **Northern Ireland** readers may like to note that there are some differences between how to bring complaints in their countries compared with England and Wales. Where significant, these are noted in the book but it has been impossible to list all details. If you are in any doubt, call the **Scottish Consumer Council** or the **General Consumer Council for Northern Ireland** for precise information.

CHAPTER ONE

WHY COMPLAIN?

Have you ever wanted to refuse to pay for an unappetising meal in a restaurant? Or needed to put an end to blaring pop music from your new neighbours? Have you ever got mad about a new toaster that always produces burnt bread? Or felt aggrieved about waiting two hours at your local doctor's surgery with no explanation or excuse offered? In this book, we will tell you how to complain about these and hundreds of other everyday annoyances. And tell you, too, how you can get satisfaction or your money back. Read on.

But don't just take *our* word for it. Every year, thousands of *You and Yours* listeners contact us when they have got a bad deal – and tell us how they went about making a complaint.

Take Malcolm Bell's experience of a rogue washing machine, for example. The machine broke down 10 times in two years, despite several attempts by the manufacturer to repair it under Malcolm's guarantee. The manufacturer then suggested it was Malcolm's fault for using the machine too much! Malcolm considered such an excuse ridiculous: 'I thought washing machines were meant to be in constant use'. He persevered with his complaint – and eventually won a replacement.

Or, take Susan Barnard's experience with a competition organised for children by Clarks shoes. The prizes for boys included a bike and a toy spaceship; the prizes for girls were a visit to Alton Towers and a necklace. Susan thought this was unfair: 'Why should girls not be allowed to win a bike'? She was one of many par-

ents who complained, and Clarks eventually gave in, allowing boys and girls to enter both competitions.

Susan and Malcolm are just two of the many successful complainers we have heard about in the 20 years *You and Yours* has been on the air. This book will tell you some of their stories – and pass on some of their tips and advice about complaining, too.

But why bother to complain in the first place? Isn't it better most times just to put it all down to experience, and not to go back, for example, to the restaurant or shop that gave you such a bad deal? Or, move to a quieter neighbourhood, or change to another doctor who offers a better service?

Surprisingly, it isn't. When *You and Yours* commissioned a poll about complaining in Britain today, six out of 10 people said they were satisfied when they had taken the trouble to make a complaint. When we asked them what they got out of complaining, they told us it was that good feeling of getting their own back, that sense of satisfaction that comes from not allowing someone else to exploit them or rip them off.

Experts go along with all this as well. Ask anybody who works in the 'people business', psychologist, agony aunt, personnel manager, and they will tell you that people who complain, who make a fuss and fight when they feel they have been wronged, are less likely to suffer from feelings of inadequacy or depression. People who complain are even more likely to live longer than those who just accept that things have gone wrong, according to psychologists.

We can, of course, take all this too far sometimes. We all know people who seem to complain all the time, the Dot Cottons or the Linda Snells of this world, people who seem to spend their whole lives figuring out who they can make a complaint to next, people who whinge all the time.

The travel industry – one of the most common targets for complaints, according to our poll – even has a term for these people. 'Professional complainers' the people in the industry call them – although the tour operators seem to use this term a little too often to take them entirely seriously! But yes, such people do exist – and for some, a particular complaint becomes so much a matter of principle they ruin their lives in pursuing it.

But most people have a sense of balance. One thing we have learnt at *You and Yours* is to know when to draw the line, when following up a complaint will be more trouble than it's worth, and the end result – even if it is a success – will not have been worth the effort.

When 42-year-old Sheila travelled by coach from London to her home in Bristol one hot summer evening, she was looking forward to a pleasant journey through the Berkshire and Wiltshire countrysides, interrupted only by the noise of motorway traffic. Her journey, though, was spoilt by noise of another kind – two teenage girls sitting nearby who preferred the latest pop sounds to the steady hum of the coach's engine. When Sheila complained to them about their cassette player and asked them to turn it down, the girls not only refused, they taunted Sheila throughout the journey. And, worse was to come. At Bristol, Sheila got off the coach only to be followed by the girls, who then beat her up and ran away leaving poor Sheila with a cracked jaw and broken teeth. An example, perhaps, of when making a complaint might not have been the best option.

But fortunately such examples are very rare. The great majority of times it *is* worth complaining, and it is surprising how often the most aggressive-looking person can become reasonable and compliant when you make a well-justified complaint to them in the right way.

And when you complain, it doesn't just do you good. In the past 30 years, there has been a tremendous development in the scope of protection that stops the consumer getting a bad deal.

Laws like the 1979 Sale of Goods Act and the 1987 Consumer Protection Act give us all the necessary backing to press home a complaint about shoddy or unsafe goods. Industries from the motor trade through to shoe manufacturers now have codes of practice which we can all use to help our complaints along. In most town centres, we can get advice and support from organisations like the **Citizens Advice Bureau** (CAB) or the council's trading standards or consumer protection departments. These organisations, codes of practice and consumer laws often owe their existence – and certainly keep going –

because people have been determined to press home complaints.

It is a small consolation to **Sheila** – but an important one all the same – that her complaint led to calls by coach operators for new regulations to ban the use of personal radios on coaches.

You and Yours listeners **Debby Tombs** and **Corraine Foster** had even more success with their complaints.

Debby bought a new washing machine from Comet and she paid for a five-year guarantee to cover anything that might go wrong. When the machine broke down, the Comet engineer who turned up to repair the machine insisted Debby paid for the work, then claim a refund. Debby contacted *You and Yours*. **When we put her complaint to Comet, they not only agreed it was unfair to ask Debby to put money up-front, they also decided to introduce a new customers' charter ensuring no one in Debby's position in the future would have to pay the repairman first.**

When Corraine Foster started using some new pills she had bought to help her tan, she found that her fingernails began to disintegrate. Her complaint encouraged the government to withdraw these types of tanning pills from general sale.

Just like Debby and Corraine, the complaint you may be considering making at this moment may lead, in the end, not only to you getting satisfaction, but to better protection for your family, neighbours and friends. At the very least, it will force the thoughtless or incompetent manufacturer or supplier to think twice in the future.

Some of us are, of course, better at making complaints than others. We all know people who seem to have just the right instincts when it comes to working out what they are entitled to, and the right, persuasive manner to get what they want. What we have discovered at *You and Yours* is that making a complaint is more a matter of learning a skill than having an in-bred assertive character. A skill, moreover, which can be quite easily learnt and gets better the more you use it. We hope this book will put you on the road to becoming a good complainer, because in the end, the more good complainers we have, the better our society will be.

CHAPTER TWO

WHO COMPLAINS?

The French have four different words for it, each one reflecting a more serious or more important complaint. The Americans claim to have invented complaining. That so-called home of consumerism has always argued it is not just an American's right to complain, but a duty as well.

Here in the British Isles, however, complaining is almost an afterthought, something to be done reluctantly if a product or a service you have purchased is not quite right . . . and then done quietly, if at all. Better not to cause a fuss, make a scene, or, heaven help us, embarrass people.

There is no doubt that we as a nation have not been brought up to complain. The forebearance that was once a distinguishing quality of British character, that saw us through the wars, still lives on.

Or, does it? At *You and Yours*, we received a letter from **Bridget Olisa** of Nottingham. **Bridget described complaints she had made over the last couple of years about unsatisfactory sewing materials, an ionizer and chocolate, amongst other things, which were all resolved to her satisfaction. She had also written to her local council to complain about housing, and questioned local trading standards officers about what they were doing to make sure local auctioneers and estate agents were operating honestly.**

And Bridget is not alone. Recent surveys to discover how likely the British are to complain indicate we are slowly becoming a nation more willing to stand up for our rights.

The **Office of Fair Trading**, the government body responsible for ensuring consumers get a good deal, tried to find out a few years ago how often people complain. They discovered four out of 10 people were dissatisfied with a product or a service they had purchased over the last year, the worst being motor vehicles, household goods and building repairs.

But the survey also found out the vast majority of dissatisfied customers, 75 per cent of them, did something about it. When the BBC's Broadcasting Research Department conducted a similar poll for *You and Yours*, almost half of the people questioned said they felt more confident about complaining than they did five years ago. Such evidence confirms we are slowly changing from the *laissez faire* attitude that used to characterise the British, perhaps as a result of being more in touch with our more assertive foreign neighbours across the channel!

Consumer experts like Janet Graham, vice chairman of the National Consumer Council, reckon it is just a matter of time. She is already noticing that the younger generation is more likely to press a complaint than its elders, and she thinks by the year 2000, the United Kingdom will no longer be a nation of reluctant complainers.

The *You and Yours* poll showed this, too. The group least likely to complain were people in their 60s and 70s. Young people were the most likely. Liverpudlians were just as likely to complain, on average, as Londoners, but the worst complainers were those who live in Northern Ireland, who, perhaps as a result, expressed the highest dissatisfaction with goods and services.

But wherever they lived, the people who were most likely to complain were the middle classes, because they generally knew their rights and also knew how to go about making sure they got them.

The *You and Yours* poll did still indicate, however, that seven out of 10 people had not made a complaint over the last five years, middle class or not. Some of these people may just have been fortunate that everything they bought was fine. The majority couldn't be bothered to do anything about it. So, what stops people complaining? We asked people in shopping centres around Britain why they didn't complain when something went wrong. This is what they told us:

REASON 1: 'It's not worth the trouble'.

True, a lot of the time it clearly isn't. If you bought a food mixer for £15 on a trip to town, and it starts going wrong after a few weeks of use, it may well not be worth the effort to take it back and convince the salesman it's not your fault the mixer doesn't work any longer. But what about phoning the shop, registering your complaint and putting the mixer away until you go back to the shop on another errand? Complaining can take much less time than you think – and if you don't complain, you are often left with feelings of dissatisfaction and being taken advantage of.

LESSON 1: Complaining does not have to be hard work.

REASON 2: 'I don't want to make a fuss. I'd be too embarrassed'.

Maybe. Complaining is about making a fuss, and it can lead to other customers noticing, and talking about, you, especially if it is a busy shopping day.

But hold on a bit. Whose fault is it? Why should *you* feel you are making the fuss? Why should *you* be embarrassed? In practice, the manufacturer, retailer or professional to whom you are complaining is far more likely to feel embarrassed that their standards have fallen.

*LESSON 2: Complaining is about making **them** feel bad, not you.*

REASON 3: 'It was really my fault. I didn't use the product properly'. 'I threw away the receipt'. 'I wasn't paying attention when the shop explained how it should be used'.

We all know these situations. Not reading the small print. Hoping something will manage to do what we would like it to do when it clearly will not. Not reading the instructions properly. Throwing away any evidence that we did buy it from that shop. And yet, are all these situations entirely our own fault? What we often do is swallow 'fob-offs' some traders are quick to try on. After all, meeting a complaint is going to cost them time or money. The fact is, we know in our own minds when something has not worked when it should have. It is often a sense of injustice that compels us to try and get our money back, irrespective of small print or lost receipts.

LESSON 3: *Complaining more often than not is about using common sense. Just ask 'is it reasonable for me to be making a complaint' and common sense will tell you the answer.*

CHAPTER THREE

THE BEST WAYS TO COMPLAIN

Making a point about a new traffic scheme you think will destroy your neighbourhood; standing up for your child if you think his exam results did not in any way reflect his abilities; protesting to a builder that the superb extension you were promised turned out to be a botched job: each of these is a different kind of complaint and each implies different rights and obligations from all the people involved. And the list of situations where we might want to complain goes on . . . and on.

Yet, there are some general principles we can use for almost all occasions when we want to make a complaint. They are not exactly rules, and there is no guarantee they will always bring success. Complaining about some of the new forms of alternative medicine that seem to be springing up all around us is a damn sight trickier than making a complaint about your local GP. And, getting your money back for a lousy package holiday to the Costa del Sol can require a different kind of tenacity to writing to your council about the cutbacks in the bus service that takes you to work.

Our experience at *You and Yours* of observing why some complainers are successful and why others fall at the first hurdle, however, has taught us some approaches to complaining work much better than others.

Complaining is not a science but a skill and an art. Like

most skills, the more you practice, the better you become. Like most arts, the trick is to recognise your abilities and when it's best to use them. What complaining involves is a little psychology, a worked-out strategy, an awareness of tactics and an appreciation of the resistances you are likely to meet. If all this makes it seem like a battle, sometimes it is . . .

PSYCHING YOURSELF UP

So, you've had a raw deal and you're fuming, angry, annoyed, vowing never to make the same mistake again and determined that someone is going to pay for it.

Fine. If you keep feeling like that, however, you stand very little chance of succeeding with your complaint. The trick is to convert these feelings into ones of determination and controlled indignation.

First, ask yourself what you want to achieve. Things that immediately come to mind may be revenge, getting someone sacked, making them feel small, showing you can't be taken advantage of . . . all very understandable but unlikely, in the long run, to do you much good.

If you burst into a shop determined to teach a lesson to the sales assistant who sold you a sofa that has just fallen apart, chances are you're more likely to fall apart than the sales assistant. And shop managers, like any other people in charge, do not respond kindly to accusations. They will start covering their tracks, and make accusations about you. You will end up having a nasty argument, and possibly forget why you were making the complaint in the first place.

So sit down calmly and work out, perhaps with your family or friends, what you want and what you might be prepared to settle for. You will then have a target to aim for, and your chances of getting what you want will improve.

Ask yourself, is it worth the effort of complaining? For some, perhaps the majority of complaints, there will be little effort involved, other than going back to the trader and stating your case. In other situations, however, making a complaint about a dentist who has mucked up your teeth, for example, or complaining about a solicitor who has mucked up your house conveyancing, you may become involved in a long, complicated and potentially costly fight.

Think carefully before you start. Be prepared to be persistent but recognise when you may have to give up. Complaints are important – but not *that* important.

Try, too, to remain patient and reasonable when you are making a complaint. There will be times when a little unreasonableness can help cut through red-tape, but even then, try and use unreasonableness as a tactic, and not as your overwhelming style of complaining. When you go into what can often be a hostile situation, it pays to keep your head, remain polite and not to lose your temper.

Time and time again we hear about it at *You and Yours*. The kinds of complainers who get what they want, keep their cool, are assertive without being aggressive, and above all, don't lose thier sense of humour. Most people you will be complaining to are much like yourself – they're just doing their job. If you can convince them that if they were in your shoes, they would be complaining too, then half the battle has been won.

At least most times. Inevitably, there will sometimes be rudeness or evasion ('it's more than my jobsworth') from those who are dealing with your complaint. The catch is not to be taken in by this and just to keep plodding on, making sure they know you are going to keep plodding on until you get what you want.

Try and adopt a tone more of disappointment than of anger, and don't be distracted into turning the complaint into a personality clash between you and the person responding to your complaint. Not easy, but at least it will stop you becoming more stressed by the complaining than by the original cause for complaint!

If you can keep calm and determined, you are well on the way to being a good complainer. In the end, if you have been treated well, and your complaint listened to and met, thank people for their courtesy: it will encourage them to deal properly and well with future complaints.

Strategy and tactics

Ah, but if only getting in the right frame of mind was enough. Unfortunately, a little more than this is needed. Even the most reasonable approach will get you little if you can't support your case, and get to whoever makes the decisions. You also have to work out what you have going for you – and how best to use it.

Write down all the facts about your complaint, why it arose and when. Include all evidence you have to back up the facts. Do you have a receipt proving you bought the faulty good from that specific shop? Or, a photo of a badly-performed service: a roof repair, for instance, that looks worse after it was repaired than before? For some kind of complaints, such as those involving your local council, it might be helpful to find out if other people have been affected the same way.

Then, stop using anything you are going to complain about. You will look very silly if you complain about an alarm clock which fails to go off in the morning but you are still using it to tell you the time when you do wake up. And, it will be all the more difficult to show that the alarm clock was faulty when you bought it and didn't stop working due to bad handling on your part.

Complain as soon as you can. For some complaints, like those about something you have bought, your legal rights can be affected seriously if you don't complain promptly. If you can't go back to your supplier as soon as you have noticed the fault, drop them a note about the complaint and send it recorded delivery, just in case.

Next, **decide which is the best way to make your complaint.** Sometimes things can be resolved simply by going back to your supplier and verbally complaining to someone in authority, such as a manager or supervisor. Other complaints will need to be put in writing: complaining to your local cinema manager about the fact that the cinema prefers to show Clint Eastwood films rather than family musicals is not really worthwhile, as he or she will usually just be following head office instructions. Instead, get the cinema chain's address from the manager and write to the head office.

Whichever way you choose, complaining in person, making a phone call or writing a letter, always **take a note or keep a**

copy. If you are writing, find out who is the best person to write to, then write to them by name, and send the letter by recorded delivery: you will almost certainly get some kind of reply. Try, too, and type the letter, and keep all your correspondence together.

Keep a note as well of all the people or organisations that might be on your side. Work out if the law can help you or not (see the relevant chapters in this book), and which experts you may be able to bring in to back your case. Work out your rights, but try not to quote laws and regulations until it looks as if your complaint is not going to be met.

Finally, although you may be sorely tempted to extend your complaint to a general critique of the person or organisation you are complaining about, stick to the original complaint and try not to exaggerate or lie about your grievances.

It might be a lot of fun to start moaning to your bank manager about his bank's callous attitude to customers when he has just unfairly bounced one of your cheques, but it will just distract you and him away from your complaint. You may even end up forgetting what you wanted him to do in the first place. In some other situations, particularly when you make a written complaint about a professional person, you could find yourself in a lot of trouble if you make unprovable allegations against a named individual: they could sue you for libel. Take care.

Follow all the suggestions above – keep reasonable and persistent, know who to approach and how, be aware of your rights, and aware, too, of who can help you – and, in most cases, your complaint will be dealt with satisfactorily. In most cases. But there will be times when this does not happen.

All traders and suppliers at some time (and some particularly dodgy traders and suppliers all the time) will try and fob you off, confuse you or sometimes deliberately mislead you into not pursuing your complaint. Here are some common evasion tactics we've heard about at *You and Yours* – and how you can get around them:

1 **'They never reply to my letters – even when I send them recorded delivery'.**
This is the old lawyers' technique of not responding to an accu-

14 Acacia Avenue

Anytown

AT4 PDQ

The Manager

Helpful Trading Co   Tel: 0090 11111

Lemmings Lane

Smalltown   *try and write to someone by name*

July 1st 1990

*be specific: this just puts
him on the defensive*

Dear Sir

Well, I don't know but your goods are really
lousy and as for your service... *say exactly what went wrong*

I recently bought.....and it just didn't do

*try not to
attack staff:
he will feel
obliged to
defend them*

what I wanted it to do. It was terribly made,
a waste of money if you ask me and when I went
back to the shop, well you really shouldn't
employ such people. The lady there said she
couldn't deal with it and I gave her a piece of

*decide what
you do want
and don't
change horses
in mid-complaint*

my mind. What I want to know is when you are
going to get some decent staff... the whole
country is going to pieces.

And look, let me get to the point. I want
a full apology and an explanation about why
your shops are like they are, and if you don't
give me what I want, then I'm never going to
use your shops again. I might even contact my
solicitor about all this. There must be a law
to protect people like myself, or a least there
should be.

Thank you for your attention and sorry to
bring all this up.

*don't apologise: it is
his problem not yours*

Yours sincerely

John Citizen

John Citizen

An example of how *not* to complain

14 Acacia Avenue
Anytown
AT4 PDQ
Tel: 0090 11111

Mr I. Incharge
Customer Relations Office
Helpful Trading Co
Lemmings Lane
Smalltown

July 1st 1990

Dear Mr Incharge

I recently bought a (<u>detail of purchase</u>).
When I tried to use this item after
returning home, I discovered (<u>what happened</u>).
I went back to your shop and was told all
complaints are dealt with by your department.
I enclose (<u>evidence backing your complaint</u>).
I would like you to (<u>what you want them to
do</u>).

I look forward to your reply within (<u>give
them a deadline</u>) and hope this matter can be
dealt with speedily.

Yours sincerely

Jane Citizen

Jane Citizen

An example of how to complain

sation, in the hope that eventually the person will get bored and go away. It's surprising how many companies and organisations still use this today. When this happens, the trick is to set them deadlines – and stick to them.

If a letter of complaint has not been acknowledged within four weeks, write to the chairman, managing director or company secretary saying if you have not heard from him in another 14 days, you will take the matter further. Throughout your complaint, give people a reasonable time to look into the complaint but get them to conform to your deadlines and not you to theirs.

2   'They told me "the cheque's in the post".'

Sometimes it seems as if there are far more cheques caught up in our postal services than ever actually arrive. But give them the benefit of the doubt – for a few days. Ask them when it was posted, and then if it has not arrived in a week's time, ring up and ask for another cheque to be issued and sent recorded delivery. Don't let them get away with any excuse about the cheque being lost by the postal services: it is their problem sorting this out and not yours. Simply ask them to cancel the 'lost' cheque and issue you another, immediately. The Post Office, by the way, says that letters very rarely go missing if they are addressed properly, so it is pretty unlikely your cheque will have got lost.

3   'They kept telling me it was all due to staff shortages'.

The old excuse. It seems as if staff shortages have been with us ever since 'staff' were employed in the first place. The thing to remember is that staff shortages or staff incompetence are their problems not yours. And they have to pay for them, not you.

4   'They told me "we've never had any complaints before".'

Well, they're getting one now, aren't they? And since they haven't got any other complaints to deal with, they should be able to deal with yours pretty quickly. But this is yet another psychological try-on: they are trying to make you feel that you are in the wrong and not them. It is irrelevant to your complaint how many other complaints they have had: you are not asking them to sort out other people's grievances, merely your own.

5 **'They offered me half of what I thought I was entitled to'.**

Another trick, but one more difficult to deal with. Inevitably, any person or organisation you are complaining to will try and negotiate, do a deal, buy you off. Irrespective of the rights of your case, sometimes it will be better for you to negotiate if the alternative is a long struggle to get all the money or redress that you feel you deserve.

For example, if you have got into a dispute about a botched building job and the builder offers you half the £2000 you paid him back, then it might be better to accept this than persevere with a court case when the result is uncertain. So, learn when to strike a deal. But two tips may help. The first offer might just be a try-on and it should pay to negotiate for a higher amount. If you do negotiate, make sure you write to them with the words 'without prejudice' on top of your letter. This legal phrase allows you to change your mind later if you decide to pursue the money you think you are entitled to through the courts.

6 **'They just said they were sorry but it was not their fault, and I would have to take it up with someone else'.**

Like the shop that says you have to contact the manufacturer about the faulty item you've bought. Or the council that claims not sweeping your streets is a result of government cut-backs in their grant. When you complain, you will find many examples of people trying to pass the buck, pushing you on to someone else. But shops, councils, suppliers and professionals all have to operate under rules and regulations, many of them laid down by law; the buck often stops with them. And when you come across this kind of excuse, that's the time to find out about those laws and talk to the people on your side as a consumer who can help you with your complaint.

CHAPTER FOUR

ON YOUR SIDE

If it was simply you pressing your complaint against large companies, elusive traders or unresponsive bureaucracies, then, frankly, you wouldn't stand much chance. They have resources, staff and power, and all you could do is resolve not to deal with them again. If it was all up to you.

One of the great benefits of people complaining over the years, however, is that there is now a wide range of law to protect consumers, a number of organisations to give advice and occasionally represent you when you have a complaint battle and a number of procedures for certain kinds of complaints. These are less formal than the law, but sometimes just as effective and much easier to use.

THE LAW

It may come as a surprise, but many of the cases dealt with in court every day are not prosecutions of alleged criminals, but attempted resolutions of disputes between private companies or individuals. In fact, the law in the United Kingdom divides quite neatly into **criminal law** and **civil law**.

Civil law covers disputes about the rights and duties between two parties in which usually no criminal law has been broken. An example is when someone breaks a contract with you. You can then take civil action for compensation. Civil cases are heard mainly in Small Claims, County or High Courts.

Criminal law is when somebody has behaved in a way society deems unacceptable and faces prosecution by the police or by other law enforcement officers in the criminal courts: the Magistrates or Crown Courts.

As consumers, we are protected by some civil and some criminal laws. If an organisation or individual has broken a criminal law, law enforcement officers will usually prosecute. If they have just broken a civil law, however, it is up to you to get redress.

If you buy a new toy, for example, and it falls apart when your child plays with it, your ultimate weapon to get your money back will be for you to make a claim in the civil courts against the toy shop. If that toy turns out to be too dangerous for your child to play with, however, your local council's trading standards department will step in and may prosecute under criminal law. In the first example, the shop has broken the 1979 Sale of Goods Act, a civil law; in the second, it is guilty of breaking the 1987 Consumer Protection Act, a criminal law.

There are some differences between the law in Scotland and the law in England and Wales. Civil cases in Scotland, for example, are heard mainly in the Sheriff's Court, which also now have a small claims procedure. Northern Ireland law is almost identical to that of England and Wales.

The most important laws which give us consumers' rights and impose obligations on the people and organisations which supply us with goods and services will be explained throughout this book. These laws are the basis on which we can make complaints, and taking legal action is our ultimate sanction to force our complaints home.

And, using the civil courts to get redress and compensation doesn't have to be expensive or daunting. In Chapter 17, there is a step-by-step guide to using the law, including how to get the best deal out of solicitors and how to bring a claim in the cheap Small Claims Courts without using specialist legal advice. Thousands of people do this successfully each year, and many more find the occasional use of a solicitor to draft a letter of complaint, for example, resolves matters quickly and relatively cheaply.

But taking legal action in court should always be a last resort of complaining, a final weapon up your sleeve. It's far better to try and resolve your complaint with the help of some of the people listed below before contemplating the courts.

1   Trading standards officers

Trading standards officers are the modern equivalent of the old weights and measures' officials who made sure merchants' 'half pound of butter' was exactly that. One of the officers' duties is still short weight, which involves checking measures of glasses in pubs and wine bars. They have other jobs as well, and every county, regional and metropolitan council now to have a trading standards department. (Some councils call them consumer services or consumer protection departments. In Northern Ireland, they are part of the department of economic development.)

You can contact your local trading standards officers for any of the following complaints:

- if food you have bought is not up to the quality promised;
- if goods or services you have purchased have been misleadingly described;
- if the price of something you have bought was misleading or not displayed;
- if you have certain problems with credit, for example, if the wrong interest rate was advertised;
- if you've been sent goods you didn't order;
- if goods you bought are unsafe;
- if you were served short weight or measure.

In any of these situations, trading standards officers can prosecute traders for breaking criminal consumer law. The court can also order the trader to pay you compensation if you have suffered financial loss. (Let trading standards officers know if you want to claim for this.)

Trading standards officers can also give you advice about your rights when you think you have been cheated but no criminal law has been broken. They can also tell you how to pursue a complaint yourself. It is best to ring them first – the number will be under your local council in the phone book.

2   Environmental health officers

These people normally work at district council level but in some areas they work closely with trading standards officers. They would like to hear from you:

♦   if food you have bought contained 'foreign bodies', for example, fly spawn in a bag of rice;
♦   if the food was mouldy or contaminated or generally unfit for consumption;
♦   if restaurants or shops are dirty or contained vermin;
♦   any concerns you have about noise or other forms of pollution;
♦   if houses, flats or hotels are unfit for occupation.

Or, indeed, any other worries about public health. Like trading standards officers, environmental health officers can prosecute the offending party. You can also ask them to claim compensation if you have suffered distress or inconvenience; criminal courts now have the power to award compensation.

Alternatively, you could use the prosecution as evidence to claim compensation in the civil courts. In Northern Ireland, by the way, environmental health officers also deal with food quality, food labelling and consumer safety, all of which are the responsibility of trading standards in Great Britain.

3   Citizens Advice Bureaux (CABs)

Unlike trading standards or environmental health departments, CABs are independent of local councils – sometimes fiercely so, although they may receive funding from councils. It is also much easier to pop in and see an advisor since there is a CAB in over 1000 towns and cities across the United Kingdom. The CABs provide free and independent advice on any problem people face in their daily lives and the majority of their trained advisors are volunteers.

If you have a dispute with a trader, the CAB can intervene. The advisor can put you in touch with solicitors who offer free or inexpensive legal advice. CAB advisors also know about the many organisations and groups which offer specialist advice for particular problems. Unlike trading standards or environmental health officers, however, the CAB doesn't have any law enforcement powers, and in some of the smaller bureaux, the expertise of their volunteers in consumer law may be limited. In recent years, CABs have tended to concentrate on areas where environmental health or trading standards officers cannot intervene like worries about debt, social security, employment and immigration.

4 National consumer organisations

Four organisations to safeguard the consumer now exist in the United Kingdom. With their experience and expertise they make this country the envy of our European neighbours.

The Office of Fair Trading does not deal with individual complaints but rather keeps an eye on general trading practices, working closely with trading standards officers around the country. It often investigates industries or particular firms which may be trading or operating against consumers' interests. It can take direct action against unsatisfactory credit businesses and estate agents, and against any trader who persistently breaks the law. It also encourages trade associations to publish **codes of practice** for their members. Although a government body, this organisation has a degree of independence from the government and can exert pressure for changes in consumer law. It also publishes a wide range of leaflets and booklets on consumer advice which can be obtained free from CABs or trading standards departments.

The National Consumer Council and its sister organisations, the **Scottish Consumer Council**, the **Welsh Consumer Council** and the **General Consumer Council for Northern Ireland**, specifically represent the interests of less well-off consumers. Like the Office of Fair Trading, they, too, are funded by government and cannot deal with individual complaints. Their brief, however, is wider, taking into account all areas consumers may have a legitimate concern about. Recent Council reports, for example, include a survey of the legal system and a report on social security changes.

The Consumers' Association, by contrast, is entirely funded by its members, currently 1 million, which makes it amongst the largest consumer organisations in the world. Independent of government and any political party, it lobbies and campaigns for better protection and better deals for consumers.

Membership at around £50 a year is not cheap but it brings with it the monthly magazine *Which?*, famous for its best-buys surveys. For an additional fee of £20, members can subscribe to *Which? Personal Service*, which advises and helps with individual complaints.

The National Federation of Consumer Groups co-ordinates the activities of local consumer groups, and can put you in touch with a group or individual member near you. There are about 30 local groups nationwide, run by volunteers, which conduct surveys and organise campaigns. They can probably advise you on more straightforward consumer complaints, although one consequence may be joining in with other activities!

5 Other kinds of help

While not allowed to intervene in civil disputes, the **police** may be interested if you have evidence of fraud or intimidation against you, for example, if a debt collection agency is harassing you or your family. In some parts of the UK, there are **law centres** which offer free or cheap legal help.

Your local **councillor** or **MP** may take up complaints you may have against institutions like housing departments or the DSS: check in your local library for their surgery times. If they do help you with your complaint – and that is one of their duties as elected representatives – they can really get things moving.

If you feel your basic human rights or freedoms have been interfered with, and you have exhausted all possible UK legal remedies, you can appeal direct to the **European Commission of Human Rights**. Write to them for an application form. Do take legal advice about this first, though, because the Commission's procedure is long drawn out and expensive, although there is financial help available.

Nearer home, both the **Local Government Ombudsmen** and the **Parliamentary Ombudsman** can take up complaints about maladministration in local and central governments (see p. 158 and p. 167 for more details).

With some complaints about banks, insurance companies and the National Health Service, for example, there are **spe-**

cific ombudsmen to whom you can appeal. They are mentioned in the appropriate chapters in this book.

Also, it may well be worth contacting the appropriate **government department** if your complaint is a very serious one. Try and get your MP, or another important person like a bishop, to write to the government on your behalf: you're more likely to get a reply from someone 'high-up' if you do.

If you are concerned about any information held about you on computer, you have the right to inspect most of it under the **1984 Data Protection Act**. CABs can tell you more about this or you can write to the **Data Protection Registrar**. The registrar will also look into complaints about how an organisation has dealt with your application to look at any records or how it has handled computer information about you.

Finally, you can always write to the **Queen** at Buckingham Palace, London SW1. Her Majesty probably won't be all that interested in complaints about faulty fridges but she will be interested if you have suffered what seems to her an appalling injustice, especially if it was due to her government's action or inaction. Her aides will pass your letter on to the appropriate government department with a recommendation that they try and resolve your complaint.

6   Complaining procedures

From trading standards officers to Her Majesty herself, there are a wide range of people who will at least listen to your complaint if not try and help you resolve it. One effect of all these people being 'on your side' when you complain is that it has encouraged at least the larger shops, manufacturers and suppliers to set up their own procedures for dealing with complaints. Far better, their logic is, to try and sort things out directly with their customers than get involved with some troublesome advisor who may open up a whole can of worms.

Most large chain stores and big manufacturers have a **customer relations department** and some, like the banks, their own internal complaints bureau. These people will not put your interests before their firm's but they are more likely than the average shop manager to appreciate that resolving your complaint may be in the firm's interest, too.

Research shows that people who successfully resolve their complaint with a trader are much more likely to carry on shopping with the trader than people who do not bother to complain. In America, companies have worked out that the average customer who has a complaint will tell at least nine other people about it: that is nine potential customers probably lost. But customers who have had their complaints dealt with satisfactorily will tell five people about the treatment they received: that's potentially five new customers won.

So it is good business practice to take complaints seriously, and some more enlightened American firms now see customer complaints as the first indication that something may be wrong with their product or service. This positive approach to complainers is slowly spreading to Britain.

Don't be too suspicious, then, if your complaint is answered by a customer relations manager; often it is the quick and easy way to sort things out. If you are complaining about a household store or manufacturer, find out the name and address of the customer relations officer and write to him with your complaint. If need be, send a copy of it to the managing director just to let them know you cannot be easily fobbed off!

7   Trade associations and codes of practice

Many *You and Yours* listeners, however, find companies' own complaining procedures a waste of time, and for some smaller traders, they simply don't exist. Fortunately, there is another way of complaining about certain types of goods and services and one that is considerably more independent than traders' own complaining procedures.

One of the first activities of the Office of Fair Trading – and one it still pursues today – was to agree with trade associations codes of practice for their members to follow. These act as a bonus to your legal rights and aim to improve standards and offer customers a better deal. The codes also lay down proper methods of handling complaints, including low-cost, independent arbitration schemes.

For example, if you've had double-glazing fitted in your home and it turns out to be faulty or unsightly, you can take your case to the Glass and Glazing Federation Arbitration scheme, under the Federation's code of practice. An independent arbitrator may then agree with you and order the firm to repay some or all of your money.

The Office of Fair Trading has now agreed codes of practice with trade associations covering the following goods and services: cars, motorcycles, holidays, holiday caravans, household electrical appliance servicing, laundry services, glass and glazing, photographic equipment, catalogue mail-order, furniture, funerals, footwear, postal services and credit. These codes normally include access to arbitration schemes most of which are run by the **Chartered Institute of Arbitrators**, which for a set fee will adjudicate your complaint. The fee is on average £15 per person, slightly more for complaints about the motor industry or holidays, but all refundable if you win. Additionally, some industries and suppliers, such as electrical manufacturers, timeshare holidays and British Rail, have their own codes of practice and arbitration schemes independent of the Office of Fair Trading.

Details of these arbitration schemes are explained in the relevant chapters in this book; on p. 282, there's an easy guide on how to use them. But it is as well to be aware of a couple of drawbacks.

♦ You can only use an arbitration scheme to resolve your complaint with a trader or supplier who is a member of the relevant trade association. So for all major purchases, but particularly with services, check whether the firm you intend to use belongs to a trade association. Many do.

♦ Arbitration awards are normally legally binding on you and the trader. That means you can't then pursue the case in court if you lose. You have to choose at the outset whether to go to arbitration or go to court – you can't do both. If the trader does not pay you any award made to you by arbitration, however, you can then go to court to get the payment enforced.

By the way, there are still some contracts particularly in the building and removal industries, which have a **compulsory arbitration clause**. These are supposed to **require** you to settle any dispute through arbitration. Since the **1988 Consumer Arbitration Agreements Act**, however, you can't any longer be bound by this clause: you can go to court if you want instead.

8 User committees

Most of the major utilities like electricity companies, British Telecom and the Post Office have codes of practice and arbitration schemes. Additionally, they have their own watchdog committees which are the first port-of-call for consumers pursuing complaints. For more details see Chapter Eight.

9 Other methods of complaining

Using the law or an arbitration scheme, or enlisting the help of trading standards officers or a national consumer body, usually resolves most complaints. But some complaints are more difficult to resolve on an individual level. These may require a major change in government or council policy or a major shift of strategy for a company. And to do that, you will need allies.

Villagers in Wymondham, Norfolk, were horrified to discover that a proposed by-pass for the A11 road would go straight through a stretch of woodland and meadow called the Lizard, one of the few places left in the area for wildflowers and wildlife. The villagers could, of course, have waited for the official inquiry to make their views known – but there was no guarantee of success there. So, with the help of the local Friends of the Earth group, they decided on a different strategy: they bought up land adjacent to the Lizard, and sold it off in very small plots to 1000 different individuals. Because the government would have to purchase this land to build the road – and have to find and serve notices on all 1000 owners – the villagers reckoned this tactic would make the Department of Transport's task so time-consuming and complicated, it would abandon the route and leave the Lizard intact. As this book was going to press, the villagers were still waiting for the government's decision.

A very different problem bothered the residents of

the Acorn council estate in north-west London. They could hear virtually everything going on in each others' flats; toilets being flushed, all comings and goings. They didn't even need to turn on the radio if. there was one on in the flat next door. It wasn't because any of the residents were particularly noisy. Instead, it was simply because the sound insulation between the flats was totally inadequate. Through the tenants' association, the residents took the council to the County Court – and won. The council was ordered to improve insulation between the flats.

Both these kinds of action are examples of how a group can press home a complaint with much more force and vigour than an individual. Pressure groups vary tremendously from a local one-off committee to obtain a new pedestrian crossing, through to large, national organisations like Friends of the Earth and National Association of Mental Health (MIND), which successfully influence government policy. Many will give you help and support with your complaint. Your library probably has names and addresses.

As well as using more traditional methods of influencing decisions, some pressure groups have turned to a relatively new way of harnessing complaints, the **consumer boycott**. When *You and Yours* carried out a survey of company boycotts recently, half the people questioned had boycotted a product at some time or another, and two thirds had thought about it. The major reason was because they felt a company was damaging the environment. Indeed, consumer unease about buying aerosols that affect the ozone layer was one reason why aerosol manufacturers have recently introduced less damaging alternatives. So, if all else fails with your complaint, boycott the product, make sure the trader knows why and tell all your friends about your boycott!

Finally, one of the things that most worries traders, suppliers or government departments about complaints is **publicity**. If your complaint is justified, publicising it will encourage other complainers to come forward. That means the organisation has to deal with other people as well as you, not to mention the damage done against their public image.

Local papers or your local radio station are often useful places to contact, particularly if you have exhausted all other methods of complaining, if you have what you think is a very reasonable case and have found the person to whom you are complaining incompetent or entirely unreasonable.

And if your complaint seems likely to affect many other people as well, contact us at *You and Yours*. Since we started broadcasting in 1970, we have heard from thousands of listeners who had complaints about goods, services, professions and government departments which they were unable to resolve. We have been able to put many of these complaints, on behalf of our listeners, to the person who is responsible, usually with a radio microphone present to record their answer for broadcast. It is hardly surprising that dealing with the complaint suddenly then takes on a remarkable urgency – and more times than most, we have got at least some satisfaction for the listeners who asked us to intervene.

If you have a complaint you can't resolve, write to us at *You and Yours*, **BBC Broadcasting House, London W1A 1AA**. We can't promise to intervene because our time-on-air is limited, but we will certainly read your letter.

In the remaining chapters, we look at how to complain about particular areas or concerns, and we feature some of the people who have contacted us in the past with their complaints. **In future editions, you could be one of them.**

GOODS

Two years ago, Chris and Alison Rah bought a Hotpoint Microprofile washing machine. 'It did everything but tap dance', Alison told *You and Yours*. 'It worked brilliantly, but when I examined the clothes after the wash, some of them had holes in them'.

The Rahs complained to Hotpoint, which fixed the rogue machine. Or, so it seemed. Then the machine started savaging their clothes again. Hotpoint visited once more and replaced the machine, which Chris and Alison were pleased with until machine number two started producing holes in their clothes as well. They complained once more. Machine number three was the worst of the lot, shredding poor Alison's clothes and her nerves as well. At this point, Hotpoint refunded the Rah's money and offered them compensation for the damaged clothes. A successful complaint but one that took Alison and Chris a very long time and was only helped along by neighbours who let Alison use their machine during the times when she was waiting for Hotpoint to call.

Fortunately, there is an easier way to get your money back when you buy things from shops, markets or through the post. This allows you to complain to the shop where you bought them, not the manufacturer.

It's by using the **1979 Sale of Goods Act**, perhaps the most important of all our consumer laws. And most of the time, it works.

The Sale of Goods Act states quite simply that all goods sold by a trader must meet three reasonably simple conditions: they must be 'of merchantable quality', 'as described' and 'fit for purpose'. And if they do not, you can get your money back. Let's look at each of these in turn:

♦ **of merchantable quality**
This rather quaint phrase (soon to be re-named as 'satisfactory quality') simply means that all goods sold must meet the kind of standard you could normally expect them to meet given their price. An expensive washing machine should meet higher standards than one at the bottom of the range, but both machines

should wash clothes without mangling them or producing holes as the Rahs experienced. Yet, as their machine was one of the dearest available, they also could expect it to last much longer than a cheaper model. As it clearly did not, that machine was not of 'merchantable quality' and the same condition applies to any goods you buy from a car to a container of ice cream. The shop must give you your money back if the item isn't.

◆ **as described**
For £450, Malcolm Adams' new desk was hardly cheap but he thought worth the money. After all, it was real oak – or at least it was described as such in the catalogue Mr Adams had ordered it from. When the desk arrived in his office, however, only the desk's top and drawers were made of wood – the rest was plastic. Quite simply, the desk was not what its description claimed it was. This was rather embarrassing for Mr Adams, and rather unfortunate for the desk's manufacturer, since he was no ordinary customer but chief trading standards officer for Hereford and Worcester.

Because of his position, Mr Adams decided to prosecute the manufacturer who had not only broken the Sale of Goods Act but criminal consumer law as well – and the company was fined £500.

As ordinary customers, we don't have to go quite that far. Any goods sold must match any description provided which can be on the label, the box, a sign in the shop or even the shop assistant's own words. If they do not, you're entitled to a refund under the Sale of Goods Act.

◆ **fit for purpose**
This means that any goods you buy must fulfil the job they were meant to do. If you ask a shop assistant if a particular item can be used for a particular purpose and he says 'yes' or doesn't say 'no', you can get your money back if it turns out that the item wasn't up to it. If the shop assistant denies giving you that advice, ask to speak to the manager and give him your word.

When Cathy Halloran went shopping for a skirt for work, she wanted something both fashionable and

hard-wearing. At a London branch of the Jigsaw clothes chain, she chose a mini-skirt made out of stretch material. Cathy takes up the story:

'I wore it to work the next day with a long cardigan over it. As the morning progressed, the skirt disappeared up my legs and several people asked me if I forgot to put a skirt on that morning! I had to keep pulling it down all morning as goodness knows where it would have ended up'.

She complained to Jigsaw who offered her a credit note but Cathy didn't accept this and held out for a refund. She was right. The skirt was clearly not fit for the purpose Cathy wanted it for, to cover her legs. The Sale of Goods Act says that all goods sold, including clothes, must do what we should reasonably expect them to or meet the purpose we said we wanted them for.

WHAT YOU'RE ENTITLED TO

As long as you act swiftly to reject any item you buy from a trader which does not meet the conditions of the Sale of Goods Act, you are entitled to your money back. It's as straightforward as that. Or, almost so. There are a few exceptions such as buying something from a private seller or buying goods for your business which we cover later. And you are not entitled to your money back if you just change your mind, you damaged the item yourself or if defects were pointed out to you before you paid for it. But most times when you buy something and it turns out to be faulty or shoddy, you have a right to a refund.

And the shop may have to pay you compensation, as well. When Katerina Mickayledees bought a new dishwasher, faults in the machine caused it to overheat, resulting in considerable damage to her kitchen and home. She claimed not just the price of the dishwasher from the shop, but compensation for the damage as well – and eventually won £30 000.

An extreme case, perhaps, but the law does give you the

right to claim for any damage caused by the item, for the cost of hiring a replacement if you needed to use it straight away, for any postage or travel costs incurred in taking it back to the shop or, indeed, for any distress or inconvenience you have experienced by not being able to use the item when you wanted to. The only conditions are that these costs are reasonable and that you don't try to profit out of your complaint.

Despite the 1979 Sale of Goods Act now being over 10 years old (and previous laws dating back to the last century), some shops claim not to know about your rights! Some smaller shops also display notices saying 'no refunds': these notices are illegal and should be reported to trading standards officers. (If you look carefully, though, they usually include a small phrase such as 'this does not affect your statutory rights', that is, your rights under this Act.)

Here are some more 'try-ons' which turn up regularly in the *You and Yours* postbag, ones that could happen to you.

♦ **'They said I had to have the receipt'.**
Reasonable perhaps but not legally necessary. All you have to do is show that you did buy the item from the shop. While a receipt is usually the best way to do this, sometimes we throw them away or they just get lost. After all, we buy things in good faith not expecting them to go wrong. If you haven't got the receipt, simply tell the shop manager you did buy the item from the shop, giving the date of purchase and say you will provide them with a written assurance. That should be enough, both for the shop, and, if you need to take them to court, for the court, too. Obviously it helps if you can point out similar items to yours on sale as well, and if you can remember the time of day, how you paid and perhaps also the shop assistant who served you.

♦ **'They offered me a credit note'.**
Be very wary about this tactic. Here's what happened to retired British Airways Captain **Heinz Lipshuck** when he purchased a portable tape recorder from his local branch of Currys in South Wales:

'I wanted one that would record at double-speed. I explained that to an assistant, but I wasn't able to

examine the tape recorder properly because the shop was so noisy. I bought it, though, because I'd always been happy with other purchases from the shop. When I got home, there was an enormous background hum on the speakers and on the tapes as well. I took it back to the shop and saw the manager and he offered me a gift-voucher in place of the tape recorder. I accepted this but then decided I wanted my money back instead, so went back once more. The shop wouldn't give me any refund.' And the shop was perfectly within its legal rights.

The problem for Capt. Lipshuck, and anyone else who accepts a credit note from a shop for a faulty item, is that the credit note cancels all rights you have for a cash refund. Under the Sale of Goods Act, these rights are quite clear: you're entitled to your money back, or compensation, if you buy faulty goods. Your money back, not a credit note. But if you accept a credit note, you can't then change your mind and ask for a refund instead. Capt. Lipshuck had to buy something else from the shop. Sometimes this is convenient, but often it is not. So stick out for the money and refuse any offers of credit notes or vouchers.

♦ **'They offered to repair the item for me'.**
If the item you've bought has just minor damage, for example, a screw is missing or an additional warning light doesn't come on, it is probably better to let the shop repair it rather than push for your money back. But make sure you get a definite time for how long the repair will take, and if you need the item before this, ask them for a replacement while it is being repaired.

If a major repair is needed, think whether you would prefer your money back before you hand over the item. Write a note to the shop, keeping a copy, reserving your rights to reject the item if you are not satisfied after the repair. Something like 'I reject this item under the 1979 Sale of Goods Act but will reconsider after it has been repaired' will do. *Otherwise, you lose your right to a refund.* Only ask for or accept a repair if you are happy with a repaired product. If the shop offers to replace the item, however, you have the same rights if the replacement doesn't work.

♦ **'They said it was second-hand so what could I expect'.**
George Gomersall paid £239 cash for a video from a TV
shop in Yorkshire. Eleven months later, it developed a
fault which a qualified engineer said was with the
video heads. The engineer pointed out a ticket on the
base of the video which gave an address and date stat-
ing that it had been repaired two years before. George
took the video back to the shop but the salesman said
George should have known that at that price it was not
new – and refused him his money back. Was the sales-
man right?

Perhaps. If he had not told George the video was reconditioned, and there was no notice with the video that it wasn't
new, then George could not have been expected to deduce this
just from the price. After all, £239 is a reasonable price to pay
for some new videos. But what if the salesman *did* tell George it
wasn't new? Second-hand and reconditioned goods **are** covered
by the Sale of Goods Act just as new goods are. We just can't
expect them to last as long. Still, reconditioned videos should
last more than 11 months.

In the end, George could not get his money back but his
experience illustrated the general point. If an item is sold as
'second-hand' or 'not new', your rights are the same. And if it
breaks down, don't let them fob you off.

♦ **'They said they don't give refunds on "sale" goods'.**
The shop assistant or manager might say that – but it's not
true. Any item sold in a shop, in a market or by any other kind
of trader must be of merchantable quality, fit for purpose and
'as described', sale or not. The only difference between sales
goods and others is that, if they are described as 'seconds' or
faults are pointed out, then you can't claim a refund for the fault
or expect the same absence of blemishes you would with a brand
new item.

♦ **'They said it was shop policy not to give refunds'.**
If a sales assistant tries to fob you off with this excuse, simply ask
to see the manager and quietly tell him that, if that is his shop's

policy, then he is breaking the law and you will inform your local trading standards officer. That should get you a refund pretty quick.

Under the Sales of Goods Act, traders have to give you a refund if the item is faulty, irrespective of any policy or notice they may put up. And, for the sake of other customers, tell the trading standards officer anyway even if you do get a refund.

♦ **'They said I would have to take it up with the manufacturer'.**

Absolutely untrue. Your right to a refund applies to the shop you bought it from, not to whoever was the manufacturer. Indeed, you have no legal comeback with the manufacturer at all if the product is faulty because you only have a contract with the shop not the people who made it. So stick to your guns and don't let them sidetrack you into writing off to the manufacturer to get your money back.

Of course, there are times when it is too difficult for you to go back to the shop where you bought an item, for example, when you bought it a long way from your home or if the shop has gone bust. Then you may prefer to use the manufacturer's **guarantee** but there are many problems with guarantees so only use them as a last resort (see p. 49).

♦ **'They said I did the damage' – 'They said I was too late because I had the item for a long time before it went wrong'.**

This is a more difficult excuse to argue against or get around. If the product goes wrong while you are using it, what you have to show is that you were using it in a reasonable way and it was the product's fault and not yours.

For example, if a new electric kettle suddenly stops boiling water after it has been working perfectly for a few weeks, you can claim that there was something inherently wrong with it in the first place. But if sparks start flying and it blows a fuse after you have been using it near pools of spilt water, then it was your fault and not the shop's.

Most of the time though, it is usually clear whose fault it is.

But it becomes more complicated when items break down *after a period of time*. The Sale of Goods Act is ambiguous about these kind of situations.

On the one hand, the Act gives you the right to compensation up to six years after you have bought a faulty product. But on the other hand, the Act says that once you have 'accepted' an item you lose your rights of refund. The definition of 'acceptance' includes keeping and using the item beyond a reasonable time. A court case a few years ago, to the dismay of consumer organisations, illustrated that this can work quite fiercely.

Leslie Bernstein bought a new Nissan car from a garage in North London. He used it in the following three weeks driving 140 miles and then the engine seized up. He wanted his money back – and took the garage to court when they refused to pay up. But the judge ruled that Leslie had 'accepted' the car by having it for three weeks without going back to the garage – so he had no right to a refund, only a right to compensation. Backed by the AA, Leslie lodged an appeal and, fortunately for him, the garage settled up before the appeal was heard. But unfortunately for everybody else. Because that case was held in a High Court, it is binding on County Courts and Small Claims Courts where most disputes over faulty goods end up if they can't be settled.

So, it's a confusing situation which is one reason why consumer organisations want to update and clarify the Act. The best advice at the moment is *to stop using an item when it goes wrong and take it back promptly*.

If you have used an item for a period of time before it goes wrong, you could always take the trader to the Small Claims Court or full County Court under the Sale of Goods Act *not for your money back, but for compensation because the item did not last as long as you might have expected it to*. Compensation, in this situation, may be the difference between the value of the item as it should have been and its actual value in a faulty condition, or the cost of getting it repaired.

Most faulty items that people buy, however, tend to show their faults straight away, and most traders will not want to chance court action if you have got a reasonable complaint – and if you go about it the right way.

HOW TO COMPLAIN ABOUT FAULTY GOODS

1   Take the item back to the shop and ask for the manager or some-one in charge – there always is. If they cannot deal with you straight away, offer to wait or make an appointment to see them later. If you can't go back to the shop soon after you discover the fault, telephone and tell the manager about the item and arrange a convenient time when you can bring it in. Take a note of the conversation and the name of the person you talked to.

2   Ask the manager for your money back or if you are willing to consider a repair or replacement (see 'try-ons', p. 43). If they refuse, quote the Sale of Goods Act. If they disagree with the fault and want to examine the item themselves – for example to 'send it to their laboratories for testing' – get a new receipt for the item and give them a copy of your old receipt if you still have it, keeping the original yourself. Ask them for a replacement while it is being tested and if they refuse, say you will claim the cost of hiring one.

3   If the manager refuses to give you a refund, get the name and address of their head office and write to the customer relations department.

4   If you don't get a satisfactory reply – or if the shop does not have a head office – write to the shop again saying that you intend to take it to court under the 1979 Sale of Goods Act to claim either a refund or compensation unless your claim is dealt with within 14 days. Keep a copy of your letter.

5   If after 14 days, you still have not received a reply or offer which satisfies you, pursue your claim in the Small Claims Court (see p. 274 for details of how to do this).

Follow these steps and you should get your money back –

and you will not have to use a solicitor at all. Occasionally, though, a solicitor could be helpful: **one of our listeners, Guy Miller from Buckingham, wrote to us saying that a letter from his solicitor to a furniture shop about a new carpet which never arrived got his money back within a few days.** Trading standards officers or CABs can also give you support in pressing your case.

Trader 'gone bust'

If a trader has disappeared, then it is up to you to decide if it is worth the effort of trying to trace him. You could ask the shop next door or see if your local trading standards department knows about him. If the trader was a limited company, check with the **Companies Registration Office** to see if he has gone into liquidation. If so, you could press your claim with the liquidator in charge of the case – but you're unlikely to get much after 'preferential creditors' like the taxman have taken their share.

If a trader has put his company into liquidation, there is nothing to stop him starting up another company under a different name unless he has been declared bankrupt – and you cannot press your claim against the new company, unfortunately.

But there are some other remedies for these situations, or indeed if you run into problems pursuing any claim and can't be bothered to go to court.

Buying on credit

If you paid for an item using a credit card, for example, you can claim your right to a refund against the credit card firm instead, *provided the item cost more than £100*. Under the **1974 Consumer Credit Act**, finance companies are as responsible for faulty goods as the shop from where they were bought. This is true even if, as in most cases where credit cards are used, the credit company had no idea of your intention to buy – nor ever saw the item. To claim a refund, contact the credit card company quoting the Act and ask for a refund on your next statement, they will probably want to see the goods before they give you your money back.

The Act also applies to any credit company the shop has

arranged for you to pay, including their own 'store card' company. But it doesn't apply to your bank even if you told your bank manager you wanted a bank loan to pay for the item.

Hire purchase arrangements are the same but you do not have *any* claim against the shop at all, only against the hire purchase firm.

Guarantees

These days, guarantees are offered by most well-known (and some not so well-known) manufacturers of household items and large consumer goods like cycles and cars. Sometimes you have to fill your name, address and other details in the card provided, then you're covered if anything goes wrong. At least, that is what they say. If it was only so simple.

Every time we broadcast an item about 'guarantees' on our programme, we get dozens of letters from listeners about their problems with manufacturers' guarantees, many concluding that they were not worth the paper they were written on. **Paula Pugsley from Devon, for example, sent us a 'six-month guarantee form' from Matsushiro, which the firm enclosed with one of their remote-control toy buggies. The form said that if the buggy went wrong within this time, send it back to them 'enclosing £3.50 to cover post, packing and handling'. The cost of the buggy? Only £16.99. As Paula pointed out, 'with me having to pay postage costs to get the buggy to them, it's going to cost me at least a third of the price of the toy simply to get the manufacturer to repair their own faults'.**

Remember, guarantees are in addition to and not instead of your rights against the shop under the Sale of Goods Act. You should treat the guarantee's promise accordingly. *Try the shop first*. If you buy something costing more than £100 on credit, the credit firm next. And then – or if it really is too much trouble to go back to the shop – use the guarantee. When you do use a guarantee, put on your letter that you are 'reserving your rights under the Sale of Goods Act' if the repair doesn't turn out satisfactorily.

While there aren't any laws regulating guarantees, the manufacturers are under a contractual responsibility to repair a faulty item if you meet the conditions of the guarantee since the guarantee is often one of the main reasons why people buy their products. So you could press them for a replacement if the repair is going to take a long time, and certainly claim compensation if their faulty product caused damage. (The National Consumer Council is at the time of writing pressing the government to introduce a new, legally enforceable 'total guarantee' from manufacturers which should give consumers much better protection than the present haphazard system.)

The most you can ever expect from a guarantee, however, is a replacement or a repair. To get your money back you will have to go to the shop you bought the item from, and then take the shop to court if it refuses to pay up. Except, that is, for a small number of goods whose specialist retailers conform to a 'code of practice'. Fortunately, they are amongst our most popular purchases – and often the ones that are most likely to go wrong.

Complaining by using a code of practice

Codes of practice are drawn up by trade associations usually under the auspices of the Office of Fair Trading. The main advantage they offer when you want to complain is that they allow you to use independent, low-cost arbitration instead of going to court. Because for many of the items covered by a code of practice, like new or used cars, you may want to claim more than the maximum amount allowed in a Small Claims Court, these schemes are a very useful alternative.

Goods covered by codes of practice include shoes, cars, furniture, motorcycles, photographic equipment, holiday caravans (on permanent sites) and electrical products. The **Chartered Institute of Arbitrators** can send you a copy of these codes of practice and details of how to apply for arbitration. You can complain about these items not only if they are faulty but if the retailer has broken any of the commitments included in the code.

For example, shoe shops that are members of the **Multiple Shoe Retailers Association** must conform to their code of practice which lays down that they must have properly trained staff and must provide proper information to customers to allow them to make the right decision about what purpose the shoe can be used for. If the sales assistant didn't know very much about the shoes he was selling, you can complain to the Association.

Similarly, new car dealers who are members of the **Society of Motor Manufacturers and Traders** must, amongst other obligations, give you the vehicle handbook and the terms of warranty when you buy a car. And any car dealer they appoint must repair a car under warranty, even if you bought it from another garage. Otherwise the car dealer is breaking the Society's code of conduct – and you can complain. Second-hand car traders who are members of the **Motor Agents Association** or its **Scottish equivalent** also have a code of practice, and you can use their arbitration procedure if things go wrong.

All these motor trade associations, by the way, have also worked out with the Office of Fair Trading a code of practice and an arbitration scheme for **vehicle servicing and repairs**. Again, contact the appropriate association if you get into a dispute about the cost or quality of how your car is serviced or repaired. You do have the right to take a garage to court instead of using arbitration for a shoddy repair or service, but not under the **Sale of Goods Act**. Instead, you use the **1982 Supply of Goods and Services Act** (see p. 110).

You can only use arbitration if both you and the trader agree to it and if the trader belongs to the trade association that offers the scheme, although most reputable traders do. And if you choose arbitration, you almost always lose your right to go to court if you are not satisfied with the arbitrator's decision. (See p. 282 for how to use arbitration schemes.)

Complaining about 'standards' marks

Some goods we buy include a British Standard 'kitemark' or 'safety mark' on them, or simply have a written description saying they conform to a British Standard number. These types of standards are worked out by the **British Standards Institution (BSI)** which has drawn up a relevant standard signifying safety and quality for thousands of different consumer items. Many items like tyres have to meet a British Standard by law, but most are voluntary. If a BSI kitemark or safety mark is on a product, the item has been tested independently to make sure it conforms to the standard required.

If you buy an item which does not have a kitemark or safety mark but simply says that it conforms to a BSI number, you don't have any guarantee it has been tested by the BSI. But if the item does not meet BSI standards, this would be an offence against the 1968 Trade Descriptions Act and you should tell trading standards officers.

SOME EXCEPTIONS TO THE SALE OF GOODS ACT

The Sale of Goods Act does not cover you in every situation. If a builder goes out and buys a new door for you when he is renovating your home and the door turns out to be full of holes, you *can't* claim against the shop which supplied the door but you *can* claim against the builder (see p. 115).

Also, if you buy an item as part of a business deal, your rights under the Sale of Goods Act can be cancelled in any agreement you make. But the main exceptions to watch out for in everyday purchases are the following.

Presents

If you give a new item as a present and it turns out to be faulty, the **recipient** cannot claim the money back since the shop has a contract with you, not him. That's the law and to make sure of a refund, you will have to take the item back. In practice, however, if you've received something as a present and it goes wrong, just take it back to the shop and nine times out of ten, you will get a replacement. It will help if you have the receipt as well. There is also a way around the law which is by you writing a note assigning your rights to the person you give the present to – but that will probably appeal only to the legally minded.

Private sales

When you buy goods from shops, they must be of merchantable quality, fit for purpose and 'as described'. But when you buy something from a private seller, a friend, perhaps, or through a small ad in the newspaper, it only has to be 'as described'. If you see a lawnmower for sale in the small ads, for example, and you buy it only to discover it conks out when cutting the lawn, you are not entitled to a refund if the previous owner was a private seller. Nor are you entitled to any compensation if it ran amock through your prize chrysanthemums. But if it was described as 'new', and turned out to be second-hand, or if it was described as battery operated and you found out it had to be run off the mains, or if it was described as 'trouble-free' and it turns out to be anything but, then you can claim your money back. *So always ask a private seller about the quality of an item before you buy.* And if the private seller turns out to be a trader masquerading as an ordinary individual, all your rights under the Sale of Goods Act still apply.

Auctions

Auctions are often places where you can save yourself a lot of money – and one reason is that they don't have to meet any ordinary traders' conditions of sale as laid down by the Sale of Goods Act but can set out their own ones. And, surprise, surprise, most auctions' conditions of sale, which you are entitled to inspect, do not allow you to claim a refund if the item is faulty, or even get your money back if it turns out not to be '18th century' – though in this case, trading standards officers may be interested if the description is intentionally misleading.

The problem with deposits

And now here's some good news for traders and shopkeepers. You have rights when you buy goods from them – but they have rights, too, when you promise to buy something. If you put a deposit down on an item and then you change your mind, they can legally keep your deposit. But there's more. If they ordered the item especially or incurred some loss due to you changing your mind, they could insist you buy the item or pay them some compensation. If that happens to you, take legal advice or see a CAB advisor. Try and only leave deposits with shops you completely trust.

Deliveries that go wrong

Anne Grant from London bought some furniture from Habitat, and was given a four week delivery date. That

was in July. The furniture arrived in November, and when it finally came there was a blemish on it. Anne complained to Habitat and eventually got the furniture replaced. When she complained about the trouble it caused her, she received a £10 voucher.

If a shop has given you a firm delivery date and the item doesn't arrive, you can ask for your money back. If you agree to wait some more time, press them for a free loan of a replacement, a refund or compensation. They will almost certainly come up with a replacement which they have to deliver and collect free of charge.

Of course, most furniture shops do not give a firm delivery date. They would go out of business if they did. What usually happens is they say 'in about six weeks, depending on . . . etc . . . etc . . .' And that's fair enough: furniture often has to be ordered from the supplier, and this can and does take time.

What is unfair is a shop taking six months instead of the expected six weeks. So if an item of furniture – or, indeed, any other goods you have ordered and paid for – doesn't arrive when you expected it, go back to the shop and give them a delivery date that seems reasonable to you – say, two or three more weeks. And put it in writing, keeping a copy. This is called 'making time of the essence' and if the furniture does not arrive within this new time limit, you can then get your money back. If you have to have an item by a fixed date, write this on their **and** your receipt when you buy it.

But what if the item does arrive on time and it turns out to be faulty? Most shops will accept their responsibility for this but we have heard of the occasional rogue who tries to get out of it by saying that the customer signed a delivery note and therefore accepted the item, faults, blemishes or scratches and all. This is hardly fair since most deliveries these days are done by delivery men in a dreadful hurry who certainly don't seem to have the time to wait for you to open the package up and check carefully for damage. To be absolutely sure you won't lose your rights, write on the delivery note 'not inspected'. That will do the trick.

And what about a situation when the furniture you have ordered and paid for will not fit into your front door or up your stairs? This is what consumer lawyers call a grey area: it depends on the circumstances, but certainly a furniture shop could claim it was your fault for not ensuring the item would fit in, not theirs. The best thing to do when you buy a large item of furniture and you are not sure that it will fit in is to ask the shop to promise in writing that they will give you your money back if it does not.

Buying goods by mail-order

Whether you buy an item from a shop, through a mail-order catalogue or through an advertisement in the colour supplements, your rights are the same. And most mail-order companies are pretty quick to offer you a refund, or a replacement if you want it, if their product is not up to it. But problems do occur when the item you ordered didn't match the picture you had of it in your mind – or the picture you saw in the magazine.

Sara Cooper from London was looking for something to store her garden tools and barbecue set in. She noted an advertisement in the Innovations catalogue for a 'storette', a do-it-yourself shed. In the ad, there was a photo of this storette complete with walls and floor and described as 'fully waterproof from top to bottom'. She sent off £69.95. Soon the storette arrived and with it came an order form for a storette base which Sara could purchase for another £28. This rather surprised Sara since she thought the base would be included as it seemed to be in the picture. She didn't think she'd have to pay another £28.

And she was right: she didn't have to. Any item bought on mail-order must correspond to any description given, whether in writing or in a photo. And in any illustration, if something is an extra or not included in the purchase price, the ad must say so. Otherwise customers are not buying what they think they are buying.

The procedures for claiming a refund for mail-order goods are exactly the same as claiming from a shop – but remember your contract is with the firm to whom you pay your money and not with any other firm that may send you the product. Remember, too, that if you pay by credit or by hire purchase, you may have the right to a refund from the finance company (see p. 48).

You also have some other protections as well. Many mail order firms are members of the **Mail Order Traders Association**, the **British Direct Marketing Association** or the **Association of Mail Order Publishers**. These trade associations have codes of practice and arbitration schemes run by the Office of Fair Trading.

Also, for any advertisement, apart from catalogues, where the ad is not 'legal, decent, honest and truthful', you can complain about it to the **Advertising Standards Authority**, or, if it was on radio or television, the **Independent Broadcasting Authority** (see p. 213). These organisations cannot compensate you if you lose money because of a false advertisement.

Some publications, however, will compensate you if you have lost money because of an ad it carried. Contact the advertising manager within three months for newspapers or two months for magazines.

Finally, any promise made when you shop by mail must be honoured. If they promise a refund with no questions asked, refund they must. If they promise delivery 'within 28 days', cancel if the item doesn't turn up. And if the goods are faulty and you have to send them back, claim postage and packing charges as well.

Unsolicited goods

If you are sent something out of the blue that you didn't order, you do not, of course, have to pay for it. But can you keep it? Yes you can *if you don't hear from the firm within six months*. Then, it's yours. You can also write to the firm pointing out that the good was unsolicited and give them 30 days to arrange to collect it. If they do not, you can then regard it as your own. There is *no* responsibility on you to send any unsolicited item back. And, if the firm tries to make you pay for such an item, contact your local trading standards department – the firm is breaking the law.

Telephone selling and doorstep salesmen

If someone makes what is known as a 'cold call', that is, they turn up at your door or ring you up without invitation, you have some additional rights under the Sale of Goods Act. The most important of these is that you have an automatic 'cooling off period' of five days if you spend more than £35. You can then cancel the sale at any point during this time if you change your mind, and many customers do: sometimes the salesman's patter just doesn't seem the same when repeated to a partner in the evening.

Some less-reputable doorstep firms have come up with ruses to get around this. Two we've heard about at *You and Yours* in recent months are:

1   Firms call potential customers on the phone first and invite themselves around. *This way, their visit to your home is no longer 'cold'.*

2   Firms say you must sign an agreement at the office, and offer to take you there right away – 'I can do you a deal with £20 off if you can come'. *Your cooling-off rights only apply if you sign away from business premises.*

If any doorstep or telephone sales company tries these ruses, steer well clear even if they seem to be selling the best bargain you've heard about for many a while. The odds are they've had many customers in the past using the cooling off period to reassess the purchase.

Or, alternatively, ask them if they are members of the **Direct Selling Association**. This trade organisation has a code of practice and an arbitration scheme for complaints similar to those of the mail-order associations.

Repairing goods

Sheila Store was the proud owner of a pair of spectacles which she described as 'Edna Everage' like. She decided she'd like new lenses in them and a local optician was quite happy to do the job. When Sheila called to pick up her glasses, however, the frames they gave her were not hers at all. A shop assistant explained Sheila's frames had got broken so the optician had put new lenses in the 'next best thing'. But to Sheila, the

**new frames were nothing like the originals. She no
longer looked like the Australian superstar, for one
thing. What could she do?**

She could sue the opticians under an ancient but still applicable law of '**bailment**'. This law imposes a duty of reasonable skill and care on anybody who has something of yours even if you have asked them to repair it. It applies to situations like a radio repair shop losing your radio or a garage denting your car when you put it in for a service, and many more. In Sheila's case, the opticians agreed they were in the wrong and offered her the choice of compensation or some brand new specs.

Prices

Contrary to popular belief, a shop does not always have to sell you an item at the price it has displayed. If there is a price sticker on a tin of cat food which makes that tin half the price of others on the shelf, for example, the shop can claim it was a mistake and ask you to pay the normal price instead. But if, for example, there is a large notice by the cat food offering tins at half-price and then the shop refuses to honour this, tell your local trading standards department as the shop is breaking the **1968 Trade Descriptions Act**, a criminal law.

Bargains

Bargains are difficult to resist. So much so, that every trader at some time or another tries to persuade you that their prices are cheaper than elsewhere. But their methods of persuasion are now quite rigorously controlled, or at least it seems that way.

The **1987 Consumer Protection Act** tried to clarify all the laws that have previously been used to control misleading pricing and bargain offers. The Act makes it a criminal offence to 'give consumers a misleading price indication about goods, services, accommodation (including new homes), or facilities'. So traders should not add on VAT to the price they display in shops, nor should they make bogus comparisons like comparing a good with a bogus manufacturer's recommended price or simply saying '£35 cheaper than elsewhere'. Any product offered at a sale price should have been offered at the original price for a 28-day period by the shopkeepers. Tell trading standards officers if you suspect a shop is breaking any of these regulations.

It all sounds too good to be true. Especially since there is now a code of practice issued under this Act about prices for traders. But this code has not yet been tested in court – and consumer organisations and trading standards officers think it is by no means tough enough. So we will all just have to live with notices like 'closing down sale' when the shop seems to have no intention of stopping trading. Treat those supposed bargains with the scepticism they deserve.

Unsafe goods

Occasionally we buy something to discover not only it is faulty, but that it is potentially dangerous as well. A toy with hidden spikes in it, for example, or a second-hand car which turns out to be a 'death-trap' and many other horrors.

While we at *You and Yours* encourage listeners when they have had a raw deal to contact their local trading standards officers, we don't just encourage them to when they have bought a dangerous item, *we beseech them*. We've seen and interviewed children who have lost their sight, adults who have broken bones and worse, as a result of dangerous items still being on sale. And trading standards officers, or the police if the unsafe item is a car, will move fast to prosecute the seller and manufacturer and make sure the item is withdrawn from sale. But they can only do this if they are told about the item. So, *please* call them if you buy a good that turns out to be unsafe.

Under the **1987 Consumer Protection Act**, all suppliers of goods, including wholesalers as well as manufacturers and retailers, have a general duty to ensure their products are safe. Breach of this duty is normally a criminal offence but action cannot be taken if you don't let trading standards officers know.

The Act says suppliers are still responsible for injury even if it wasn't their fault the product turned out to be defective. You can also claim compensation under this law if the product has caused damage to your property of more than £275.

You can sue any or all of the suppliers for any injury you've received as a result of using defective goods. The only goods which are exempt are unprocessed agricultural products like meat, dairy products, fruit and vegetables and so on, although you may still be able to sue the immediate supplier, such as the shop.

There are some drawbacks, however. You cannot claim damages just because the product was of poor quality or did not do the job you wanted. It must have caused you injury – and that injury must have happened by you using the product in the way one might reasonably expect it to be used. You will have to prove everything in court.

And it is possible for suppliers to deny liability by putting forward what has become known as the 'development risks defence'. This defence is particularly likely if you claim against large companies like drug manufacturers for unfortunate side-effects of their drugs. The suppliers can claim they could not be expected to know the harmful effects of their products given the scientific or technological knowledge available at the time. What you will have to do, to win compensation, is to show that they could have done.

But in these kinds of cases – and indeed in most situations where you feel you are entitled to compensation due to injury from a faulty good – take specialist legal advice before you start any legal action (see Chapter 17).

AND FINALLY . . .

Another bit of goods news for traders, if not for consumers. Shops do not have to sell that wonderful new cooker displayed in their window. Or the new car in their saleroom. Or that bar of chocolate by the till. The simple reason is that no trader has to sell us anything if he doesn't want to. And this time, there is nothing you can do to complain about it all. Except, well, yes there are a couple of exceptions to this, too!

If you are refused sale of an item because of your sex or race, the trader *would* be breaking the law. And if a shop advertised something for sale and then refused to sell it they may be breaking the 1968 Trade Descriptions Act!

FOOD

In the last couple of years, concern about the quality of food on sale in shops or restaurants has become headline news. Successive scares about salmonella, listeria, botulism and the cattle disease bovine spongiform encephalopathy (BSE), have certainly thrown into question old feelings that British food, if not the best in the world, was certainly renowned for its basic freshness and purity. And if all that was not enough, there have been frequent calls for an end to preservatives in food, and frequent advice from health experts that we should all cut down on red meat, fat, sugar and salt in our diets. It sometimes makes you wary of eating anything at all!

There are signs, however, that all these worries about food are resulting in higher standards and better protection for consumers. The major supermarkets are all now vying with each other to produce more 'natural' food, chemical free and refrigerated and stored to discourage any chance of food poisoning. Domestic science and food hygiene have been given an increased priority in school education. And, as this book goes to press, the government is finalising plans for a new Food Bill, which will increase controls on the processing, manufacture, preparation and sale of food. This new Bill should become law in 1990. The government has also announced, 'in the interests of food safety', its intention to allow irradation of certain foods, a prospect which has alarmed some food experts. All irradiated food on sale will be clearly labelled as such.

It is uncertain, at the moment, how the new Food Bill will increase the scope for complaints about bad or poor quality food. But here's how to complain by using the present laws and regulations.

COMPLAINING ABOUT BAD FOOD

Just like all goods, food must be 'fit for its purpose' which is, of course, to be eaten. If it is not, you can get your money back from the retailer under the Sale of Goods Act (see Chapter 5). Food on public sale must also conform to regulations laid down in the **1984 Food Act**. This Act makes it a criminal offence to sell food unfit for consumption or harmful to health. The Food

Act applies not just to shops, but to wholesalers, manufacturers and restaurants as well.

Food shops, cafés and restaurants must also meet strict hygiene rules which lay down standards for work surfaces, basic cleanliness, how food is handled and so on. The officials responsible for enforcing food law and regulations are environmental health officers (for concerns about health), and trading standards officers (for concerns about food quality, labelling and short measure). You should contact them straight away if you are worried about any food you have bought. Here's why:

Twenty-seven-year-old Heather Main, a nurse who lives in North London, bought a tin of green beans from her local branch of Safeway to make a salad.

'I opened the green beans up and took them out one at a time, and half way down I came across something quite black. I saw its teeth, eyes and ears, and on a closer look discovered it was a mouse with its tail and one back leg missing. I had to rush to the toilet and vomit. I was really pretty ill, and I kept wondering what had happened to the missing leg and tail, whether I had eaten them already.'

Heather phoned Safeway, which had representatives 'at my door within 10 minutes. They couldn't wait to get their hands on it to take it away and me, like a fool, gave it to them'.

After several months of not hearing anything from Safeway, Heather eventually received a letter saying the 'little bit more' she had received with her green beans was due to mistakes with the crop-gathering at the bean's German manufacturers. Safeway, they told her, had withdrawn all tins of these beans from sale at their shops. And they sent her a £20 voucher to spend at her next visit to the store.

That was little consolation to Heather since she needed to take two weeks off work to get over the shock and had no plans on shopping at Safeway in the future.

When you discover something wrong in the food you buy – or indeed any mould, degeneration or dirt – *do not take it back* to the shop but take it straight to your local environmental health officer.

It is a question of evidence – environmental health officers need the unfit or dangerous food as proof if they decide to prosecute the shop or manufacturer. And if they do prosecute and the shop is found guilty, you can use this decision to claim compensation for any loss you have suffered. Heather, in fact, could have sued anyway since Safeway admitted the mouse but she would have been in a stronger position with environmental health officer backing.

To complain about food which is unfit for consumption:

1   Stop eating the food and hold on to it, preferably with the receipt from the shop.

2   Take it as soon as you can to your local environmental health officer or call and ask them to collect it.

3   If you are ill as a result of eating the food, for example, any vomiting due to food poisoning, get a note from your doctor confirming this. Keep a note of your losses, such as lost wages.

4   Press for compensation by either writing to the company outlining your case, and enclosing any evidence, like a doctor's note if you have lost time off work. (Threaten to take them to the civil courts if they don't pay up.) Or ask the environmental health officer to claim compensation for you if they prosecute the offending supplier in the criminal courts.

'Best-before' dates

Food manufacturers must stamp a 'best before' or a 'sell-by' date on processed food, tins, packets and cartons. But contrary to what most people think, there is nothing illegal about selling food that is past these dates, as long as the date is clearly labelled.

When a *You and Yours* **reporter went round with consumer protection officers in Birmingham recently, he discovered dozens of smaller shops and supermarkets selling food like honey and nuts, weeks and sometimes months after the 'best-before' date on their labels.**

Many of those Birmingham shops were prosecuted or

warned, however, because the food sold way past the sell-by dates turned out to be mouldy or unfit for consumption. If you discover food being sold after a 'sell-by' or 'best-before' date, let trading standards officers know – it's often a sign that other unwholesome food is on sale.

Weights and measures

Richard Penny's favourite snack was cheesy corn puffs which Golden Wonder market under the name 'Wotsits'. Once when he opened a new pack, however, Richard discovered the contents 'were none too generous'. Now Richard is a man of a mathematical frame of mind. He bought another five packs and decided to weigh them all – and they all turned out to be different, the lowest was 20 grams of puffs, the highest 32 grams, even though they were the same price. This rather annoyed Richard so he contacted *You and Yours*. **Surely, he asked us, don't all packs of Wotsits have to weigh the same?**

No, they don't. At least in Richard's case, they didn't have to when he bought them. Golden Wonder could then put as many Wotsits in each packet as they wanted to – and still charge the same price, as long as the net weight was under 50 grams and not mentioned on the pack.

Most of the food we buy, though, is heavier than Wotsits and since Richard's experience, any food item over 25 grams *must* have its net weight on the pack. If you buy food and its weight is less than you paid for, contact trading standards officers who will take the matter up with the offending retailer or manufacturer.

Trading standards officers can also prosecute for **short measure** and for any food or drink that has been **falsely described**.

A few years ago, I visited a wine bar in London and asked for a glass of white wine. The wine that came certainly reminded me of wine in the way fruit flavouring reminds you of fruit, and when I held it up against the lights to see its colour, it certainly wasn't just water. But then neither was it completely wine. I

took it back and complained. The barman quickly took another bottle off the shelf and poured me a glass of, this time, pure wine.

I got what I wanted but, ever since, it nagged me that many other customers were being ripped off – by diluted wine. If you ever go to a similar wine bar or pub and you suspect this kind of carry-on, ring up your local trading standards department so they can stamp it out.

Food labels

The Food Act also states that most packed food must contain on its label the name of the food, a list of the ingredients (including additives with E numbers if appropriate), a best-before date (see p. 64), storage conditions and country of origin if it is misleading not to. All of this information must be printed legibly on the packet.

You and Yours **listener Diana Fitzgerald, from Devon, sent us a carton of Birds Eye Chocolate Mousse with a challenge. 'Can you tell me what the ingredients are?' Well no, we couldn't because they were in black type on a dark brown background. And when we put her challenge to Birds Eye, they admitted defeat as well saying it was a 'very unfortunate mishap' and promised to recall all cartons for relabelling.**

If you buy a label which is unreadable, contact trading standards officers. They will take it up with the manufacturers. Incidentally, the information can be anywhere on the packet as long as it is conspicuous.

Since the Food Act was passed, the government has also issued guidelines for the labelling of nutritional information on food packets, including protein and fat content. Soon we can expect food manufacturers to start conforming to European Community proposals giving precise information about how, for example, their food is 'low fat' or 'high fibre'.

All this sounds, then, as if we are getting a pretty good deal. Unfortunately, it is not as good as it sounds. A recent survey by the Consumers' Association revealed that food manufacturers are ignoring the government guidelines on a 'massive scale'. Only 15 out of 100 food items the Association bought were labelled in line with the guidelines, and one quarter did not have any nutritional labelling at all. And there is nothing you can do to complain because these guidelines are not compulsory but voluntary.

You can complain, however, if the food you have bought is not 'as described', by using the Sale of Goods Act (see Chapter 5). The problem is that some descriptions are so vague that it is unclear what they really mean. What exactly, for example, does 'natural' imply?

And what if the food is described as 'fresh'? **Dr Stefan Buczacki, one of the regular experts on Radio 4's** *Gardeners' Question Time*, **bought some 'fresh garden mint' from Sainsbury. Underneath this description, in smaller letters, were the words 'in vinegar' and when Dr Buczacki looked on the side of the packet, he saw a list of ingredients including salt, acetic acid and colours E104 and E142. This seemed to him an odd way of selling 'fresh' mint, so he wrote to Sainsbury asking why the mint was described as 'fresh' when it was obviously preserved. After all, he said, 'you wouldn't describe pickled onions as "fresh onions", would you?' Sainsbury's response was that the mint was fresh before it was processed. This did not please Dr Buczacki. 'You would expect all grocery produce to be fresh before it was put in a jar anyway'.**

There was, however, nothing illegal about Sainsbury's description since 'fresh' is one of those terms like 'natural' and 'wholesome' which is not defined by the 1984 Food Act. Some food suppliers have been prosecuted for selling frozen or defrosted food as 'fresh' but in this case, Sainsbury was quite within its rights. **It did, however, take Dr Buczacki's complaint seriously and have since relabelled the product 'Norfolk mint in vinegar'.**

So, if you think a manufacturer is overstepping the mark in its lyrical description of its food, write and tell them so. If they get enough complaints, they may think again.

COMPLAINING ABOUT RESTAURANTS

Rachel Greenberg joined a group of friends to celebrate the Jewish New Year in a London restaurant. The food, to put it mildly, was unsatisfactory and so was the atmosphere: the rowdiness of other customers remained unchecked by the management despite Rachel's complaints. When the meal was completed, one of her friends tried to settle the bill by offering £50, half of its cost, and volunteering her name and address. The manageress refused the offer, and attempted to keep the friend inside the restaurant while ringing the police.

'My friend felt very threatened by this', Rachel wrote to us, 'so she escaped. She dropped a £50 note through the door but in her panic neglected to leave her name and address. The police stopped our car and told us a criminal offence had been committed, forcing my friend to pay the additional £50. They said that as the food had been consumed without strong complaint, we could not complain afterwards. We had to pay the money'.

Unfortunately for Rachel, none of her friends had wanted to complain very strongly during the meal because they felt it would dampen the celebration. And as the police pointed out, that was their downfall.

Restaurants, cafés, wine bars or anywhere selling food for consumption on their premises must deliver what they promise; a reasonable standard of food, given the price, and prepared accordingly. If they do not, *complain at once* and not after you have eaten the meal. If you do not, the restaurant can claim you accepted the food and are just trying to avoid payment. If you do complain about the standard of food during your meal and it is not improved, here's what to do:

1   Offer a reasonable amount for the meal instead of the bill.

2   Write down your name and address and give this to the manager.

3   If the police are called, explain to them that this is a 'civil'

matter. Say you complained during the meal about the food and you are within your civil rights deducting money from the bill because the food was not up to the standard promised. As long as you appear to the police not to be trying to avoid any payment or committing any 'breach of the peace', they have no power to intervene.

4   If the restaurant tries to detain you until you pay all the bill, tell them *you* will phone the police to report them for wrongful arrest.

With persistence and calm, you will usually win your case. It helps, too, if other customers agree with you that the food was not up to standard.

But all this does mean making a fuss, and it can be embarrassing or ruin an evening (if the evening hasn't been ruined already by the food!). You can pay the whole amount and announce to the restaurant you will take them to the Small Claims Court for the difference of what you think the meal was worth. You can say all that to the manager – and say it loud so other customers can hear as well – but it may not be worth the effort when you get home nor will it make up for an annoying evening. If the restaurant is part of a chain, it's better to say you will write to the head office complaining about the food or to any guidebook that praises the place.

Service in restaurants

If the service in a restaurant is poor during the meal and you point this out, you are entitled to deduct some or all of the 'service charge' on your bill, even if this amount is automatically included and is notified on the menu. You do not, of course, ever have to give a tip if you don't want to, even if a 'voluntary' service charge had been added to the bill. If the waiter spills food over your clothes, tell the manager you intend to claim the cleaning bill – he might knock the amount off the bill as recompense.

Restaurant charges

For some time now, the law has required restaurants to display their menus so prices can be checked before you order. New regulations about misleading prices mean that 'non-optional extras' should not be added on at the end but should be included in the price of the food. And other extras such as a cover charge should be displayed as prominently as the price of the dishes. This should mean the bill you receive at the end of your meal corresponds more closely to the prices on the menu. If you eat in a restaurant where this is not happening, tell your local trading standards officers.

Also, you cannot *compel* a restaurant to accept either a cheque or a credit card, unless it has a sign stating it does accept these methods of payment.

Not turning up

If all this puts an onus on restaurateurs to behave as properly as other suppliers of services, the signs are that they are hitting back when customers don't meet their part of the bargain. **Antony Worral-Thompson, manager of a restaurant in London's West End, is increasingly fed up with customers who book tables and don't show up.**

'Sometimes on a Saturday night, we find 20–30 per cent of our customers don't show. They book three restaurants in advance and then decide on the evening which one to go to. They very rarely call and cancel, and the result is that we lose money'.

Along with 500 other up-market restaurants, Mr Worral-Thompson now intends to take down not just the person's address when they book, but their credit card number as well, so he can deduct a set amount from the card if the customer does not show.

Whether this can be done or not is, as yet, unclear – it has not been tested by the courts. What amount, for example, would the customer have spent if they had turned up? But you are quite within your rights to refuse to give your credit card number when you book, although the restaurant may then refuse your booking. All restaurants are, however, entitled to sue you for any loss they have incurred if you make a booking and do not show up. So, always telephone if you change your mind, especially if they have your phone number or address.

FOOD IN HOSPITALS

Hospital food is, so health authorities say, getting better and becoming more varied. This is partly because of the greater attention paid to diet these days but also, one suspects, because hospitals can no longer claim 'crown immunity' if their food is unfit for consumption. They can now be prosecuted just like any shop, restaurant or café by environmental health officers if their food is 'off'. To complain about hospital food, first speak to the staff and then, if not satisfied, to the hospital's catering manager.

If the kind of food served seems to you inadequate or unvaried, you can take this up with the hospital's unit general manager or through your local Community Health Council (see Chapter 11).

MEALS ON WHEELS

Meals on wheels are provided by local **social services** and usually ordered by your doctor. If you don't think the food is the standard it should be, have a word with the person delivering the meals and then, if you're still not satisfied, contact your local social services department.

SCHOOL FOOD

This kind of food has also made great strides recently. There is even a campaign by school caterers to try and convince parents school food is no longer the butt of all schoolboy and schoolgirl jokes. This is partly due to the removal of obligations on schools to provide meals at all, except for children whose parents are claiming certain state benefits. Meals for these children must be provided free but schools can charge other children what they like for meals, as long as they are not making a profit.

If you are dissatisfied with the cost of school food or the choice provided for your children, complain first to the school's head, then to the local education authority. Just as with other complaints about schools (see Chapter 14), you can then take up your complaint with your local councillor.

Incidentally, and surprisingly, there are no minimum nutrition requirements for food provided by schools or hospitals. Or, indeed, at staff canteens.

FOOD AT WORK

There is no legal obligation on employers to provide food at work at all, apart from in certain heavy industries, such as the docks. Most large and many small firms, however, do offer snacks and lunch as an incentive to their employees. If your work does not have this facility, your trade union can try to negotiate one for you. And a union can also deal with any complaints about the food, although it's probably better to have a word first with your firm's catering committee. Just as with any restaurant, you have the same rights for complaining at your work about food which is unfit for consumption.

FOOD WHEN YOU TRAVEL

Most long-distance public transport now provides a range of food for customers. Even coaches find it more attractive to bring around sandwiches and drinks, rather than dropping into a motorway service café. If you are dissatisfied with the food provided on any kind of journey, complain to the waiter or, if the food is so bad you can't eat it, ask the on-board catering manager for a refund. If you still want to pursue your complaint when your journey has finished, here's what to do:

Airlines: For scheduled airlines, complain to the airline's customer relations officer. For charters, complain to the tour operator. Ask for a nominal payment back, as payment for the food was included in the price you paid for your flight.

Ferries: Complain to the operator's customer relations department.

Coaches: Complain to the coach company.

British Rail: For on-board food, write to the **Manager Inter-**

City On-board Services at **Tournament House, Paddington Station, London W2 1HQ**, or contact the regional office of the **Transport Users Consultative Committee**, the consumer watchdog. For food in stations, contact the station manager.

Motorway service stations: Complain as you would in a restaurant and ask for your money back. Or write to the company's customer relations department – the address will be at the service station.

Finally, it is worth repeating that all food served in hospitals, schools, at work or when you travel in the UK must meet the general requirements of being fit for consumption. If you have been served with food that does not, contact your local environmental health officer.

YOUR HOME: BUYING AND RENTING

PROBLEMS WITH PAYING THE MORTGAGE

Jean and Chris took out a mortgage to buy a house in the West Country for themselves and their five children. The house cost £33 000, and they took out a mortgage for half. Chris then had his overtime reduced, losing £75 a week. Jean takes up their story:

'We were managing very well with the mortgage payments. We had no other debts and we were comfortable. But in January, Chris lost his overtime, and by May, we were really desperate. We just couldn't afford to meet the repayments. By August, we owed the mortgage company £700 and we were evicted. We had to go and live in bed and breakfast and it was absolutely devastating and all for the sake of £700. We didn't have any other debts at all. The bed and breakfast was only a two minute walk from our old house, and every morning I had to walk past it. It was heartbreaking'.

Jean and Chris are by no means alone. In the seven years from 1980 to 1987, mortgage repossessions increased threefold. One in 14 homeless people lost their home through being repossessed by their bank, building society or finance company. How can you prevent this happening to you?

Whether you have your mortgage with a building society, bank, mortgage broker or local council, the most important thing to do if you have problems making repayments *is to let them know as soon as possible*. This sounds obvious, but it is surprising how many people only do this when their situation has turned from the serious to the drastic.

If you are apprehensive about this, or if you have other debts as well, contact your local **Citizens Advice Bureau (CAB)** first. In many parts of the country, CAB workers have access to specialist money advisors (in some cities these are run by the local council themselves), and they will help you structure your debts and then contact your mortgage company to try and avoid repossession. This may mean delaying other payments until your mortgage arrears are sorted out. For more details of how this works, see the section on Debt on p. 142.

If your personal finances are under control but you have just been unable to make the odd repayment or you can foresee problems with repayments in the future, here's what to do:

1 Write to the mortgage company as soon as you have missed a payment, and explain your circumstances. Arrange to pay back the amount missed over the next few months. In general, mortgage companies are not bothered by the odd payment missed, but they do get worried if you have to cancel a regular standing order.

2 If it looks as if you will have trouble meeting future repayments ask the mortgage company to extend the period of the loan. This will mean that your regular repayment will be reduced. Or ask the mortgage company if you can convert your mortgage into one that is 'low start': a mortgage where you pay less now but more in the future.

3 If your mortgage is several years old and the repayments are too high, ask the lender to consider a period when you only pay the interest on the mortgage and not the capital repayments. If you have an endowment mortgage – where your insurance premium is effectively the repayment charge – see if you can convert to a repayment one, although you may sacrifice the premiums you have paid.

4 If you start claiming **income support**, tell your local DSS office about your mortgage. They can help cover the interest payments.

All these steps will at least buy you time and convince the mortgage company you are taking your problems seriously. With all the recent publicity about house repossessions, most reputable companies will try and sort out repayment problems before going to court. They all have the flexibility to restructure the loan if they choose. Many will.

But if none of these steps work – or if the company proves bloody-minded – they may threaten repossession. Remember, they have to get a court order for this. And if this seems likely to happen, get legal advice as soon as you can via a CAB. *Don't try to defend a possible court order on your own.*

If it seems likely you will lose your home, try and negotiate a period with the mortgage company for *you* to sell it and not them. You will almost certainly get more money for your home than a mortgage company will, even if you go for a 'cut-price' quick sell. If the mortgage company does repossess, it must pay you the difference between your mortgage and the price it gets.

Apart from the worry of repossession and missed payments, there are, of course, many other types of complaints that occur with mortgage companies. These are dealt with under the appropriate sections in Chapter 9.

PROBLEMS WITH LEASES

A couple of years ago, we heard from a number of listeners in Lancashire about letters they had received from a property company. These listeners owned their houses on a 'leasehold' rather than a 'freehold' basis, a situation far more common with flats. A freeholder is the absolute owner of the property. A leaseholder, in return for an annual fee and some other conditions, owns the lease on a property for a fixed number of years, usually 80–100, occasionally more, sometimes less. If you are a leaseholder, you pay an annual fee, usually called ground rent, to the freeholder or his managing agent.

The property company had bought the freehold of our Lancashire listeners' homes, then wrote to them demanding the annual ground rent, even though many people who received the letters had already paid. The firm threatened to call in the bailiffs if the money was not paid, and said they would charge a set fee of £28.75 to answer any queries about the letter for 'administration and computer-time' costs.

This seemed to us at *You and Yours* extraordinary – and also to housing experts we consulted. The advice we gave to listeners who received threatening and unjustified letters from anybody owning or managing the freehold of their home was to ignore them as the demands are a try-on, unenforceable by law. We also said they should go to a CAB or housing advice centre and get other advice as well.

But, what if you do not pay your ground rent? The freeholder can take you to court for not paying, and can, in theory, ask for repossession of the property. But this is only after he has given you every opportunity to pay the amount owed. It is extremely unlikely any court will grant him repossession or bailiff's rights until all possibilities of paying back the money have been tried.

While it is up to you to pay the annual ground rent to the freeholder, some older houses with long leases and small ground rents seem not to have any person who owns the freehold at all. Or at least any owner who takes any interest in the property. You may be able to find out who owns the lease, if it is not clear from the deeds of the property, by writing to the **Land Registry**, as long as the property is registered with them.

Finally, if your **house** is leasehold, you have an absolute right under the **Leasehold Reform Act** to buy the freehold after three years of residence. If the freeholder asks what you think is too high a price, you can contact the **district valuer** at your local council. He has the power to lay down a fee which is binding.

The same right does not currently apply if your property is a **flat**. However, if the freeholder wants to sell the whole building, he is obliged to offer first refusal to a majority of the flat residents in the property. There is no restriction on this fee, except that the freeholder cannot then sell the freehold for a lower price to someone else.

Obligations and conditions in leases

All leases lay down certain types of conditions and obligations on the freeholder and leaseholder. These include the ground rent and responsibility for repairs. The lease may also include the cost of service charges and caretaking charges, particularly in the case of flats. So get your solicitor to study it carefully before you buy.

It is possible to change the terms of the lease if you and the freeholder agree by a simple act of 'deed': there is not any need to go to court. But if one party wants to change the lease and the other does not, this can only be resolved in court.

Repairs: Sue Jenkins owns the lease of a flat in Somerset, quite near the sea. One day a hole appeared in the flat's roof. It didn't produce exactly the sea view Sue desired, so she asked the freeholder of the flat to repair the roof, an obligation on him under the terms of her lease. He kept telling her he couldn't find the 'right kind of builder' to do the work. What could she do?

Depending on the terms of your lease, you can usually take the freeholder to court for a court order forcing him to do the repairs and for compensation for any inconvenience suffered. Or you can ask the local environmental health officer to issue a notice for repair if the state of the property is affecting your health, for example, if rain or damp comes in. *What you should not do is stop paying any charges owed under the lease.*

Service charges These must be 'reasonably incurred' and the freeholder or his agent must provide you with a clear breakdown if you query the charge: it is a criminal offence not to do this. This allows you, for example, to challenge a '£200 caretaking charge' if you have never seen a caretaker around your flats. Newer leases and flats recently bought from councils have arbitration procedures to sort out disputes instead of having to go to court, so check if these are mentioned in your lease.

Extending leases: Sylvia Jones bought a 90-year lease on her London mansion flat 20 years ago. Fearful that the value of her flat might start tumbling, she decided to renew her lease. The landlord agreed but said it would cost her £6000. This seemed an extortionate amount to Sylvia and she beat the landlord down to £5000 but he wouldn't go any lower. She wrote to us at *You and Yours.* **What could she do?**

The only thing she could really do was to keep negotiating with the landlord. She could point out that 40 or 50 years is a long time to wait around for the property to revert to him, and he may be dead by then. Besides, who knows what might happen in the meantime. Still, if a landlord refuses point-blank to

extend a lease, there is nothing you can do at all *at the moment*.

However, there have been several attempts in the past few years to give flat leaseholders similar rights as house leaseholders to be able to buy their lease even if the freeholder does not want to sell. It seems extremely likely the government will introduce new legislation soon to sort this out. Therefore, it is probably best to sit back and wait for this to happen. Or move to Scotland: the Scots abandoned lease ownership years ago.

COMPLAINTS ABOUT ESTATE AGENTS

When we broadcast a *You and Yours* programme about estate agents, the calls came thick and fast.

Some listeners felt their estate agent was too pushy, some felt not pushy enough. Some felt their agent had priced their property too low, some that their agent had no real interest in selling it at all. And to be fair to estate agents, many listeners were more than complimentary about the service they had received.

Let's get one kind of complaint out of the way first. Many people who buy houses or flats through estate agents complain that the description provided bears little relationship to the actual property – 'close to all facilities' turns out to mean on a busy main road, that kind of thing. (Interestingly enough, sellers rarely complain about this kind of hyperbole!) Unfortunately, there is nothing to stop estate agents doing this because house descriptions are, at the moment, exempt from the **1968 Trade Descriptions Act.**

If you see an estate agent's ad in a newspaper and magazine, though, and it turns out to be less than honest, you can complain to the **Advertising Standards Authority** (see p. 213). The Authority has ruled, for example, that a house in Sussex, described as 14 miles from Hastings when it was really 21, was against their code and the ad was stopped. The best advice, though, is to treat all estate agents' descriptions with a very sceptical eye.

The government has, however, recently announced plans to

crack down on estate agent descriptions which go beyond 'poetic licence'. As this book was being prepared for publication, it was too early to know exactly what kind of description will be banned, but the intention is to strengthen the **1979 Estate Agents Act**.

New controls on estate agents should become law in 1990 and 'undesirable practices' like agents forcing up house prices by inventing bids or not disclosing any financial interest they may have in a property look likely to be outlawed. The Office of Fair Trading will have new powers to strike off estate agents who break these new rules.

At the moment, the 1979 Act says estate agents must tell you their fees, how and when they are to be paid, and if they have any interest in the property. If your estate agent has not done this, contact the Office of Fair Trading.

If you think an estate agent has **overcharged** you or **behaved reprehensibly**, write to the manager of the local branch and then, if not successful, to the firm's head office.

One important thing to remember when dealing with estate agents is to read the information they provide carefully before signing up. Try and avoid giving them 'sole selling rights', as this means they will get their fee even if you sell the property yourself. And if you are giving them 'sole agency', lay down a deadline after which you can hand it over to someone else. Remember, too, an estate agent represents the interests of the seller and not those of the buyer. If you are buying, don't be misled into thinking they are neutral arbiters!

We have also heard stories at *You and Yours* of estate agents not selling a property on their books to a buyer unless he takes out a mortgage with their firm. **Graham Rider from Manchester complained that he had offered the asking price on a property through an estate agent – and been accepted until shortly before exchange of contracts. Then his offer was turned down and he later learned the property had been sold to another buyer for £2500 less. What stuck in his mind was that the estate agent also offered mortgages and had asked him if he wanted one from their firm, but he had said no. Perhaps the**

new buyer had offered to take out such a mortgage, Graham was left wondering.

As more and more estate agents are now owned by financial institutions, this kind of carry-on is bound to happen occasionally. If it does, the agent is not operating in the interests of his client, the seller (unless, that is, the seller prefers a lower price, say, for a quick sale). If you have any evidence of this happening, write to the Office of Fair Trading, which will soon have new powers to investigate and crack down.

Finally, some good news for dissatisfied estate agent customers. There is increasing pressure from consumer organisations and the **National Association of Estate Agents** to draw up a code of practice which would provide a benchmark of good estate-agenting. The government has indicated its support for this so it should happen soon.

And the complaints made by many, many people about estate agent boards littering their neighbourhood have had an effect. The 1988 regulations in England and Wales restricting one small estate agent sign to one property seem to be working. If you see a private house or flat with more than one small sign, contact trading standards officers. Unfortunately, this law does not apply to commercial property.

COMPLAINTS ABOUT SURVEYORS

When you buy a house or flat, you buy it as it is. If two weeks after you have moved in, the roof collapses, you cannot usually claim a refund from the person you bought it from. Building societies appoint a surveyor to do a property **valuation** for them which you pay for. You can now normally see a copy of the valuation before you fully commit yourself to the mortgage. You may also hire a surveyor (more often than not, the same person), to do a **full structural survey** for you or a less comprehensive **home-buyer's report** at a price less than the full survey but more than the valuation.

In theory, this means that if anything major is wrong with the property, the surveyor will advise you and if they miss something, you can sue them.

There are, however, two problems. First, what exactly should a surveyor's report, valuation or survey cover? And, second, the expense and expertise needed to take a surveyor to court. Many complaints about surveyors have languished against one or the other.

Surveyors have always argued that a valuation, which usually costs up to £100, cannot be expected to spot as many defects as a home-buyers' report (£200–400) or a full structural survey (£400 and upwards). You get what you pay for, they say. Their advice is always go for the full works – not surprisingly because they make more money. In general, however, it is pretty good advice, and is essential for any older property.

Surveyors can no longer get away with claiming that a low-cost valuation can't be expected to spot major defects.

Jean Smith, from Norwich, paid a surveyor to do a mortgage valuation for a terraced house which she was interested in buying. The surveyor valued the property at £16 500, and Jean bought the house for £18 000. After she moved in, however, the chimney collapsed and fell through Jean's bedroom. Jean took the surveyor to court – and the case went all the way to the House of Lords. The Law Lords ruled in 1989 that the surveyor had to pay Jean £4379 in damages.

The Lords also ruled that any exemption clauses surveyors insert into their contract disclaiming liability for the accuracy of their valuations cannot be used by them to get out of paying compensation if their survey was wrong. This means that if you buy a house for £100 000 after a surveyor has told you, effectively, it's worth the money, you can claim compensation from him if the house turns out to need a lot of essential building work he did not warn you about.

That's not bad, is it? Especially since the Law Lords' decisions are binding on all the courts in the land. The only trouble is it still remains both hazardous and expensive taking a surveyor to court.

There is a new arbitration scheme developed by the **Royal Institution of Chartered Surveyors**, the profession's regulatory body, which is designed as an alternative to court action.

It works by an independent arbitrator looking at the complaint and the surveyor's answer, and then deciding between the two. It costs the complainant about £57 and there is no upper limit on any award which is binding on both sides. There are drawbacks, however. First, the surveyor must agree to the arbitration as well as you. Second, it is probably not a good idea to use the scheme if you want to claim a lot of money in damages (say £5000 plus) or if your case is a complicated one. Third, it is extremely unlikely this arbitration service can be used if you just had a valuation and not a house-buying report or full survey. For these kind of cases, use the courts.

Get good legal advice before you start court proceedings. Ask your CAB for a solicitor who specialises in these kinds of cases: the law most helpful to you is the **1982 Supply of Goods and Services Act**, explained on p. 110.

If you take legal action, you will almost certainly have to pay for an independent report from another surveyor or a structural engineer. If you lose, the court costs can be high. But take heart. If you have a very strong case, confirmed by your solicitor and an independent expert, the recent Law Lords' decisions mean you have a very good chance of winning and getting all your costs repaid. You cannot, by the way, sue for the cost of the repairs needed, but only for the difference in value of your property if the defects the surveyor should have noticed were taken into account.

A new alternative to legal action for disputes about surveys or valuations obtained for a building society is to contact the **Building Societies Ombudsman** (see p. 125). He should soon have the power to deal with these kind of complaints.

Finally, all chartered surveyors must belong to the **Royal Institution of Chartered Surveyors** and follow the institution's professional rules. If you come across bad or sloppy practice by a surveyor, write to that Institution's professional practices committee. The committee has the power to discipline or expel.

FIXTURES, FITTINGS, CONTRACTS AND CLAUSES

Most house and flat buyers use a solicitor to sort out the contract of sale and to liaise with the seller, the local authority, the Land Registry and the mortgage company. It is as well to remember, irrespective of how well you get on with the seller, the mortgage firm and estate agent, your solicitor is the only person who is completely on your side, who represents your interests and no one else's. This is what you are paying him for! If your solicitor botches up the job, you can complain and, if necessary, sue (see p. 291).

It is up to you to scrutinise the contract the solicitor draws up and make sure the solicitor knows exactly what conditions you are prepared to agree with the seller.

In Scotland, once you have made an offer on a property, and it has been accepted by the seller, it is binding on both of you. In the rest of the United Kingdom, you and your seller only become committed to the sale of the property when you have 'exchanged contracts'. It is important to make sure this contract says what you want it to say.

The contract lays down the price and conditions of sale. If either are broken, you can claim damages. If, for example, the seller cannot move out on the day and time agreed, you can claim compensation. The contract can also include details of what is included in the price, the so-called fixtures, fittings and extras. This is where problems can occur.

Mary Smith was expecting her first day in her new home in the West Country to be a pleasurable surprise. It was certainly a surprise but not a pleasurable one. 'We suddenly noticed there wasn't any seat left on the toilet and there wasn't a door knob on the bathroom door so we couldn't close it. We looked around a little more closely and discovered there weren't any door knobs in the house at all! And when we tried to turn on the lights, there weren't any light bulbs left either'.

George and Christina Melton-White, from Northamptonshire, had a similar shock when they moved into their new home. 'We were very impressed by the curtains in the house. They fitted into the decor very

well. We decided to buy them and wrote "curtains" into the contract. When we moved into the house, there were curtains there all right, but they were tatty old things which looked like they were dragged up from the cellar. It was legalised robbery'.

Both the Smiths and the Melton-Whites were victims of 'fixtures and fittings', a nice, easy phrase that conceals as much as it allows. If your contract does not specify what is to stay and what can go, the general rule is that 'fixtures' automatically stay with the property and 'fittings' don't. Fixtures are things stuck to the building or the land and not simply put up for decoration or display, things like garages, fitted carpets and boilers. Fittings are decorations and the seller can take them. Unfortunately, there are several anomalies.

TV aerials, flowers and trees, light fittings and fitted cupboards, for example, can be either fixtures or fittings. Make sure these – and, indeed, any object you want to remain in the house and you don't think qualifies as a fixture – are inserted into your contract and described precisely. Do not, like George and Mary did, rely on goodwill. If these items are taken away, you can make a claim in the Small Claims Court (see p. 274).

NEWLY-BUILT HOMES

Almost all new houses and flats are protected by a warranty issued by the **National House Building Council (NHBC).** *Do not buy if the builder is not a member of this scheme.* The NHBC inspects a new home before issuing this warranty which covers most (but not all) major defects that may arise for 10 years. If major faults develop within the first two years of the warranty, complain to the builder, who should put them right for free. If you are not satisfied with the builder's response, write to the NHBC which will attempt to negotiate between you and the builder. If this does not work, NHBC will arrange arbitration.

If something major goes wrong after two years, the warranty is treated much like any other insurance claim. Contact the NHBC and it will inspect and then approve the work needed to put the property right. You pay a builder to do the work and the

NHBC then reimburses you. If the NHBC does not agree with you that the defects in the property are covered by the warranty, you can go to arbitration. They will explain how to do this.

If you buy a recently built house, check that it has a NHBC warranty and get it signed over to you. There is also a voluntary six-year warranty the NHBC offers for **new conversions** of old houses. Not very many builders offer this but check if it is available.

If you are employing a builder to build you a new house, always employ a surveyor as well, to check the builder's work. Although the builder will usually find out from the local authority about building and planning regulations and restrictions, do a double-check either yourself or through your solicitor because if any regulations are broken, you will be responsible, **as John and Sue Jones found out.**

They bought an old cottage in Herefordshire through a builder which was a 'tumble-down shell, virtually derelict with a red corrugated roof'. John and Sue, however, saw the house differently. They imagined it 'looking like a photo on a chocolate box with a lovely thatched roof'. And it was the thatched roof that proved the problem.

The builder restored the cottage to its former glory and the Jones family moved in. Three months later, however, they were visited by the chief building inspector of the local council. The problem, as the council saw it, was that the Jones' cottage was semi-detached and the roof of the house next door was not thatched at all. That meant the restored thatch on the Jones' house might be a fire risk to their neighbours. Even though many other houses in the village were thatched, they were not, unlike the Jones', attached to a non-thatched house. The council told John and Sue their builder had contravened building regulations and they would have to remove the thatched roof within 28 days. In the end, the situation was resolved without the Jones losing the thatch of their dreams, but the council was technically in the right.

Any major building, restoration or improvement work to a

house or flat may need local authority consent. This includes, for example, shifting an interior load-bearing wall or staircase. Always check with the local council's building control and planning department officers before beginning any work. If you disagree with their decision, you can apply to the Department of the Environment which may over rule the council, *but only before the building work is done, not afterwards.*

Finally, if you employ an **architect** to design your new home and they do a bad job, you can complain to their disciplinary body, **Architect's Registration Council of the United Kingdom (ARCUK)**, in the case of disgraceful conduct, or to their professional association, **Royal Institute of British Architects (RIBA)**, or its equivalent in Scotland and Northern Ireland, if the architect has breached professional standards. These organisations, however, cannot get your money back if the work was badly done or exorbitantly charged: just like any other service (see p. 110), you will have to go to court for this. RIBA, however, can help with a second architect's opinion which you will need for your case. If an architect employs a builder to do work for you and the work goes wrong, you cannot sue the builder; you have to sue the architect.

COUNCIL TENANTS

It may come as a surprise but recent research by University of Glasgow academics amongst others has revealed most council tenants think that their council is a good landlord, approachable and sensitive to their needs. They have to be. The **1980 and 1985 Housing Acts** gave all council tenants the right to buy their flat or house if they have been in residence more than two years.

As a result of all this, the number of council tenants has gone down in the last 10 years and may go down much further under more recent legislation.

If, by the way, you want to buy and you disagree with the price the council asks for, you can put your case to the district valuer (the council will provide you with details). You also have the right to a mortgage from the council.

Council tenants now also have the right to 'opt out', if a majority of tenants on their estate want to, to another landlord, most likely a housing association of some sort. If you want to do this – and each council must inform tenants of this right – contact the **Housing Corporation**.

One effect of all these changes is that councils have become much more tenant-friendly to their remaining tenants. And that's no bad thing given the kind of complaints that have come into the *You and Yours* office over the years about council housing.

A few – not very many – have been about increases in rent, and, unfortunately, there is very little you can do about this, at least in the short term. Councils are not bound by any of the 'fair rent' regulations which apply to some private tenancies. So, if you think your rent is too high, lobby your local councillor to change council policy – or don't vote him in next time.

Most complaints, though, are about repair. And the most bizarre one we have heard about at *You and Yours* was from **Bernard Jones**.

Bernard moved into his council house in Birmingham in August 1965. He noticed that his garden fence needed mending, and pointed this out to the council. He wanted a proper fence so his young children could play safely. Nothing, however, was done. Over the years, he tried to patch the fence and kept pointing out to the council that it needed repairing. He even stopped paying rent for a while but that didn't work. Finally, the council repaired the fence – in January 1988, 23 years after he had moved in. It wasn't because of Bernard's complaints, but instead due to a new system the council had introduced when any repair that had not been done for 12 months was automatically reviewed. 'He should have put more pressure on us', a council spokesman said, a little sheepishly. 'Two dozen complaints in 23 years is not good enough!'

All councils are under a legal obligation to repair and look after any structural problems with your house or flat. If the repair is 'minor' (say, less than £20) and the council cannot do it quickly, you can pay for the repair yourself and deduct it from your rent. Be careful, however, because the law which allows you to do this is confusing. It is best to give the council a reasonable time to make the repair and then get a couple of estimates and write to the council announcing your intentions.

The situation is more complicated for major repairs involving, for example, better insulation or rebuilding. You will have to take legal action and will certainly need a solicitor who specialises in housing law. **This is exactly what council tenants Jean and Bill Ireland from Sheffield did – and they won.**

Jean and Bill's council house had deteriorated to a quite dreadful state. The walls went black, fungus grew everywhere and the place stank. They kept reporting the matter to Sheffield City Council, but nothing was done and the Irelands' health suffered: they were constantly under doctor's care for depression and bronchitis. Through a solicitor, provided for them by the local law centre, the Irelands took Sheffield City Council to court under the 1985 Landlord and Tenants Act, claiming compensation for the nine years of distress they suffered due to the house not being in a 'reasonable state of repair'. They also asked the court for an injunction on the council to oblige them to repair the house. On the day of the court action, the council caved in and gave the Irelands £5000 compensation and offered to re-house them.

So, it is possible by using the law to force the council to make major repairs on your home. However, it is not an easy option: you have to show that the state of your home has a demonstrable effect on your family's health and you will need a hospital consultant's opinion confirming this. If your home is not that bad but you still think it is a health hazard, complain to your local environmental health officer, who can instruct the council to repair, under the Public Health Acts.

HOUSING ASSOCIATION TENANTS

Housing associations were invented in the middle ages, although they first came to wide public notice in the late nineteenth century when associations like the Guinness Trust and the Peabody Trust were set up to provide low-rent homes for the (so-called) 'deserving poor'. Since 1974, they have been regulated by a government body, the **Housing Corporation**, and they received a fillip recently when the government gave council tenants the right to opt-out of council control, usually by joining a housing association instead.

Although housing associations vary considerably in size – some have more tenants than some councils – they fall into two categories: *those which have charitable status and those which do not.* If you are a tenant of an association which is not charitable, you have an absolute right to buy your home just as if you were a council tenant. But if your housing association has charitable status, you don't have this right, although you may be able to claim a discount towards the price of a private house or flat.

That only applies, however, to existing tenancies taken out before the 1988 Housing Act came into force in January 1989. New tenants now have a different form of agreement called an **assured tenancy**, which does not give you any right to buy at all even if your housing association is non-charitable, although you may have preserved your 'right to buy' if your home has been transferred from council to housing association ownership.

All housing associations have a similar responsibility to repair your home as councils do for their tenants. Additionally, housing associations have to provide their tenants with targets for repair and also a way for tenants to monitor progress.

To complain about lack of repair or managerial incompetence, first write to the manager of the association and then, if not satisfied, to the housing association's board of management or trustees. Some charitable housing associations also allow their tenants representation on their board of management so you could try and make sure these members take up your complaint or vote them off next time. For serious 'breaches of rules' by the association, you can contact the Housing Corporation, which will look into the matter.

You can also take the association to court if your flat has become a statutory nuisance and they are not doing anything about it under the same laws as council tenants (see p. 89). Contact your local housing advice centre, via the CAB, or environmental health officer. All housing association rents must be assessed and agreed by a council rent officer. You have the right to examine this register and, if your rent is more, deduct the difference. If your rent has not been assessed, you can also apply for registration with the rent officer.

Finally, most housing association tenancies give you as much protection against eviction as council tenancies, as long as you conform to the association's rules. If you break the rules, however, the association still can't generally evict you unless you have suitable alternative accommodation arranged.

PRIVATE TENANTS

Your rights as a tenant of a private landlord are somewhat different from those of council or housing association tenants. In general, you have less rights, but you do have some protections. The most important thing that determines your rights is your contract with the landlord **which does not have to be written down**. It is worked out by the way you use your home and the date when you moved in.

If you rented your flat before 24 October 1974, your rights are different if your flat is **furnished** or **unfurnished**. Generally, unfurnished flats have security of tenure and are rent controlled.

If you rented after this date but before 15 January 1989, it does not matter whether your flat is furnished or not. All that matters is if it is a **protected tenancy** or a **short-hold** one, or one **where the landlord lives on the premises**. If it is protected, you cannot be evicted unless you stop paying the rent or bring the property into disrepair. Your rent is also controlled by the rent officer at your local council who can set a fair rent if you think the rent is too high. But if the landlord lives on the premises or the time of a short-hold agreement is up, he can evict you. He must, however, give you four weeks' notice in writing and inform you of your rights. And when this notice expires, he has to get a court order before any eviction takes place.

Tenancies taken out since 15 January 1989 are either

assured or **short-hold**. Assured tenants do have some security of tenure although there are several grounds for repossession that the landlord can use to get you out. He must still, however, go to court to do this. If your tenancy is assured, you can ask your council's **Rent Assessment Committee** to assess your rent, although they are now bound to work out not a 'fair' rent, but a 'reasonable market rent' instead.

For all types of tenancies, your landlord has a duty to keep the flat or house in a reasonable state of repair. If it needs repair, write and tell him so, and give him access to agree the repair. If he is not forthcoming, you will have to take him to court: local council housing departments can usually help you with this. Whatever you decide, *do not stop paying the rent, otherwise you could be evicted*. And if you are threatened with eviction, contact your local CAB or housing advice centre.

All letters from landlords of furnished or unfurnished property must now include their name and address, and the landlord must tell tenants if they sell the property and who the new landlord is. If you feel your landlord is harassing you, write to him and ask him to stop, saying that you will contact your local council's harassment officer or the police if he persists. You can also apply to the courts for an injunction but do take local authority advice first.

YOUR HOME: SERVICES AND BILLS

THE POLL TAX/COMMUNITY CHARGE

From April 1990, rates will be replaced in England and Wales by a new bill from local councils called, officially, the **community charge** but more popularly known as the '**poll tax**'. In Scotland, the community charge was introduced in 1989, and there are, as yet, no plans to introduce it into Northern Ireland – there you still have to pay rates.

Rates were assessed according to your property's rateable value, but the poll tax is an individual charge on all adults living in the house.

There are some over 18s who are exempt from this new charge, such as those still at school, long-term hospital in-patients and the severely mentally handicapped. Most people, however, will have to pay.

It is still too early to assess both how this tax is going to work and what the most effective ways are of sorting out any problems. But here are some general pointers:

1 Councils will set their own poll tax bill and these will vary across the country.

2 It is an offence not to register with your local community charge registration office or not to fill in registration forms. Offenders will be fined.

3 Married or cohabiting couples will be legally responsible for each other's poll tax. But they will not be responsible for other adults in the house such as grown-up children or elderly parents.

4 People on low incomes can apply for a rebate, although this will not cover the whole amount of the bill. Check with your council's local registration officer if you qualify. Most people on income support will.

5 If you have another home, you will have to pay the **standard community charge** assessed by the council where this home is, unless you have rented it out. Landlords are not responsible for their tenant's poll tax.

6 If you live in a short-stay residential home, such as a hostel, you will have to pay the **collective community charge**, assessed

by the local council for residents in that home. Some homes, like those providing care, will be exempt. Your registration officer can tell you which ones.

If you live in Scotland, you can complain about your assessment for poll tax to the **Community Charge Registration Officer** at your local council. If you are not satisfied, your only option is to take your complaint to the local Sheriff Court. If you live in England and Wales, the registration officer is also the first person to complain to but there will be, in addition, a **Community Charge and Valuation Tribunal**, which can have complaints referred to it.

GAS

British Gas has been operating as a private company for several years now, but its service to consumers leaves a lot to be desired. And that's not our opinion at *You and Yours* but that of **James McKinnon**, director general of **OFGAS**, the organisation the government set up to watch over the industry when gas was privatised.

Mr McKinnon told the 1989 Consumer Congress that British Gas' 17 million domestic consumers get a worse level of service than British Telecom, water industry and electricity customers. Even Mr McKinnon's own experience as a customer was not a happy one. 'People think I automatically get good service because of who I am, but it is not true. Following an unfortunate incident between a gas man and my German shepherd dog, I was told not to expect any more service'.

A case, then, of British Gas shooting itself in the foot. If they can't make sure the country's chief gas watchdog (and the watchdog's watchdog at that) is happy with the gasman, what chance do the rest of us have?

To be fair, though, British Gas' record on the most important part of their service, safety, is good. And they have pledged to introduce a **customer's charter** which should give us all a benchmark to measure their performance against.

OFGAS regulates the industry and particularly regulates its prices. But there is another organisation which deals with most consumer complaints: the **Gas Consumers Council**.

The Gas Consumers Council has 12 regional offices, including Scotland, that consumers can complain to. (There is not an office in Northern Ireland for the simple reason that British Gas does not operate there.) These offices have consumer advisors who can help sort out your complaint if you don't have any luck with your local gas region: the address is on your gas bill. The advisors refer some complaints to OFGAS itself.

Complaints about bills Try first to sort out any complaints with your local gas region. If you don't have any luck, contact the regional office of the Gas Consumers Council, which will take the matter up, right to the top, if necessary.

If you can't pay your bill, you can arrange to have a prepayment meter installed. This meter is free and it works by crediting a small amount towards your past bill when you pay for gas you need. Most meters work on tokens which are not, at the moment, widely sold. Your local gas showroom should sell them.

If you think your meter is faulty, ask the gas region to replace it and to send the old meter to the **Department of Energy Testing Station**. If you are right, you will get a refund, but if the meter turns out not to be faulty, you will have to pay a fee of about £20.

Disconnection Three years ago, the rate of disconnections rose alarmingly and British Gas was heavily criticised for not taking into account some customers' inability to pay. British Gas now generally does not cut off people who are in debt as long, of course, as they know about it. *Tell them at once, if you cannot pay your bill*. Involve your Citizens Advice Bureau or Gas Consumers Council regional customer advisor if necessary. For any disconnection that involves entering your home, the gas company has to go to court to get a warrant.

Right of supply This is still one of the main areas of complaint: there are many villages in the remoter parts of Britain which are not on the mains supply. It is worth complaining to British Gas if your village is still not connected: the Gas Consumers Council recently pushed Scottish Gas to put the village of Dyce, near Aberdeen, on the mains. You have a right to be connected free only if you live within 25 yards of an existing mains.

Service Gas servicing seems to be improving although we have heard at *You and Yours* of stories about emergency insurance contracts taken out with local gas companies not being met with emergency-like haste.

You have the same rights against gas company servicemen or installers as you have with any service provided (see p. 110). And you can also claim compensation if they do not turn up when you agreed they should. The gas board, however, can say they had to break the appointment because of an emergency concerning safety elsewhere, such as a gas leak. Emergency call-outs take priority over anything else.

There is nothing to stop you using tradesmen other than British Gas' to repair your cooker or central heating system but it is then up to you to ensure the servicing is done according to British Gas' regulations.

Safety Any worries or concerns about gas safety must be dealt with by your gas board straight away, even in the middle of the night. Call the emergency number in the telephone directory if you are concerned. That's not just sensible advice: there is a statutory duty on people to call the gas board if they smell gas or suspect a gas leak. You can be held responsible for any accident or explosion if you don't.

Calor gas Portable gas canisters are not supplied by British Gas. They come from 'portable gas' companies, the best known of which is Calor Gas. Complaints should be made first to their regional office's customer services department and then directly to their head office. If you have no luck, however, or if your complaint is about safety, you could contact the trade association, **Liquefied Petroleum Gas Industry Technical Association (LPGITA)**. They enforce safety procedures and codes of conduct on all portable gas suppliers.

ELECTRICITY

As this book goes to press, the final details of how British electricity will be transferred from public to private ownership have yet to be worked out. What seems likely, however, is that electricity boards will become **public electricity supply companies** and they will be regulated by a new organisation called **OFFER**. This body will operate like OFGAS (see p. 97), but it will have more staff and also, unlike OFGAS, regional offices.

As well as OFFER, there will probably be regional **consumer committees**. These committees will be the main places to take any complaints. They will work closely with OFFER. In Northern Ireland, electricity will remain under public ownership and all complaints should be made with the help of the **General Consumer Council for Northern Ireland**.

To complain about electricity services in England, Scotland and Wales under the new private system of ownership, here's probably what you'll have to do:

1 Complain to your area electricity company's customer services department first, then to the general manager.
2 Then with most complaints contact your regional **consumer committee**. It will look into the matter and negotiate with the company for you. Its address should be on your bill.
3 If the complaint still isn't resolved, the **committee** can then refer it to OFFER, either to a regional office or to its director general. If you think your complaint is sufficiently serious, you can contact OFFER direct without going to the consumer committee first.

OFFER will have the power to order the electricity company to pay you compensation if it is appropriate. It will also be able to make sure electricity companies follow their code of practice about disconnections, for example, or connecting people to the mains.

Right of supply You have the right to be connected to the mains even if you live in the most remote part of the UK mainland. The electricity company will, though, charge you for this. But this charge must be **reasonable**, and if you don't think it is, contact your regional consumer committee.

Size of bill You can get your meter checked in the same way as for your gas bill (see p. 97).

Problems paying the bill Ask the accounts department if you can pay in instalments. Make sure they know at once if you do not think you can meet your commitments. Also seek help from your local CAB: the advisors can advise about any state benefits you might be able to claim to help with heating costs. A CAB advisor might also be able to negotiate with the electricity company for you to get a pre-payment meter. Make sure this is set at a realistic rate so you can afford to keep the electricity on.

Disconnection Just like British Gas, the electricity companies have committed themselves to not automatically cutting off people who have difficulty paying their bill, providing, of course, they know about any problems. They will negotiate with you about paying in instalments or having a pre-payment meter (see above).

If you are threatened with disconnection, write to the company explaining your circumstances and be sure to say if there are any dependent people in the house. A CAB advisor can probably help as well. If the company cuts you off when they should not have done (for example, if they lost your cheque), you can sue them for breach of contract and claim compensation for inconvenience.

Goods bought at electricity showrooms Under the Sale of Goods Act, you have the same rights for electrical goods bought at showrooms as you have with items bought at any other shop.

Also, if you still owe money for any item and you have agreed to have a pre-payment meter installed to help you pay off your old bill, the electricity company cannot try and reclaim the money for the item by fixing the meter. If they do try this, contact your regional consumer committee.

WATER

Just as with the electricity industry, the water services are in the midst of being transferred from public to private ownership as this book is being prepared for publication. What is likely to happen is that the regional water authorities will become private companies, and they will be regulated by two organisations, **OfWat**, responsible for supply and standards of service, etc.

and the **National Rivers Authority**, responsible for wider environmental matters.

There will also be **customer service committees**, which will work closely with OfWat and will be the first port-of-call for consumer complaints.

This only applies, by the way, to England and Wales: the **Northern Ireland Office** will still control water there, and complaints should go either to it or to the **Northern Ireland Consumer Council**. In Scotland, water will remain the responsibility of **regional councils**: contact them with complaints.

In England and Wales the new water companies have said they will pay you £5 if they do not respond promptly to a complaint, if they break an appointment or if they cut your supply for more than 24 hours, excluding situations like droughts. Hold them to this.

Paying for water Some water companies can provide you with a meter. This is a good idea if your water consumption is below average, but you will have to pay more if you use a lot of water. There are experiments being conducted with compulsory water meters, and some water companies look likely to adopt this method of working out your bill once they get going. Others will go for a flat rate for everybody in their area.

Disconnection If you have problems paying your water bill, let the company know at once. They can arrange, for example, for a pre-payment meter to be installed (see p. 100). There is a strict code of conduct that the water companies must conform with before disconnecting someone. They have to offer you the chance of paying by instalments, and they should not cut you off during any dispute about an old bill. Also, they are not allowed to cut you off if you are getting DSS or social services help.

If you cannot pay your water bill, get in touch with your local CAB. If you think a water company has breached its code of conduct, contact OfWat.

Colour and taste: Merseyside newsagent Lynn Claire thought her water was beginning to taste fishy. When she looked more closely at it, she found freshwater shrimps swimming around, several of them in each cup. It put her and her children off drinking the water

completely, although the local water authority said the water was quite safe! Lynn refused to pay her water rates until the shrimps were removed.

If your water doesn't have shrimps in it, but still doesn't taste as it should, or, to take another example, the water seems a funny colour, contact the water company's district office. If it does not resolve the matter, go to the head office, to the top if necessary. You can then write to your local customer services committee and warn it about the situation, or alternatively, tell OfWat. OfWat has a duty to make sure water companies provide safe and drinkable water so it may take the matter up and order independent testing. The 1989 Water Act makes it a criminal offence to supply water which is unfit for consumption.

OfWat will also be interested if you have any evidence or strong suspicions that there may be unacceptable levels of chemicals in the water supply. But contact the water company first: it will almost certainly take up the matter. After all, it could be prosecuted – and fined heavily – if it is allowing the water supply to be polluted. You can also bring any worries you have about the health of your water to your local environmental health officer.

To challenge the *allowable* level of chemicals in water, contact environmental pressure groups like **Friends of the Earth**, which campaign on water issues.

POST

Complaints about the post are handled differently from the other basic services. The postal services are split up into three different sections: letter post (controlled by 64 district head postmasters); parcels (controlled by 12 district parcel managers) and counter services (controlled by 32 district counter managers).

To complain about any aspect of the postal services, ask at your local post office for the address of the appropriate district and write to the **customer care department**. This is the Post Office's equivalent of a large firm's 'customer services'. If you are dissatisfied with the answer, write to the postmaster or manager direct, preferably by name.

If this doesn't work, you can then involve two consumer organisations, the locally based **Post Office Advisory Committees** (ask the customer care department for their address), or the four **Post Office Users National Council (POUNC)** – one for England, Wales, Scotland and Northern Ireland.

Complaints about delivery: Bill Thorne, a retired civil servant, discovered a lot of the mail to his central London flat was going missing. He started checking with people who had sent him mail, and discovered that in three months, eight letters didn't arrive, including a cheque from York and some sheet music he had ordered. He complained, pointing out that perhaps the postman did not go to his flat because there was not a lift. Bill's post still did not appear. In the end, he used a post office box number, costing £72 a year, to make sure his post got to him. 'It was sheer frustration', Bill told us. 'Complaining just did not make the post appear'.

Bill went through all the channels suggested above – with no avail. There was one more thing he could have done, which would have needed POUNC help. That was to ask the Post Office to examine their system of delivery to Bill's flat.

If mail persistently does not arrive, POUNC can press the Post Office to revise and change its local delivery system. That should eventually do the trick.

Bill Thorne's case was an extreme example of what many people have faced at one time or another: letters and parcels that do not arrive. Post Office customer care departments will send you a form which enables them to trace a letter through their network. It will also circulate the 'returned letters' branch to check if the letter was badly addressed. But you cannot get *compensation* for lost mail unless the mail is **registered** (not just recorded) for inland mail or **insured** if you send something overseas.

If your missing mail was registered, the Post Office has to deal with your complaint within six weeks under their **code of practice**. If it is not dealt with satisfactorily, or if you are not offered enough compensation, you can take the case to the Post Office's arbitration scheme which is run by independent arbiters. You will have to pay a fee for this (currently £15) which is refundable if the arbitrator decides in your favour. Details of the arbitration scheme can be provided by POUNC or the local advisory committee.

You can also use the scheme if your mail is damaged. What often happens when arbitration proceedings start is that the Post Office offers an *ex gratia* payment without admitting liability.

Complaints about **parcels** are dealt with in the same way, as are those about **counter services**. To complain about your local post office **closing down**, contact the district head postmaster. You will need to get a petition started at least, and to enlist your local post office advisory committee's support to win your case.

TELEPHONE

The main association that deals with consumer complaints about telephone services is **OfTel,** which is also the regulatory organisation as well, the industry watchdog. Unlike gas, electricity and water, there is no separation of a consumers council and a national watchdog for the telephone industry which makes things a good deal simpler!

OfTel takes up individual complaints about all telephone services for **Mercury** as well as **British Telecom** and **Hull Council's** own local service. It also has two specialist committees which handle complaints on behalf of elderly and disabled telephone users (DIEL) and small businesses (BACT).

In addition to OfTel, there are also some 170 local **Telephone Advisory Committees (TACs)** which can help you with your complaint. British Telecom will give you their address. Both the committees and OfTel itself will want you first to try and sort things out with the telephone company.

Bills Complaints about telephone bills are by far the most contentious and common. Virtually everybody is surprised by the amount of a telephone bill at one time or another, and some people cannot understand why it is so high at all. If you want to challenge your bill, here's what to do:

1 Write to the area accounts office and ask for the bill to be checked. All telephones have a meter at the exchange which logs calls. British Telecom first check this meter and then use logging equipment to make sure your phone is working properly.

    If you are not satisfied with the response from the accounts office, you can contact the general manager and then the regional director. Make sure no one is using your phone surreptiously, for example, by phoning expensive chatlines.

2 If you still do not have a satisfactory response, contact your local TAC or OfTel. They will make sure British Telecom have done all the checks they can.

3 If the situation is still unresolved, you can use the British Telecom **code of practice** which gives you the right to take your case to arbitration. BT, however, must agree as well, although they usually do. This will cost you £15 which is refundable if you win. You will have to produce some pretty strong evidence to convince the arbitrator: perhaps a meter you have had installed at home and certainly past bills. Alternatively, you can take BT to court but your chances of success are pretty slim.

Disconnection Under their code of practice, BT cannot disconnect you while you are in dispute with them about a bill, although it is probably better to pay the portion of the bill you do not dispute. This shows good faith. BT also cannot disconnect you straight away if your phone is essential to your health. If this is so, contact your local social services or if you are elderly or disabled, DIEL via OfTel.

Faults with your phone BT are committed to sending engineers to check faults within two working days of the fault being reported. Hold BT to this – and complain to the district service manager if it takes any longer. The engineers must check the line and find out if it is at fault. If your phone is rented from BT, any equipment fault must be repaired free or you have to be given a replacement.

    If you have bought your phone and it goes wrong, you have all the normal rights under the Sale of Goods Act (see p. 39) to get you money back from the shop.

Metering calls You have no automatic right to a meter at home nor to a phone bill which itemises each call, although in some parts of the United Kingdom it is now possible to get an itemised bill. You can, however, ask BT to meter calls for a set period of time.

Carol Gibson from Berkshire asked BT to monitor her calls over Christmas while she put up some visitors from Australia. BT promised – but they then forgot. Carol complained and eventually received 200 free units from BT as compensation for their broken promise: the price of a couple of calls to Australia to tell her visitors what they owed her!

Callboxes If you can't get through, ask the operator who must charge you at normal dialling rates and refund you if you have had a crossed line. If your local callbox is out of action, contact BT or Mercury. BT have promised that 95 per cent of callboxes should be working at any one time. Let OfTel know if the other 5 per cent all seem to be in your local area.

Directory listings: Derek Barnes used to look forward to his Sunday lie-in. That was until he started getting calls asking him the times of trains from Dundee. Which was a little surprising since Derek lived in Cumbria. And it was not just the odd call, but regularly from 6.30 every Sunday morning. He complained and eventually discovered the Dundee telephone directory included this information for British Rail passenger enquiries. 'Sunday 0900–2200'. That was Derek's number in Cumbria, 100 miles away.

What had happened was that the real number for passenger enquiries was next to 'British Rail', and the number next to 'Sunday' was, in fact, the opening hours. 'Anybody must be thick not to realise that', said a British Telecom spokesman. 'Can't imagine people making that mistake', said a British Rail spokesman. But a lot of people did make the mistake, and they weren't all 'thick' by any means.

British Rail promised Derek they would remove the ambiguity in the next edition. Derek could, how-

ever, have taken BT to court for the inconvenience he
suffered due to the misleading description.

The same applies to any mistake made in the telephone
directory, for example, excluding you or including you if you
requested ex-directory. Ask the area office for compensation.

Chatlines and other special services The range of services
offered over the telephone is increasing each year, anything and
everything from the weather to soft pornography. Chatlines
have recognisable codes like 0898, 0077 and 0836, and each
chatline advertisement must carry a note of the cost per minute:
this is usually quite considerable. OfTel control the cost of these
services, but a different organisation, **Independent Committee for the Supervision of Standards of Telephone
Information Services (ICSTIS)** watches out for problems
concerning taste and decency.

Because of so many complaints from parents about large
bills run up by their children using chatlines, OfTel are examining ways to control these lines. Stricter controls should be in
place by the time this book is published.

Some parents who were horrified by the size of their telephone bill because their child was phoning a chatline and they
didn't know have been able to negotiate a reduction with BT.

Decency is another matter. Some people have complained
about sexually explicit phone services which are advertised in
national newspapers. Others have complained they were misled
because the service was not explicit enough! Just as with sex on
television, public standards change. If you want to complain,
contact ICSTIS. They have a free 24-hour complaints line:
0800 500 212.

**Janice Brown called the complaint line. Her com-
plaint wasn't over a pornographic service but an abusive one called 'Mr Bates'.**

**Janice discovered a message on her answering
machine one evening simply saying to phone a 'Mr
Bates' about some money she owed. She did not know
anything about this at all, but phoned to find out what
it was about. 'Mr Bates' then proceeded to shout abuse
down the phone to her for a couple of minutes before
another voice cut in to tell her it was only a spoof.**

Janice, however, did not share the joke. She was upset by the abuse and also by the fact that the call had cost her £1. She complained to ICSTIS, along with many others – and 'Mr Bates', who turned out to be not a person, but a very clever recorded message, was taken off the air by ICSTIS. 'He' was only allowed back with a preface telling people it was a 'recorded, entertainment line' and how much it cost to listen.

All service lines, by the way, have to be licensed by BT, and there will soon be a code of practice, prepared by ICSTIS, under which they will have to operate. This will include sexually explicit lines.

COAL

All coal merchants must belong to a **Regional Panel of Approved Coal Merchants**. Try to resolve any complaint you may have about coal quality or service with the merchant first but if you do not have any success, contact the regional panel. The panel sets standards of quality and service, and it can take up your complaint. If you do not have any luck with this association, you can then write to the **Domestic Coal Consumers Council**, which operates much like the consumer councils in the gas and electricity industries.

MISSED APPOINTMENTS

The gas man, the electricity company repairman and the water officer have to visit straight away if there is any problem that looks as if it may threaten life. And, by and large, they all respond quickly and promptly to emergencies. But for other appointments . . . isn't it funny that you wait in all day and then pop out for a moment and often they have been and gone with one of their horrible notes saying 'we called . . . but you were out'. It is almost as if they wait around the corner in their vans until they see you leave. Maybe it is not quite that bad, but virtually everybody has lost days at work waiting for repairmen to call.

Fortunately, the situation looks as if it is improving. The gas companies, for example, have even gone as far as offering compensation for missed appointments which were clearly their fault. Check any obligations with the appropriate consumer council or committee if you have taken time off work or lost money due to waiting for a repairman who has not shown.

What you can do as well is to deduct a small amount off the final bill when it finally arrives – write and tell the company concerned you are doing this and why, giving precise details of what you were promised and what actually happened.

This also applies, by the way, to all the services you pay money for at home, such as builders, plumbers, electricians, removal men and so on.

SERVICES PROVIDED AT HOME

Patricia Parsons, a retired civil servant, decided she needed some essential plumbing work done in her small, studio flat in West London. She rang a free advice line to put her in touch with a plumber near her who could do the work. Two plumbers were suggested but both turned out to be unsatisfactory. The advice line then recommended another plumber from South London, who told Patricia he could do the job with the materials she wanted. He did, or at least she thought he had, for Patricia is blind and she had to take the work on trust.

She paid him £650 for the plumbing work and then asked the plumber if he knew a decorator who could redecorate her flat and put in new work surfaces. The plumber volunteered himself, and over the next six weeks he popped into the flat to strip surfaces and repaint. At the end of the job, he charged £2300 and, despite misgivings, Patricia paid. The flat seemed to be decorated well. That was until friends who came around started, somewhat hesitantly, to point out all the mistakes, such as the wrong paint being used, paint splashed all over the kitchen and worse, much worse.

After protests from Patricia, the plumber came back and tried to rectify matters – to no avail. Patricia was left feeling that 'I would never trust people again. I had always done this, being blind for 44 years but he just took away all that trust'.

She was not, however, going to let this cowboy get away with it. Using the skills learnt from a lifetime of dealing with people, and motivated, too, by her strong sense of English fair-play, Patricia wrote to the plumber to complain, and asked for a detailed list of the work he had done.

Then she contacted a local trading standards officer who sent round an inspector. He was as horrified with the work done as she was. She then had independent expert backing to support her claim that the plumber had not done the work she had paid him for – and she could take him to court under a very useful consumer law called the 1982 Supply of Goods and Services Act.

This Act applies to virtually all of the contracts and agreements we make with anyone providing us with a service, professionals as well as tradesmen, so let's look at it in some detail.

The 1982 Supply of Goods and Services Act

This law states that all service contracts must be carried out with reasonable care and skill, within a reasonable time if no specific time was agreed, and at a reasonable price if no specific price was agreed. All materials used must also meet the conditions laid down in the **1979 Sale of Goods Act**. That is, they must be 'as described', 'fit for purpose' and 'of merchantable quality' (see p. 39).

There are, however, a few drawbacks so let's get those out the way first.

♦ The Act does not apply to a service performed by family or friends: you can't take Uncle Bill to court if he has mucked up installing your new gas cooker, unfortunately. Or perhaps fortunately, for family togetherness.

♦ Neither does it apply if the service had been done free of charge.
♦ And finally, for some reason or another, the Act does not apply in Scotland. There, you have to use common law to take the tradesman to court – although your rights are broadly similar. (Northern Ireland, however, is covered like England and Wales.)

Apart from the above exclusions, the Supply of Goods and Services Act is great news, although, just like the Sales of Goods Act, it is a *civil*, not a *criminal* law (see p. 26). You have to take the supplier to court, no one else will do it for you.

Here's how the Act works.

Price: Actor Lesley Glazer needed a plumber when one of his pipes burst at his London home one evening. A card from a local company had recently come through his door, so he rang the firm and a plumber quickly turned up. The plumber fixed the leak but then water started cascading down from other leaks in Lesley's bedroom, and Lesley asked the plumber to fix those as well. The job, according to Lesley and his mother, took a total of three hours – and was done well. But when Lesley was presented with the bill, it came to £442.75, 'the equivalent of a fortnight's holiday in Greece', Lesley told *You and Yours*. **'I was astounded and aghast'.**

Lesley complained to the firm which said he had been charged for 13 hours work. This was quite different from Lesley's estimate, which was confirmed by an independent expert who said it was an 'uncomplicated job, straightforward enough, and should take about 3–3½ hours at a cost of about £100–£120'. Lesley then offered this amount for the job. He was within his rights.

If you have not agreed a price with a plumber, builder, double glazer or indeed anybody who is providing you with a service, the price must be reasonable for the work involved. To find out if the price charged is reasonable, get an independent assessment.

Obviously, the best thing to do, however, is to agree a price beforehand. Ask the supplier for a **quote** which is legally binding on both you and him if he does the job competently. If he won't give a quote (and many will not because it is difficult sometimes to work out exactly how much a job will cost in advance), get an **estimate** instead; this means that the job may turn out to be more or less, but it shouldn't be all that much more unless something unforeseen needs to be done. If that happens, make sure you agree to this new work, and get a new estimate before it is started.

Standard The Supply of Goods and Services Act states that all services must be done to a reasonable standard. That means they must be done competently and well according to the kind of job you could expect for such work. It is no excuse if the tradesman says he is 'new to the job', or that he was using an 'inexperienced apprentice'. That's his problem, not yours. He will have to pay for his or his apprentice's incompetence, not you.

Obviously, though, you cannot expect the same standard from, say, a one-man removal firm than from a 'household name', since the price you pay may be much less. But the one-man firm still has to do a competent job and meet the standard you might reasonably expect him to meet, given the price. And if he damages your furniture during the job, you have exactly the same right to compensation as you would have against a larger company.

Time If you have not agreed a time, the time taken must be *reasonable*. A double glazing firm, for example, cannot take weeks to install your new windows by claiming they could only squeeze the job into a tight work schedule. They must do the job within the time you would reasonably expect them to take. And you can claim compensation for any period you spend with plastic sheets up instead of glass windows. But if they told you their schedule was very busy and it might take a few weeks to finish the job, you wouldn't have a claim. Try and get any tradesman to estimate the time the job will take in writing, or make a note of any time limit you agree to when you arrange the job.

Materials used Just as with goods you buy from shops, the materials used by tradesmen must be of merchantable quality, as described and fit for any purpose you may have asked for. You can claim against the firm doing the job if the materials turn out to be shoddy or not up to it. *Your claim is against the tradesman not* *against any shop or wholesaler he may have bought the materials from.* If you ask for a specific type of paint or building material, he cannot substitute a cheaper alternative. But if you do specify a particular brand or kind of material to be used, and it turns out to be inappropriate for the job, you will have to put up with it: it was, after all, your mistake. Try not to lay down precise instructions about what materials tradesmen should use unless you are convinced they are the right ones.

How to complain about shoddy work

1 Point out any badly done work as soon as you notice it, preferably while the tradesmen are still there. Don't be afraid of making a fuss; it is your home they are meant to be improving, not their own.

2 If the work done is a mess, refuse to pay the bill or only pay what you think is reasonable. Put this in writing to the firm and send the letter recorded delivery, just in case.

3 If the tradesmen demand the money before leaving your house and you refuse, they can threaten to undo the work but they must leave your house in the same condition as when they found it. In these circumstances, though, it is probably better to pay some or all of the money 'under protest'. Tell them this and write a letter confirming it.

4 If you do not receive a reply and your builder works for a firm, write to the owner or managing director complaining about the job. Give the firm a chance to put it right. If the firm disputes that the job was badly done, get an independent expert in (perhaps from a trade association) for confirmation.

5 If you still don't get satisfaction, write to the firm giving it 14 days to put the work right, otherwise you will take it to court under the 1982 Supply of Goods and Services Act. If you can afford it, get a solicitor to write for you. A trading standards officer or CAB worker may help as well. Trading standards departments cannot prosecute a tradesman for *bad workmanship*, but they can prosecute *if he provided a written account of what he has done and the reality failed to live up to this.* Therefore when

you write to the firm, ask for a description of the work done as justification for the bill, then show this to the trading standards officer.

6   If all this fails, take the firm to court under the Act. But, be sure to have independent expert backing before you do this. You can also consider claiming compensation.

7   Alternatively, you can contact any trade association the firm may belong to and use their **arbitration system** if there is one. If the firm is not a member (and it is a pretty good idea to choose a firm who does belong to a recognised association before you agree a job), the association can put you in touch with one of their members who can do an independent assessment of the work done for you to use in court.

8   Finally, if you have not paid the bill because the work was badly done, do not be dismayed by any court action the firm might threaten or use against you to get its money. The firm will have to take a civil action against you: it is not a criminal offence to withhold money if you have due cause and you have told them why you are withholding it. You can counterclaim against the firm for compensation for any loss caused by its bad workmanship.

Follow these steps and you should be able to resolve most complaints about shoddy workmanship done in your home, or, indeed, in any service you have paid for, at home or outside. For example, shoe repairing and laundry services are covered by the 1982 Supply of Goods and Services Act, as are electrical and car repairs.

If you have problems with any kind of practical service you have paid someone for, you have the same rights under the Act – and you can complain in the same way.

The Act also covers services by most **professionals**, such as surveyors, estate agents, solicitors (apart from work in court), architects and many others. *Exceptions are National Health Service employees like doctors and nurses, and anybody employed directly by the government who are all covered by crown immunity.* The only condition for using the Act is that you have a contract with the professional. This contract doesn't have to be in writing. It can just be a verbal agreement to pay for his service.

Most problems with services provided at home can be resolved by using this law – and often the threat of legal action is enough to get the work done properly or your money back. But let's just look at some of the practical services that frequently produce the most complaints at *You and Yours* – and the particular problems that come up.

Builders

On virtually every list of common complaints that have been drawn up at some time or another, building work comes out top. The so-called 'cowboy' builder has become a household word and a household fear: even the reputable building trade uses the phrase to disparage their back-street competitors. The cowboy has become almost an affectionate term of abuse, almost a joke. Except, that is, for those who have had a sorry experience when using them to repair their home, people like coal miner **Bill Jubb**.

Bill wanted a new porch for his house and saw a card in a local shop window for a firm that could do the job. He has regretted it ever since. The porch that was constructed turned out to be completely lop-sided, in Bill's words, 'it was just like the leaning tower of Pisa'. While *that* tower has lasted several hundred years and has become a tourist attraction, Bill's porch didn't have any such compensation: it made his home look awful. The firm promised Bill it would mend the porch, but it took six months. The porch was only repaired after Bill threatened to take the firm to court.

Bill's experience is by no means uncommon – and was one of many complaints that led to his local trading standards department in Yorkshire to call for a government backed 'home improvement checklist', and for registration of all builders who offer home repairs. We are still waiting for such a list, and registration seems pretty unlikely. In the meanwhile, however, the **Office of Fair Trading** has produced some rules which you could try and follow when agreeing to house repairs to avoid ending up in the same situation as Bill.

The Office recommends:

- Decide what you want done before asking a builder in, and check if the job needs planning permission from your local council.
- Shop around for at least two quotes and find out about the firms you are thinking of using. Ask them what other work they have done and get references.
- Agree a contract with them, in writing if you can, specifying the work needed, the cost, the materials to be used, cancellation rights and guarantees, the time the job will take and if they will clear up the mess.
- Be careful about deposits. Do not pay for all the work in advance, and try and pay only for work once it has been done and you approve the quality. It is, though, reasonable to pay for materials before any work is done.
- Make sure the builders need your agreement before taking on any new work that they discover might need doing – and agree the cost.
- Draw attention to any defects in the work as soon as you spot them.
- If you are still dissatisfied with the work, contact the firm and then your local trading standards department.

By following these steps, you should not end up with building work that costs you more to put right than it cost in the first place. But if you do need to complain, follow the suggestions outlined on p. 113.

It must be said, however, that good builders are in heavy demand these days and some of them can pick and choose their work. If you have been recommended a builder by friends and he does not want to give you precise times when he can do the work – 'I've got too many other jobs going, gov'ner. I can't say exactly when I can do it' – you may have to compromise about time. After all, you wouldn't want to employ a builder no one else wants! But do not compromise on agreeing beforehand about money and materials.

And there is something else you can do as well. Ask the builder if he is a member of a trade association, such as the

Building Employers Confederation, and check the trade association out as well. Find out if it is well established and if it has an arbitration procedure.

Some trade associations offer **insurance** against their members going bust, others offer a **warranty system** guaranteeing work done. And most offer a **code of practice** and an **arbitration system**, which you can use instead of taking the builder to court, if things go wrong. None of these building codes of practices have, however, Office of Fair Trade approval.

Plumbers and heating engineers

Next to builders, plumbers and central heating engineers come out top amongst complaints about services with *You and Yours* listeners – and probably with most other people, too. All the advice about builders and general complaints about services (see p. 110) applies to these people. There are several trade associations which can put you in touch with local members.

Do not, however, put all your trust in trade association help, as **David and Karen Fagan** found out:

They called in a plumbing firm when their pipes burst. They left the firm to it while they went shopping, a shopping trip which took longer than expected. They returned home to find the job complete and expected a bill of 'about £200 for 9–10 hours work'. When the bill came, it was for £496. The firm had charged for 25 hours work for the plumber and his plumber's mate.

This bill shocked the Fagans and they wrote to the Institute of Plumbing and the Heating and Ventilating Contractors Association. Both names were on the letter head of the plumber's firm which was one reason why David and Karen had felt safe using the firm in the first place. But both association's replies were unhelpful to the Fagans. The Institute and the Association both said they cannot deal with arguments about the cost of the work, only about the workmanship involved. They were not allowed to have a code of reasonable prices, they argued, because it is against the restrictive practices laws. And no one disputed that

the work had not been well done, it was merely the cost of it the Fagans were complaining about.

So, remember, trade associations are not allowed by law to fix prices for their members. There is nothing in law to stop them dealing with a complaint from the public about overcharging in a particular case but some trade associations choose not to do this. Plumbing and heating engineers trade associations will, however, provide you with a list of their members, and put you in touch with an independent expert to do an inspection if you want to take action against poor service. You will have to pay for the inspection. The best advice is to try and agree a price in advance and, if you can't, threaten legal action if the final price seems unreasonable (see p. 113).

Double glazing

Dr Paula Gosling decided that she wanted her old metal windows replaced. She rang the Glass and Glazing Federation, the trade association for this service, who gave her a list of their members from which she chose one. The firm seemed to do a good job and charged her £10 000 with a 10-year guarantee. Unfortunately, as Paula explains, the windows weren't all she expected:

'After a while, the rubber sealers on the windows started shrinking. It got very draughty and I couldn't close, let alone lock my new French doors. I couldn't go out at all. So I tried to ring the firm but found the telephone number unobtainable. I went around to the address and found it was no longer there: a shop selling rugs had taken its place. The firm had gone into liquidation'. Paula then rang the Glass and Glazing Federation – and discovered that under their rules, the Federation could do nothing at all. As their director explained, 'Once a member goes into liquidation they cease to be a member, so there is nothing we can do'.

It seems sensible, then, for glazing and double glazing work, to check the past history of a firm before asking them to replace your windows – and if you have paid a lot of money like Paula, get a check made by an independent expert after the work has been finished. If you have a complaint against a glazing firm that is still trading, you can use the Glass and Glazing Federation's code of practice and arbitration scheme, which is recognised by the Office of Fair Trading.

Removals

The British Association of Removal Firms vet firms before they are allowed to become members, and the Association will try and reconcile complaints about their members from annoyed customers. They also offer an independent arbitration scheme but this is not under Office of Fair Trading auspices. Still, it is better than nothing and the Association will give advice about pursuing complaints about non-members.

The most important thing to do when agreeing with a removal firm to move your belongings is to study carefully the contract provided. Ask for a contract if one is not offered. Some removal contracts do not state the precise time when the job will be done, and this is often quite crucial to people who have sold their house and are moving into another one. Make sure this is put in writing or inserted into the contract.

Do not be worried, however, by any clause which commits you to compulsory arbitration to resolve any dispute: these clauses are now illegal and cannot be enforced. And don't be too bothered about clauses which try and absolve the firm from delivering your belongings 'because of circumstances outside their control'. They will have to prove the circumstances were really out of their control if your furniture doesn't turn up on time – otherwise you can claim compensation.

You can threaten court action and claim compensation if the firm damages your property in transit or if it goes back on an agreement with you.

Dr Walker, from Hertfordshire, called us at *You and Yours* **to tell us about his experience of moving house. He had arranged with a local firm to do the job at a good price. But 24 hours before he had to move, the firm rang up and said it couldn't make it. Dr Walker got another firm to do the job but because of the short**

notice, they charged more. Dr Walker decided to claim the difference from the firm he had first arranged to do the job with – and after court action, he got his money.

CHAPTER NINE

MONEY

Barclays Bank recently announced a free, national complaints 'hot-line' for its customers. Anyone aggrieved can call the bank's City of London HQ on a freephone, and get through directly to someone who can deal with complaints. Barclays, of course, is by no means alone. Each high street bank these days seems to be falling over itself to provide 'customer charters', customer service managers and details prominently displayed in their branches of how you can complain.

We have come a long way from the time when financial services were provided for gentlemen and run by gentlemen who had no reason to doubt each other's word. Now banks compete with building societies, finance and insurance companies and pension funds for our money. Credit is widely available from a range of companies, old and new. There is a new kind of person, coyly referred to in TV ads as your 'personal financial advisor', who seems to pop up and down with alacrity. And even those old stalwarts, tax and state benefits, have recently felt the strong winds of change.

Money has become, then, much more complicated. While just as there are far more opportunities for people to complain about how their money is handled, the methods of complaining are by no means as straightforward as they once were.

BANKS

A bank can refuse to open an account for you, although it is pretty unlikely it will. What is more likely is that banks will refuse you a cash-card, a cheque-card or an overdraft. It is always worth challenging them if they do. What happens is that banks have various criteria to identify people they think can handle overdrafts or cheque-cards properly and they will refuse you if you don't fit into these categories.

Each bank's policy about this, however, is different, and each bank manager has considerable autonomy to waive the general rules. If your bank refuses you one of their services, write to the bank manager and point out why, in your circumstances, you think you should be granted the facility. If they still don't budge, write to the bank's district manager and say you will change your account to another bank. If you are still not satisfied with his reply, change banks: another bank might be more amenable. If you do change your account, however, you will have to pay off any overdraft or outstanding loan first, although you might be able to persuade another bank to take it on.

Your local bank manager also has discretion to waive any charges made on your account, such as overdraft administration or interest charges. So, if you have been charged an unfair amount, write and ask for a refund. All bank charges must be 'reasonable' and they must also be stated clearly by the bank, for example, in leaflets available at its branches. They can't just make them up! Therefore, if you think you have been unreasonably charged, complain.

How to complain about banks

1   Write to the manager of your branch. Your letter will almost certainly be referred to the appropriate section manager but if it is not resolved, write back to the manager by name.

2   Ask the manager to refer the complaint through the bank's complaints procedure. This will almost certainly be dealt with by the customer relations officer at a district level. But if you are still not satisfied, write to the district manager himself and threaten to take away your account. You can also write to the bank's head office, drawing attention to your complaint.

3   If this does not resolve your complaint, you can contact the **Banking Ombudsman**. This independent ombudsman was established in 1986, and now deals with over 3500 complaints from individual bank customers every year. It is a free service, and all the major UK banks and most of the smaller ones are part of the scheme. Banks must accept the ombudsman's ruling.

The Banking Ombudsman can deal with most complaints from private customers about bank services except queries about interest rates and decisions about loans or overdrafts. There is also a limit of £100 000 to any claim and it must be made within six months of the last correspondence you have received from the bank about your complaint.

Cashpoints

One of the major areas of complaints the ombudsman has dealt with is bank customers losing money through automatic cash dispensers. The ombudsman has, however, mostly upheld the banks' 'terms of contract' which make the customer liable for any use of a cashpoint card. This seems unfair to many *You and Yours* listeners who say they have lost money by unauthorised cashpoint dispensing through *no* fault of their own.

If you notice your account has been debited by a cash dispenser which you did not use, complain to the bank and get your card changed *at once*. If a cash dispenser does not pay you out any money when you use it, make an immediate note and tell the bank straight away. To win your case if the machine has not given you any money, you will need to get witnesses (for example, people in the queue with you) as evidence.

Some banks and building societies restrict their liability if your card and Personal Identification Number (PIN) is stolen. Read the small print before you get a card and if you are not happy with the restrictions, try another company.

Bouncing cheques

This is an embarrassing occasion for anyone and is usually the customer's fault for going above an agreed overdraft. But, not always. Sometimes banks are slow to credit your account with money paid in and sometimes they make mistakes. If your bank has bounced one of your cheques as a result of *its* mistake, get it to refund any charges they made to your account and to write to the person who received the bounced cheque and apologise. It has, after all, lowered your reputation.

BUILDING SOCIETIES

Building societies used to be entirely different from banks: they helped you out with your mortgage or savings and banks looked after your everyday money. Now most building societies offer you 'bank' facilities like cashpoint cards and cheque accounts, and many banks operate in the mortgage business. They have both moved with ease into investment and other financial services.

Complaining about your building society is similar to complaining about your bank. First contact your local branch manager and, if you don't have any luck, write to the head office's customer relations department. Most building societies have similar laid-down complaints procedures to banks – ask for it at your local branch and let them know you intend to use it. You can then write to the district manager with your complaint threatening to take away your account: they will try and persuade you against doing this if you have been a good customer.

If all else fails, contact the **Building Societies Ombudsman**. He cannot deal with complaints about interest rates or refusing a mortgage but he will be interested in any problems customers have had with unfair treatment, loss or inconvenience as a result of maladministration, cash machines problems and cases when the society has breached general building society rules. Like his banking counterpart, the ombudsman can arbitrate and award you compensation, and his service is free. The maximum he can award is £100 000. But unlike the banking ombudsman, his decision is not binding on the building society. Even so, almost all of his decisions are honoured by the building societies involved.

CREDIT

Mrs Hall and her husband, from Yorkshire, wanted to buy a television. They found the set they wanted in their local branch of Dixons and a salesman pointed out the advantages of buying on credit:

'He told us we would only have to pay £8 a month, including insurance cover. My husband asked how long would that be, and the salesman said 2½ years. They gave us a Dixons store card and my husband was

chuffed to bits – he thought he had got a right good deal'.

The Halls started paying the £8 – but the bill did not go down, rather it kept going up. Eventually the Halls realised the £8 was not paying off the credit at all but was, instead, a minimum payment required by Dixons to honour the agreement they had made.

'They should have told us it would "run and run" and that we were paying a high rate of interest on the set. It would have been much better to rent the television and to have saved up the money to buy it. But I thought we were getting a good deal'.

What the Halls had signed, of course, was not a **fixed repayment credit agreement** at all, but one that has become much more common these days, a **revolving interest agreement**. With this type of agreement the interest is calculated each month on the amount outstanding. If they only paid the minimum amount each month, the bill would just keep on going up.

When *You and Yours* put the Hall's case to Dixons, the store pointed out that the interest rates are displayed at all their shops and their customers also receive full written details of the agreement they had taken out through the post. Obviously, though, the Halls had been confused about what they had been offered and Dixons promised to review their case. What can you do to avoid getting into their situation?

The first thing is to be clear about the different forms of credit. **Fixed term** credit is where you agree to pay a set amount each month which will eventually pay off all the loan. Bank loans are a good example of this, and some shops still offer this form of credit. The interest rate is fixed and you must meet each monthly repayment.

Most shops, however, now offer a **revolving interest** type of credit, usually by giving you a **store card**. With these agreements, you pay off what you want when you want, as long as you meet the relatively small minimum payment each month. But interest rates can change, and every month the interest is calculated on the amount outstanding. So if you just pay off the minimum amount, what you owe will usually keep increasing.

Most store cards are, in fact, a form of **credit card** like those offered by banks. And bank credit cards work in exactly the same way, although you are not, of course, restricted to one particular store. Ten million of us have store cards now, and 20 million use the most popular credit cards, Barclaycard and Access.

Charge cards are slightly different again. Here you pay an annual fee (which you do not, at the moment, for most credit cards, although you may have to soon), and you have to pay the total amount owing at the end of each month. You don't pay any interest if you do this: many canny customers use their credit cards as charge cards, thus avoiding interest charges.

Debit cards are not really credit at all but work more like a cheque without a cheque book. When you use this kind of card, the amount you are paying is deducted automatically from your bank account without you having to write a cheque. These kind of cards are expected to become more and more common in the near future: the best known debit card at present is the Connect card.

Finally, **hire purchase** agreements are different again. With these, you effectively rent the item you buy until you have paid off the last instalment. Then the item is yours.

While most of the above forms of credit are **unsecured**, you can also take out a **secured loan**. This is by no means as good as it sounds: it does not give security to you but to the credit company. It usually means your home is on the line if you fail to pay (see p. 130).

Confused? The credit business certainly is confusing which does not stop most of us using credit, and often getting a very good deal. What happens, however, if you want to complain?

The major help is provided by the **1974 Consumer Credit Act**. This regulates virtually all forms of credit under £15 000, except mortgages for house purchase.

The Act obliges all credit companies to provide you with a written agreement about the credit you have taken out. This must contain various items of information including what the **annual percentage rate (APR)** is. Basically the lower the APR is, the better. If the agreement is made in your own home, the credit company must also send you a copy of this agreement through the post and give you five days to cancel the agreement if, on reflection, it does not seem like such a good deal. So, read the small print of the agreement carefully, even if it is extremely boring!

The Act also regulates the advertising of credit and gives you the right to ask any person offering credit for a written **quotation**. This must state the APR and how much the total cost of the item is including the interest. When a *You and Yours* reporter went around some major electrical shops in the West Midlands recently, he found many shops did not provide this properly when asked – and that's a criminal offence under the Act.

If you come across a credit company which seems to be breaking any of these rules, contact your local trading standards department. The officers have the power to enforce the Act, and to recommend that the Office of Fair Trading revokes the licence required by all firms offering credit.

If you fail to meet your side of any credit agreement, credit companies must serve you a written 'notice of default' before starting any enforcement proceedings.

Every year, *You and Yours* receives numerous complaints from listeners about credit. Here are some of the more common.

What if I'm refused credit?

Rosemary Prichard, an office worker from the West Midlands, didn't have any debts or loans outstanding. Yet, she could not get credit from shops despite trying several times. When she was refused credit to buy a camera for her husband, she decided to find out why. Rosemary wrote to the credit reference agency the shop used and back came the answer: the previous occupant of her house (who had moved out over five years ago) had several unpaid court summons against him for debt. Her address was to the credit company a 'bad address', and not worth the risk.

Credit firms usually use two methods to assess you for credit: their own **point-scoring systems** where you get points for a job, owning your home and so on, even for having another credit card! And a **credit reference agency** which checks whether there are any unpaid debts outstanding against your name and sometimes, as Rosemary found out, against your address.

If the firm has used a credit reference agency, it must provide you with the agency's name and address, if asked. If the firm refuses, report it to the Office of Fair Trading. You are entitled to see your file with the agency for a fee of £1. If the information on file is incorrect, write to the agency and tell them so. It must reply to you within 28 days. If it refuses to do anything about the wrong information, you have the right to send it 200 words stating your case. This must then be attached to your file and sent to anyone who has refused you credit in the past six months. You must send the agency that statement within 28 days.

What if the interest rate charged seems too high?

There are no laws limiting the interest charged by a credit or loan firm. However, you can challenge a credit agreement in court if you think the interest rate is extortionate, even if you agreed to it and were fully informed of your rights. Courts have the power to impose an interest rate which is binding on you and the firm. In practice, this tends to apply only to some of the less reputable credit agreements that are on offer. Get advice from your local trading standards department, which can help with your case.

Most forms of credit offered by shops and banks are perfectly reasonable under the law, even if they vary from 20 to 40 per cent APR and above. If you think the APR you are being charged on your credit card is much higher than others on the market, you can, of course, change.

Damon Speller, an engineer, switched from using Barclaycard (at that time, 26.8 per cent APR) to a Chase Manhattan Visa card (at that time, just 16 per cent APR). He told *You and Yours* **this would save him £800 a year – and Chase Manhattan also took on his unpaid balance with Barclaycard.**

So, shop around and look for the lowest APR. By the way, banks loans are usually far cheaper than, say, most store cards, and such a loan could always pay off your store card balance and save you money in interest charges.

Is it worthwhile taking out insurance to cover not being able to pay the credit back?

David Godfrey, a 50-year-old train driver with London Transport, did this. When he became ill with angina, the insurance company met his repayments. But when he was forced to retire early from his job, a long-term effect of the illness, the insurance company said he was technically available for work and refused to carry on with the repayments. The lesson here is to check carefully exactly what the insurance offered covers. Some do cover redundancy, others just cover illness. Some may even cover your spouse if you die.

What if I can't pay back the credit?

It all depends on whether your credit is **secured** or **unsecured**.

If your credit is **unsecured**, the credit company can try and get the money back you owe them – and take you to court, if necessary. But, even if they do take you to court, you are very unlikely to lose your home as a result of not being able to pay the money back.

If you cannot negotiate with a credit company about repayment, usually they put your account in the hands of a **debt collection agency**. The important thing to remember is that these agencies cannot do what they want and they certainly cannot intimidate you. They cannot, for example, enter your home without your permission or without a court order. And, if they threaten you with any form or violence, call the police straight away. It is illegal to harass debtors. The credit company will have to take you to court to get the money back: all other methods can only be persuasion.

Secured loans often seem very attractive. Their interest rates (APR) can seem low and enticing (although check out if there are any brokerage fees for the loan), or at least that is what their newspaper ads imply. The reality can be heartbreaking, as this man from London discovered:

'**We took out a secured loan for £10 000 which worked out at £170 per month over 10 years. It meant we could afford to pay off our other debts and do work**

around the house. But the interest rates soon went up, making our monthly payment £191 and, when my wife became pregnant, we started missing payments. We dreaded the postman coming because we realised we could lose our home'.

Indeed, the couple had to put their home on the line simply because they owed the loan company £1000. The company was quite within its rights: a secured loan is usually secured against your property and the company can either force you to sell your home or repossess it. But they can only do this by taking you to court. If you have any problems with a secured loan, immediately seek help from a CAB or money advice centre: your local council should be able to tell you where they are. The best advice though is to avoid secured loans, particularly from ads in the paper. Try your building society or bank instead.

If you are having trouble with paying back your credit commitments, your credit has become **debt**, and you should follow the steps outlined on p. 142.

Future changes

As this book goes to press, there are a number of changes likely to happen soon in the credit industry. The government intends to make it easier for traders to give credit and also to require secured loans to have a prominent warning about possibly losing your home printed on their advertisements.

It seems likely most credit card companies will become more competitive, offering a range of interest rates. (At the moment, British interest rates are amongst the highest in the world.) They will also probably introduce annual fees for the use of the card.

The golden rule about credit, however, will still apply: treat the buying of credit as carefully as you would any other purchase and shop around for the best deal.

INVESTMENTS AND FINANCIAL ADVISORS

This new breed of entrepreneur has sprung up in the last decade as people have started dabbling more and more in stocks and shares, unit trusts and other forms of investment and savings.

Investments are made for us by brokers, accountants, banks and other kinds of financial advisors. Their advice is regulated by a law called the **1986 Financial Services Act**. This Act covers almost all forms of investment apart from mortgages and general insurance policies. Life insurance is, however, covered under the Act.

All financial advisors must now tell you if they are independent or if they are acting on behalf of one financial company. They cannot be both or somewhere in between! The Act also obliges independent advisors to give you the 'best advice' they can once they know your circumstances and intentions. Even if they are representatives of one particular company, they cannot advise you to take out any of that company's investments if it is not appropriate for your circumstances.

That at least is what the Act says and, fortunately, it has some teeth as well. All financial advisors must be directly regulated by the Securities and Investments Board, or be members of one of five **self-regulating organisations (SROs)**. If they are, say, solicitors or accountants and are only giving financial advice as part of their work, they must be members of their own professional body.

Over 30 000 advisors are now registered under the Act, most with the five SROs, which are **FIMBRA**, **IMRO**, **TSA**, **AFBD** and **LAUTRO**. Each SRO member must carry one of these sets of initials on all its letterheads. The **Securities and Investments Board** regulates and controls the SROs and enforces the Financial Services Act.

That's a lot of initials there but it's all much more straightforward than it sounds, and *is* a great improvement on what went before. Especially if you want to complain.

All financial advisors have to have a complaints procedure and keep records of any complaints their customers make about, for example, bad advice. These procedures and records are supervised by the relevant SRO.

Therefore, to complain about your financial advisor, write to his firm and ask to use its complaints procedure. If you are not satisfied with the response, you can then contact the SRO the advisor is registered with.

Each SRO has its own way of dealing with complaints, and it is too complex to explain each in detail here. But all five of them will attempt to conciliate between you and your advisor. All SROs have arbitration schemes and give you the opportunity to use an independent referee or ombudsman, for example, the **Insurance Ombudsman** (see p. 138) or the **Unit Trust Ombudsman**, who deals with complaints about dealings with a unit trust company. These referees or ombudsmen can award you compensation.

If you are not satisfied with the way an SRO has dealt with your complaint, you can go to the Securities Investment Board. It is also more interested in hearing about breaches of the Act or if an SRO has fallen down on its obligations to customers.

If you are thinking of investing money via a financial advisor or firm, check first which SRO he belongs to. And ring the SRO up to make sure the advisor is still a member. **Linda Long** did this but, unfortunately, she came across a loop-hole.

Three years ago, Linda was advised by a company called Financial Management Services of Mayfair to invest £2000 in shares called GSS Eyepoint. The company had FIMBRA membership on its letterhead, so Linda rang up FIMBRA to see if the company was a member. FIMBRA confirmed it was. But what FIMBRA didn't tell Linda was that it was investigating Financial Management Services of Mayfair, and two weeks later, it suspended the company from trading. Linda had by then invested money with the company and lost £1800, her life savings.

FIMBRA, like the other SROs, is not allowed to tell individual investors anything about their members (even if they are being investigated) apart from the fact that they are indeed members. This is, they say, because many investigations never come to anything at all (some are just due to malicious gossip) and rumour could destroy a firm's reputation.

If you have invested money in a firm which is authorised under the Financial Services Act, a unit trust company, for example, and this firm goes into liquidation, there is a new way

in which you can get at least some of your money back. It is by
using the **Investors Compensation Scheme**. There are some
limits to the amount you can claim (the ceiling is £48 000) but
it is certainly better than nothing. A similar scheme, the Stock
Exchange Compensation Scheme, can pay you compensation
due as a result of a stockbroker's fraud or incompetence. Neither scheme shelters you from losing money if share prices go
down.

TAX

PAYE

To complain about the amount of income tax deducted from
your wages through PAYE, first find out which tax office is dealing with you: it is often in a different part of the country! Your
employer will know and it will be on your annual tax form.

Write to the tax office and ask for details of your **tax code**
and **tax assessment**. Check that the code on your wage packet
matches the code the tax office is using: basically the higher the
code, the less tax you pay. If you think all your allowances are
not being taken into account, write to the office.

The tax office can provide you with a booklet explaining all
the allowances you can claim: you can also claim back any
allowance you may have missed for the past six years. If the
taxman has not claimed enough tax off you, he can only ask you
to pay it back if it was not due to his error.

You have the right to complain about how your PAYE has
been assessed to a **tax commissioner**, but if the tax office had
taken into consideration all the allowances that you are entitled
to, it is hardly worth it.

You can complain, however, about unreasonable behaviour
by the tax office or excessive delay in dealing with your claim.
Write first to the **district inspector** and then, if no luck, to
the **regional tax controller** (ask the office for their
addresses). You could then involve the **parliamentary
ombudsman**, via your MP (see p. 167).

Self-employed

If you contract your labour to several employers or if you run your own business, you are regarded by the tax office as 'self-employed'. Each year, you have to prepare a balance sheet of income, business expenses and net earnings. You pay tax on the final net earnings figure. You also have to register with the Department of Social Security to pay national insurance. Do this at your local office.

Most self-employed people use an accountant to prepare their annual accounts although this is not strictly necessary. Your tax office can provide help and advice for you to prepare your accounts yourself. Tell the tax office as soon as you become self-employed. Almost certainly the office that will deal with you is the one nearest your registered business address or home.

If the tax office does not receive your accounts after a certain time, they will send you their assessment of how much they think you owe them along with a demand for payment. Do not worry about this but act fast and register an appeal (or better, get your accountant to do this for you): this will give you time to prepare your accounts. If you are not satisfied with the final assessment after you have presented your accounts, you can then appeal to the **tax commissioner**. But you can only appeal against the commissioner's decision on a point of law – not on fact. You can ask for time to pay your tax bill in instalments.

VAT

If you are self-employed, you have to register for VAT if you earn over a certain amount (in 1989, £23 600: it usually goes up a small amount each year). If you do not and they find out, you will be fined and you will have to pay back any VAT owing to them. You can complain about how your VAT obligations are assessed to a **VAT tribunal** (details from your local VAT office) but, most times, it is not worth it.

ACCOUNTANTS

Anyone can call themselves an accountant, so check if they are a member of a professional body. They will usually have a set of initials after their name like **FCA**, **ACA**, **FCCA** or **ACCA**, depending on whether they are qualified as cost, chartered or certified accountants. If you are still unsure about an accountant, check with the professional body and see if its members can deal with your kind of business. The best way to find an accountant is, though, by individual recommendation. Check, too, if the accountant has **professional indemnity insurance** if you are planning to invest money through him.

To complain about an accountant, write first to his firm's **senior partner**. You can then contact their professional body, which can look into bad service or misconduct. The professional body cannot, however, offer or award you any compensation for money lost: you will have to take the accountant to court for that. If the accountant has offered you bad advice about investments, his professional body must have a complaints procedure and you could then press for compensation under the Financial Services Act (see p. 132).

PENSIONS

In the last few years there has been increasing interest in 'opting out' of **SERPS**, the state pensions scheme, in favour of personal pension plans or company pensions, particularly as the government gave people a strong financial incentive to do this.

To complain about **personal pensions plans**, see the section above on investments (p. 131). All firms which arrange these plans must operate under the Financial Services Act, usually as a member of LAUTRO.

Company pension schemes have a different legal set-up from the company involved. They are run by trustees who are obliged to behave 'prudently' and are independent of the company concerned: if a company goes bust, the pension scheme will almost certainly not be affected. Some company schemes have arbitration procedures to resolve complaints, and most have insurance schemes to protect their members if the company collapses. Check these out before you sign up. For advice and help about company pensions (for example, to trace a scheme if it seems to have vanished), contact **Occupational**

Pensions Advisory Service, a charitable organisation.

Complaints about **state pensions** are made in a similar way to those about other state benefits – a Citizens Advice Bureau (CAB) advisor will help you.

INSURANCE

When we received letters from some *You and Yours* listeners recently complaining about problems they had with one of the major UK insurance businesses, AA Motor Insurance, we decided to see how common these were. We asked listeners to phone in – and they did – over 50 in half an hour. **Mrs Matthis, from London, told us how she received nine cover notes before, eventually, getting her policy. Mrs Gunning informed us she had tried to pay the AA three times for her policy – and they kept refusing her money.** And the complaints continued, although some did comment favourably.

The point of all this is not that the AA is any better or worse than other insurance brokers or companies. As one of the top businesses in motor insurance, you would expect more complaints about the AA than smaller firms since they have far more customers. And, if *You and Yours* had done something similar for the largest firms in the life insurance or home insurance business, we are sure the complaints would have come pouring in too. In general, though, most people are very satisfied with their insurance and for those who are not, there are laid-down procedures for complaining which, most of the time, help.

How to complain about insurance companies

1 Write to the company and ask it to investigate your complaint. An example would be if it intended not to pay your claim or pay it only in part.

2 If you have no success, write to the **Association of British Insurers (ABI)**, which represents most of the major insurance firms. They will take up your complaint with the insurance company's head office, and ensure it is investigated by 'someone senior'. They cannot compel a company to change its mind but

they do now have a **code of conduct** which all members must follow.

The ABI covers all types of insurance. If, however, you have life insurance you can also go to the **Linked Life Assurance Group**, which has an arbitration scheme, or if you have industrial life/home service insurance, where an agent calls to the door each week for the premium, you can go to the **Industrial Assurance Commission**.

3   If you still are not successful, then complain to the **Insurance Ombudsman** or the **Personal Insurance Arbitration Scheme (PIAS)** if the insurance company is a member: most major firms are members of one or the other. The Insurance Ombudsman has the power to make an award to you of up to £100 000. This award is binding on the insurance company although you can still go to court with your claim if you are not satisfied. The ombudsman now deals with over 1500 complaints from policyholders every year, although it can take time to decide on your case. The ombudsman is only available to personal policyholders and cannot deal with third party complaints. The PIAS scheme works in a similar way.

4   If your insurance company is part of the **Lloyds of London**, you can also complain to their **Customer Enquiries Department**, which has a procedure for dealing with complaints. Lloyds members are also now part of the Insurance Ombudsman scheme.

How to complain about an insurance broker

1   If a broker has given you wrong financial advice, you can complain by using the Financial Services Act (see p. 132). All brokers must now belong to a SRO and work under the Act.

2   All brokers must be registered with their regulatory body, **Insurance Brokers' Registration Council (IBRC)**. Many brokers are also members of **British Insurance Brokers Association (BIBA)**, the trade association, which has a code of practice, an arbitration scheme and insurance if the broker goes bust. IBRC or BIBA may be able to help you with complaints.

3   If you have used a broker who is not a member of BIBA and he goes bust, contact the Association of British Insurers. The Association now has a new indemnity scheme which will refund money to policyholders if small, unregistered brokers go out of business.

STATE BENEFITS

The **1986 Social Security Act** which came into force in April 1988, has changed the way many state benefits are worked out. Even the familiar names like Supplementary Benefit have been renamed. Here are the major benefits you may be entitled to:

Unemployment Benefit or **Income Support** (the new name for Supplementary Benefit) If you are out of work, you will usually be entitled to claim one or the other of these. Income Support is made up of a basic amount plus various **premiums**, for example, for disabilities or one-parent families.

Family Credit (the new name for family income supplement) If you have children and are in a very low paid job, you can claim.

Child Benefit All parents, regardless of income, are entitled to this.

Housing Benefit If you are claiming Income Support or if you are in a low paid job, you may be entitled to this benefit. Claim it from your local council, not the local DSS office. This benefit covers rent and 80 per cent of your community charge: you are expected to pay water charges and the remaining community charge yourself.

Mortgage payments If you are on Income Support you can ask the DSS for help with your repayments. If you are in a low paid job, you cannot get any help for mortgage payments at all – housing benefit only covers rent not mortgages.

Finally, most **allowances** (for example, for fuel) have now gone – they have been replaced by **premiums** in your income support. Also gone are **grants** for one-off purchases such as buying a cooker. These have been replaced by loans from the **social fund**, which you have to pay back from your income support benefit.

It normally takes up to several weeks for your local DSS office to work out your entitlements. You can ask for an **emergency payment** to tide you over during this time, although this will be deducted from your benefit when it does come through.

Confused? Well, yes it is confusing, but then state benefits always have been since the welfare state was first introduced. Remember many of these benefits are means-tested ones: your savings will be taken into account. There are leaflets at every DSS office which explain these benefits and other more specialised benefits as well. CABs can also explain them to you in more detail. There is also a DSS freephone service for general advice and information about benefits. The number is 0800 666 555 and it is open 9 a.m.–4 p.m. weekdays.

Complaints about amount of benefit

If you feel the DSS office has not given you all that you are entitled to, for example, they have not fully taken into account your particular circumstances, write and ask for an explanation of how your benefits were assessed. Then point out why you think they are wrong. You can do this by phone, although you will probably have trouble getting through. Better to write or call in to the office's enquiry desk. Always quote your reference number. Alternatively, start by getting advice from your local CAB.

And, CAB help is essential if you want to move on to the next stage of complaints: **registering an appeal**. After your benefit has been assessed, you have 28 days to lodge an appeal. Always do this if you think they are wrong: you can withdraw the appeal later. Your situation will then be automatically reviewed by a supervising officer at the DSS office. If the review is not satisfactory, you can then go ahead and present your case at a **Social Security Appeals Tribunal**.

The tribunals are not by any means as formal as a court but do try and get someone, like a CAB advisor, to represent you. All the evidence shows that claimants who win at tribunals usually have representation of some sort. Unfortunately, you cannot get legal aid for this but most CABs and other advice centres will give some help. In London, you may also be able to use the free services of the **Free Representation Unit** (see p. 288). The appeals procedure can often take several weeks if not months, especially for cases dealt with at a specialist tribunal like the **Medical Appeals Tribunal**. Be prepared to wait.

The tribunal's finding is binding on both you and the DSS, although you can appeal on a point of law to the **Social Security Commissioners**. Do not do this unless you have some organisation which thinks your case is sufficiently important that they will back you.

Complaints about staff

If you have experienced rudeness or incompetence from DSS staff, write to the supervisor dealing with your case, and then to the office manager if you are still not satisfied. You can then contact the regional district manager. If you feel you are being harassed by social security officers, complain at once to the regional district manager or write to your MP.

In a recent edition of *You and Yours*, we reported on a National Association of Citizens Advice Bureaux survey which featured many examples of claimants who said they had been intimidated by DSS fraud squad officers, claimants like this young woman.

'I was renting out a cottage with a male friend I knew from college. He was just a friend, we had no sexual relationship at all, and we had separate rooms. One evening when I was on my own, I was visited by two male DSS officials who said I was co-habiting and thus not entitled to benefit. They really frightened me and kept pointing to a pair of jeans in my bedroom as evidence that I was not living as a single woman. They couldn't understand that the jeans were mine, that girls wear them, too. They recommended that my benefit was to be stopped – and it was'.

That young woman had to appeal against the officers' recommendation. She eventually won but she was without any benefit for a month. If you come across any kind of intimidation from DSS officials, find out their names and report them. Your local CAB will help – as will your MP.

DEALING WITH DEBT

Five million people have had problems with repaying their credit commitments over the last five years. Many have crossed over from juggling credit to its reverse side, **debt**.

Credit becomes debt when you can no longer pay back the minimum amount you have agreed to. While *some* people get into debt simply by spending more than they can afford, the *majority* are in debt because their circumstances change, due to an accident or illness, perhaps, an unexpected pregnancy or, in **Anne's** case, her husband losing his job:

'My husband was working and I was at home looking after the children. We just had the normal household bills and a hire purchase agreement on the car of £2000, about £20 a week. We were plodding along quite happily until my husband was made redundant with no redundancy pay because he had not been in that job very long. The first few months were easy – I just kept borrowing more. The children's clothes came from a catalogue, and I even got some money from a moneylender, a friend of a friend. It just kept mounting up.

'I kept it all to myself. I thought my husband had enough to do with looking for a job. When the children wanted something, I kept making excuses, telling them they couldn't have their pocket money this week because they were out late or they hadn't cleaned their room. It wasn't because I didn't want them to have it, I just couldn't afford it. I started having sleepless nights and picking arguments with my husband so I could say to him "this is what's wrong, we're in all this debt". But I just couldn't bring myself to say it. We just stopped talking to each other'.

After a year of her husband's unemployment, Anne owed £6000, and her creditors were closing in. She heard about a local money advice centre and, one day, she took her husband there 'without telling him what it was all about'. With the help of a skilled debt coun-

sellor, they both faced up to the debts and paid everything off.

Here's what Anne did – and what you can do if you are in her position:

1 Draw up a budget of all your income and all your day-to-day spending, not including your debts or debt repayments.

2 See if there are any ways of increasing your income, such as letting a room or claiming any benefit you may be entitled to.

3 See if there are any ways of cutting down your expenditure. But be realistic and do not cut down on essential spending for day-to-day living.

4 Add up all your debts and make a list.

5 Work out the difference between your income and essential spending. The difference is what you can afford to repay. Give priority to debts that may result in you losing your home (mortgage payments, rent) or the debts you can go to prison for (mainly court orders).

6 Write to all your creditors explaining what you can afford and make them an offer which is called, in technical terms, an **equitable distribution of income**. Ask them, too, to suspend any interest owed on your debts.

If you follow the above steps, almost all creditors will accept your offer – although they may try and bargain. Resist if you have worked out your sums properly and tightly: don't let them force you into cutting out essential spending on food or heating.

You can do all this yourself but it is probably better – and essential if the money you are offering to pay back is nowhere near what you owe – to go and see a **debt counsellor** or money advisor first. In most major cities, there are specialist money advice centres: ask at your CAB. The counsellor may write the letter to your creditors with you, and back you up if any of them try and intimidate you. They can also make sure your housing payments and fuel bills are covered first and advise you on claiming benefit.

What happens if I'm taken to court?

Any creditor can reject your offer of payment and sue you in the County Court. But if you have followed the steps above, just let them do this, as Michael, a student from Swansea did:

'I had this enormous feeling of trepidation when I had to go to court. I was expecting a long dark room, very heavy with a stern judge. But in the event, it was completely different. The registrar who heard my case sat by a long, low desk and he didn't look at me as if I had done anything wrong. I came out feeling what a very reasonable person and system'.

Like Michael, if you go to court over a debt, the court normally makes a judgement ordering you to pay the debt. If the court has evidence of your personal and financial circumstances, however, it will order you to pay the debt by instalments which it thinks you can afford. This means it is *essential* to fill in the questionnaire which comes with the original court summons. If you cannot subsequently meet the instalments due to your circumstances changing, go back to the court and explain.

In practice, if you make your creditors an offer before going to court, the amount of money you will have to pay on a court order will not be very different. This is why most creditors will not bother to take you to court if they know your full circumstances.

The court procedure is slightly different in Northern Ireland and very different in Scotland. Contact your local CAB, which will explain the procedures in these countries.

What about bankruptcy and prison?

If you have a lot of debts owing, for example, to your business collapsing, any of your debtors can file for bankruptcy. They are unlikely to do this unless you have some assets as well. It might also suit *you* to file for bankruptcy as well, but take legal advice first.

You cannot be sent to prison for debt except for 'wilful' failure to pay things like rates, community charge or maintenance payments.

And, let's finish this section with some hope. Dealing with

debt does not have to bring terrible hardship and misery: here's what happened to Anne. Two years after she owed £6000, she's well on the way to paying it all back:

'**I always thought my priorities were my debts, but I learnt that everyday things are the priority. Once you get those sorted out, the debts can look after themselves. And I allowed myself a little luxury: an emergency fund, just £1 a week put away for Christmas for presents. I'm looking forward to Christmas for the first time for a very long time'.**

THE LOCAL COMMUNITY

The complaint of residents from the Rockferry estate in the Wirral was about noise. Not just any noise, but the constant hubbub from a nursery that their local council had relocated on to their estate.

Newcastle builder Roger Mason had a different type of grievance: he wanted the new owners of the posh houses he had just completed to have a 'nice' street name appropriate to the development. His local council decided otherwise – and chose 'Tethercock Street', a name that Roger thought had decidedly dubious connotations.

The village council of Wantage in Berkshire had no problems with names: its complaint was about the pollution pouring into the river, a river that used to make the village such a desirable place to live.

Noise, planning laws, pollution . . . these are just three common complaints concerning the environment and the local community we hear about at *You and Yours*. And there are many other kinds as well, for example, about neighbours or the local police. Our local community affects us all in many different ways – and it is a constant source for complaints. But how do you go about complaining when so many different organisations and laws seem to be involved? Let's take each in turn.

YOUR LOCAL COUNCIL

Most people are quite satisfied with the services provided by their local councils. At least that was the conclusion of a recent survey by the Consumers' Association. Seventy-eight per cent of the respondents in the survey felt pleased with the quality of services provided, and 64 per cent thought the services were good value for money. With the striking exception of road and pavement maintenance (about which, more shortly), the survey indicated that most people think their council is doing a good job. With one or two exceptions, of course.

Now, all that may be true but at *You and Yours* letters pour in regularly about each and every type of council department – roads, parks, social services, education and even trading standards officers. Almost all of these letters are complaints – but then, to be fair, we do not hear from listeners who are satisfied with the services provided.

The first thing to do when you want to complain is to sort out which council and which council department is responsible. A local Citizens Advice Bureau (CAB) advisor can tell you – but here's a general guide:

If you live in the 'shire areas' (most parts of England and Wales), **county councils** look after education, social services, some roads and highways, libraries and museums, trading standards, fire, waste disposal, strategic planning and conservation matters. **District councils** look after rubbish collection, planning issues, housing, local parks and leisure, environmental health and most pavements. **Parish councils** have very little direct powers: they act rather as local representative organisations to the county and district.

If you live in or near a large city or town in England or Wales, you almost certainly fall under a **metropolitan council** which combines county and district roles. There are, however, some **town** and **parish councils** inside metropolitan councils which act like other parish councils. In London, metropolitan councils are organised by **boroughs**. Just to confuse matters, some **city** councils like Sheffield are metropolitan councils; other city councils like Bristol have only district council responsibilities: there is a county council (Avon in Bristol's case) as well.

In Scotland, **regional councils** look after everything – and have some extra powers as well like looking after water. In Northern Ireland, most major council responsibilities are run by **Northern Ireland Office Boards**. There are, though, **district councils** in the Province as well, but their powers are limited. They do not, for example, look after housing.

Still, it is all much more straightforward than it sounds, at least most of the time. If your local CAB cannot tell you who to complain to, ring up any council's enquiry office and they soon will!

How to complain about council activities

In general, here is what you do:

1 Contact the council department responsible – the enquiry office will tell you its title. If you don't have any luck, write to the head of the department by name.

2 Then contact the council director's or chief executive's office and ask him to investigate.

3 Alternatively, contact your **local councillor**, and ask him to raise your complaint with the officers responsible. Councillors are in overall charge of policy; council officials put it into practice. If your local councillor can't or won't take up the issue, contact any councillor who is on the appropriate council committee.

   For example, if you want to complain about the opening hours or general state of your local swimming pool, find out which local councillors are on the **leisure** or **sports** or **recreation** committees. Again, the council's information or enquiry service can tell you this, or your local library will have the information.

   Councillors are usually pretty eager to help. After all, your vote might be at stake. They will be even more impressed if you have support from other people as well.

4 If your complaint seems to be getting nowhere, you can then try and interest the local media, or indeed your MP. There is also nothing stopping you taking legal action against the council, and for some complaints which have caused you injury, for example, badly repaired pavements, this is a good idea. But take legal advice first.

5 Finally, you can now take your complaint direct to the **local ombudsman**. He will be interested in any complaint you have about bad council practice or maladministration, and he can recommend an award in your favour (see p. 158). The award is not binding but most councils comply.

There are, then, many different ways to complain about local council activity. Some particular problems are considered below, and some like social services (p. 198) and education (p. 242), are looked at later in the book.

   But one kind of complaint is almost impossible to win. It is, unfortunately, the one we often care most about: how much we all pay the council in rates or poll tax. It is possible to organise sufficient local pressure to press for **judicial review** about council policy or to interest the **district auditor** if you think council spending (and hence its income) is unjustified. But only do this with legal advice and organisational backing.

Pavements

Elspeth Lawrence was walking near her London home one day when she tripped over a dip in the pavement. The next thing she knew was coming back to consciousness in a neighbour's house: her spectacles had fallen off, she had broken her nose and wrist, damaged her teeth and her hearing was affected. This would be serious at any time, but it was even more so for Elspeth because she was 92 at the time: 'I used to be quite spry until the accident, but I haven't been out since then. It was very, very dangerous'.

Elspeth's son-in-law took up her case. He wrote to the local council pressing for compensation for Elspeth's injuries. The Council wrote back saying it was all the gas board's fault. Then the gas board said they had contracted out the pavement work to another company. 'They were all passing the buck', he told *You and Yours*, **'but it just wasn't worth pursuing. Who would we sue?'**

The problem with complaining about pavements, as the Lawrence family discovered, is that the ownership and responsibility for repair does vary. Sometimes district councils are responsible, sometimes county councils, sometimes gas, electricity or water companies. That often deters the three million people who have pavement accidents every year and the 500 000 who end up in the local casualty ward. But what *can* you do?

The first thing is to find out from your local council who is responsible. If the council itself is responsible, complain as outlined on p. 149. If it is not, however, ask it to back your case against the organisation responsible. If council officials are reluctant to act, involve your local councillor. Councils get a lot of complaints about pavements each year – and your councillor will be aware of how annoyed other of his constituents are.

If you have suffered injury, consider suing whoever is responsible for the pavements for compensation. Get a doctor's note confirming your injury and get evidence from the 'scene of crime', such as other people who saw you fall. Take a photo of the pavement as soon after your accident as you, your family or friends can manage, and measure the depth of the crack. Then find a solicitor – through the CAB, if necessary, to press your case. And, here's some good news – from Northern Ireland.

It is not known if the pavements in Northern Ireland are worse than the rest of the United Kingdom, or if the people of the Province are just more likely to press their pavement complaints. Whatever the reason, people who suffered accidents through tripping over Northern Ireland pavements win over £4 million each year. The individual amounts are not great: a 2½-year-old girl, for example, was awarded only £450 by the courts for a permanent scar she sustained tripping over an upturned paving stone. But at least it was something – and at least she won.

So, do complain and don't let your council get away with the excuse it doesn't have any money. That's their problem not yours.

And don't take a leaf out of Mrs Thatcher's book: usually a good complainer, the Prime Minister behaved like most of us do when she tripped over the pavement outside a Conservative Party conference one year. 'Oh, I'm sorry', she was reported to have said. But why was she 'sorry'? It was not her fault – but the fault of the people responsible for repairing the pavement.

Litter and rubbish

The Prime Minsiter has, though, not been slow to complain about litter on our streets. The United Kingdom and the Irish Republic are amongst the most litter-strewn countries in Europe.

Responsibility for street cleaning and rubbish collection usually lies with the **district** council. County councils usually look after waste disposal, although this does vary in different parts of the UK, particularly in Wales. Councils have to collect your household rubbish at regular intervals, although different councils impose different conditions on residents, such as using particular kinds of bags, litterbugs and so on.

If you are unhappy with how the job is done, or dismayed that the streets in your area aren't swept, complain. If nothing is done, get a petition from your neighbours and lobby your local councillor. New government regulations impose much greater obligations on councils to keep the streets clean, and give you the right to apply for a court order to direct councils to clean up litter.

There are strict regulations concerning the **disposal of waste**, whether it is done by county councils or private companies. They have to take into account any toxic chemicals that may need to be destroyed, or any methane gas that may escape and cause havoc or worse. If you are unhappy with any waste tip near you, contact your council's waste disposal unit and get them to check the tip. If there is any possibility of danger from, for example, a possible explosion or partially-burnt chemicals being emitted into the atmosphere, take advice at once through your local environmental health officer or a national environmental pressure group like Friends of the Earth.

Roads and highways

The villagers of Shore St Gregory in Somerset were worried about a blind junction at the top of their village. Drivers could not see other cars coming without edging into the middle of the junction itself and, sooner or later, this would cause a major accident, as Sally and Angus Morris explained:

'There have been near misses, screeches, bangs. Then there was a young boy on a motorcycle who had a nasty fall. He wasn't badly hurt, but he had to go to hospital', Angus said.

The villagers complained to Somerset County Council but nothing seemed to be done. So the local parish council decided to do something about this local black-spot themselves. With the agreement of the Morris family, they altered the road so it ran on

to Angus and Sally's land making it much easier for traffic using the junction to see what was coming. 'A tremendous improvement', claims Sally.

Somerset County Council, while impressed with the villagers' ingenuity, pointed out one or two problems. What if the Morris family moves? Will the new owners still want their land used like this? And, no the county council could not reimburse the parish council for the work. 'We ought to but we are reluctant to pay for something we have not approved after it has been done', their spokesman said.

What the Council did say, however, was that people in the same situation as the Shore St Gregory residents should make a fuss. Repairing or altering roads 'depends on the availability of land, the number of accidents there have been and the keenness of locals. They have to make a nuisance of themselves'.

So there you have it, straight from a council's mouth. Whether your road is the responsibility of your council or, as in most major roads, the **Department of Transport** (see p. 165), make a nuisance of yourself until they do something about it.

Parks and cemeteries

These are usually looked after by district councils, metropolitan councils, London boroughs or Scottish regional councils. The council must keep them tidy and care for the grass, plants and amenities like swings and children's playgrounds. If they do not, complain using the steps outlined on p. 148.

Check, too, the council is meeting the regulations concerning safety in playgrounds – the **Consumers' Association** have taken this issue up in a big way and can provide you with advice and information about their campaign to make playgrounds safer.

Each district council must also provide a cemetery for burial – and, council regulations about new cemeteries are causing some *You and Yours* listeners distress. **Here's Robin and Chris Mussin's story:**

'Our eight-year-old daughter, Kate, was taken ill at

home with a brain haemorrhage. At the hospital, the doctors told us her life was over and we took the decision to turn off her life-support machine. They told us where she could be buried, and we went to see the cemetery and were pleased, because it was near where we were living. We couldn't bring ourselves to decide on a headstone so soon after her death, so we started bringing wicker baskets full of flowers to her grave. That was until we got a letter from the council'.

The council letter informed the Mussins that no flowers were allowed on the grave unless they were in a vase in the headstone. Any loose or planted flowers on the grave would be removed.

'It was very heartless and cruel', Chris Mussin told *You and Yours*. 'I cried and cried. My 10-year-old daughter kept asking me "Mummy, what are we going to do on Kate's birthday?"' 'Kate used to love flowers', Robin Mussin added. 'They were a symbol of her. It was very wrong. The council was more concerned with getting a job done than people's feelings. It would only have taken them 10 seconds to move their lawnmowers around Kate's grave'.

For that was the council's excuse. The council said they had banned loose and planted flowers because they could damage their lawnmowers and other graves' headstones. And, moreover, flowers made the cemetery untidy: 'When flowers are first planted, that's no problem', the council explained. 'It's when they die and lie strewn all over the place that it destroys the nice tidy look of the place which other people have complimented us about'. The council did, though, apologise on *You and Yours* for the distress their letter had caused the Mussins.

What can *you* do if you are in a similar situation to the Mussins', a situation which is all too common these days?

You can challenge the cemetery's regulations by finding other people whose loved ones are buried there and then lobby local councillors. Involve your local paper as well: cemeteries and distress are, in reporters' eyes, a 'good story', especially with a picture.

You may have to accept, though, that the paper will write the story up in their own way. **My sister phoned her local newspaper in Berkshire about a council ruling similar to the Mussins'. A few days later, she was on the front page described as 'grieving daughter hits out at council'.**

Apart from cemeteries and parks, councils look after many recreational activities like sports grounds and centres. See p. 148 for how to complain about these.

Noise

The kind of noise people most want to complain about is from next-door neighbours (see p. 167) but, occasionally, noise from council activities disturbs as well. And noise, too, from activities that can hardly be blamed on the council, but is up to them to do something about. **Residents of the seaside town of Folkestone, for example, were so fed up with seagulls ('noisy, dirty nuisances') that they approached the council to do something. The council hired marksmen to kill the birds but this caused a storm from other residents in the town, those who liked the birds.** Sometimes, you just cannot win if you are a council official.

That was certainly the feeling of officials in another part of the country, in the Wirral. **Officials arranged for a summer playgroup to take place in the ground floor of a block of flats. It pleased the children who used the playgroup as well as their parents. It did not please the flats' residents: some of their children were studying for GCSEs, and some adults who lived there worked nights and needed to sleep in the day. Others just wanted peace and quiet. But what could these residents do?**

They contacted their local counciilor and arranged for an independent pollution control expert to monitor the noise of the playgroup. Then they took the council to court. On the morning of the court case,

the council paid the residents sums of up to £150 as a settlement without admitting liability.

You could try this method, too. Get advice from your local environmental health officer, although whether he is prepared to go to court to testify against his employer might be open to question!

Planning

In every newspaper in the land, you will read every week about planning disputes. Someone wants to build something and someone else, usually the local council, won't let them. Here are two of the more unusual cases that have come into the *You and Yours* office.

Les Quickly, an ex-RAF officer from Harrogate, wanted to open a restaurant in the town. Being keen on the qualities of the British that were exemplified by Sir Winston Churchill and the 'Dunkirk Spirit', he decided on a Second World War theme and the name, Bunkers. The local council, however, refused him planning permission to open a restaurant.

Les was not going to take this lying down: 'It's wrong to give in. Winston Churchill wouldn't have thrown in the towel'. He opened the restaurant but he didn't charge customers for their meals but instead for the rent of a part of the building for a few hours. This, miraculously, came to a normal restaurant price. And, he went even further. He dressed up in mock-combat gear and protested outside the council offices in a mock tank!

Wyn Davies from Dyfed also went to war against his council over planning permission. The business of his general hardware store had been hit badly by new double yellow lines painted all along the High Street. His customers could no longer park outside the shop. Wyn painted a large sign on his shop's wall advertising his business and pointing out all the things he sold. The council then told him the sign needed planning permission even though it wasn't overhanging anything and was on Wyn's property. And, they said they

weren't going to give it because it was a possible traffic hazard. As Wyn pointed out, 'What about Piccadilly Circus? The signs there are far more likely to cause an accident than mine. It's a load of poppycock'. He got up a local petition backing his stand, and took his case to appeal, in his situation, with the Welsh office.

This is what you can do if you clash with your council over planning permission either for your business or simply to extend your home:

1   In general, a council must give planning permission unless there is a good reason for them to deny it. Examples are if you live in a conservation area or your new building contravenes the council's **local plan**. More than 80 per cent of people who apply for planning permission get it.

2   If you live in England and Wales, there is no obligation on you to inform any neighbours who might be affected: it is up to the local council to do this. It is probably a good idea, though, for you to discuss your plans with your neighbours to be aware of any objections they might make. In Scotland and Northern Ireland, you have to do this before you apply for planning permission.

3   If it seems likely that planning permission will be refused, put your views in writing to the council's **planning officer**. The decision will be taken by the council's appropriate committee which will usually rely heavily on the officer's advice.

4   If the committee refuses you permission, you then have six months to appeal to the appropriate **Secretary of State** (the Department of Environment or Welsh, Scottish or Northern Ireland Offices). He will then appoint an inspector who may visit the site and decide, either on the basis of written evidence only or (if you or the council request it) by a **public inquiry** whether to over-rule or uphold the council's decision.

Local ombudsman

If you exhaust all these methods of complaining about planning permission, there is one further option open to you. You can contact the **local government ombudsman**. He looks into complaints about district, borough, city or county councils, and into some other local authorities as well, such as the police (although not in London), national parks, development corporations and fire authorities. *He can only intervene, however, after you have exhausted all other ways of complaining, and only if you think you have been unfairly treated, or have suffered what you think is injustice, as a result of maladministration.*

There are three local ombudsmen for England, one each for Wales and Scotland. In Northern Ireland contact the Commissioner for Complaints. You used to have to contact the ombudsman through your local councillor but you can now write to them direct: CABs can tell you their address. Your complaint must be within 12 months of the council's decision, and there must not be any court or tribunal case pending.

In 1988, the three English ombudsmen received over 7000 complaints. The most common complaints concerned housing and planning matters, complaints like this one from **John Ayre. John got a grant from Leicester City Council to repair his home. He asked them several times if he would ever have to repay the grant and they said no. When he did sell the house, however, the council asked for the money back – and John had to pay. Aggrieved by this, he contacted his local ombudsman and the ombudsman ruled that the council would have to pay John back £4500.**

Not bad at all, and there are no limits to the amount you can claim. Councils do not have to abide by the ombudsman's ruling – but most do. You can get more details of how to complain to the local ombudsmen by writing to them.

POLICE AND TRAFFIC OFFENCES

Your local council also has some influence over policing services in their area, including traffic policing and traffic wardens. Apart from London, where police report directly to the Home Secretary, police forces are responsible to their regional **police authority**, which is made up of council representatives and magistrates.

If you have a **general** complaint about the level of police services, for example, if you are unhappy about the number of officers that patrol (or don't patrol) your neighbourhood, bring this up with the council representatives on the police authority. Your local councillor will help you with this, and the council may also have a police committee which can take up these kind of complaints. They cannot deal, however, with **individual** complaints about particular officers. These complaints you will have to make yourself.

Complaints about police behaviour

All policemen and women have to conform to certain rules and regulations when they deal with the public, question or arrest individuals. For example, they cannot compel you 'to go down to the station': they have to arrest you first, although it is probably better for you to go if you are asked. They cannot compel you to give your name and address unless they reasonably suspect you of committing a criminal offence. And 'reasonably' does not apply if your only 'offence' is being young or black.

There are also strict rules about questioning you if you are arrested or detained, laid down by the **1984 Police and Criminal Evidence Act**. You can find out more about these from your local law centre, solicitor or from **Liberty**, formerly the National Council of Civil Liberties, a pressure group.

Any of the above may be able to help you make a complaint about police behaviour but here's what you can do yourself:

1   If your complaint is relatively 'minor', for example, if a police officer has been rude to you, ask for the officer's identity number and name: he must give it to you. Your best bet then is to ring his police station – or pop in – and have a quiet word with the

duty sergeant. You will probably not hear anything else but the police officer will be spoken to by the sergeant and that should mean he will be wary of repeating his behaviour again.

2 If you are not happy about doing this or if your complaint is more serious, for example, if you have been harmed by the police or been detained unreasonably, write to the **chief constable** and ask for the complaint to be investigated and, if necessary, to be referred to the **Police Complaints Authority**. You can get the chief constable's address from the police station. You can write to the Authority direct but the effect will be the same. One of three things will then happen:

♦ For less serious complaints, a senior officer will meet you and discuss your complaint informally.

♦ **Or**, an investigating officer will be appointed who will do a formal investigation into your complaint but without any Police Complaints Authority involvement.

♦ **Or**, the Authority will become involved either by supervising the investigation or checking through the investigating officer's report.

You cannot decide which one of these three options you want to happen: it will be decided for you. Generally, the Police Complaints Authority only gets involved in serious cases of personal injury or death or complaints with special factors involved like those concerning young or old people.

3 If your complaint is upheld, either by the Authority or by the investigating officer, the most you will be offered is a written apology, although the police officer involved will almost certainly be disciplined and sometimes prosecuted. You will have to take the police to court if you want compensation, although a police apology will certainly help your case. Get legal advice before doing this.

In 1988, the Police Complaints Authority, which is independent from the police, dealt with 5500 complaints, although it only supervised 800 of these, and only one in seven of the complaints was upheld against the police. The Authority did have, though, some strong words to say about 'lack of tact and 'professionalism' of the police in dealing with complaints, words which will hopefully improve police behaviour to the public.

So, do complain: it is one way to make sure our police forces continue to serve us properly. *Beware, though, of making false and malicious accusations against individual officers. Not only can you be sued for libel, you can also be prosecuted for wasting police time.*

Complaints about traffic and parking fines

Road traffic and parking control, including traffic wardens, are mainly under the authority of the police, although some forms of car parking are controlled by local councils. If you are charged with committing a road or parking offence, you can complain in the same way as other complaints about the police (see above). Complaints about traffic wardens should be made to whichever police department is responsible: see your parking ticket for details or ask the warden himself.

Parking which is under council control, such as most residential parking places on the street, has to meet council by-laws. Before you complain then, make sure you know what these are.

One *You and Yours* **listener in London bought a year's resident parking permit from her council for a place outside her door. She went away on holiday abroad for a few weeks and when she returned found the car gone, despite it being left in her space. The council needed to use the space for road repairs while she was away and wrote to tell her. But as she was on holiday, she only got the letter when she got home. By then, the car had been towed away and she had to pay to get it back.** The council behaved perfectly properly: there was a by-law allowing them to take away the parking place at any time if needed. So check the by-laws and ring the council before going on holiday.

COMPLAINTS ABOUT THE ENVIRONMENT

Some things that affect us in our local community – and beyond – have nothing to do with our local council. Councils have little control over aircraft or railway noise, for example, and most rivers and lakes are the responsibility of the water companies. Motorways and major trunk roads come under the Department of Transport. Complaining about these kind of things not only helps you and your neighbours, it also helps provide a better quality of life for everyone.

Pollution in the countryside

The residents of Wargrave in Berkshire were proud of their village, indeed it had once won an award for the best kept village in England. Winning a future award, however, looked extremely doubtful when the state of the village's river, the Loddon, started deteriorating. And that was the least of the villagers' worries: they felt their children's health was at risk as well. Local resident Bob Grey explained:

'We've got a boatclub down on the river and our children use it to go canoeing, practice water safety and that kind of thing. Then we started noticing scum on the river, brown mess and used condoms and sanitary towels floating around it. It was really disgusting'.

What had happened was the local water authority, Thames Water, had been discharging untreated sewage into the river due, it said, to a series of mishaps and breakdowns in the local sewage plant. The villagers claimed this had been going on for many months and Thames Water had persistently put back dates to repair or upgrade the plant. The upgrading was urgently necessary, according to the villagers, because of a new large housing estate nearby.

So, what did the villagers do? They formed an action committee and asked one resident, a chemical analyst, to analyse water from the river to prove their case. Then they took Thames Water to court – and won: the court fined Thames Water £2000, the maximum possible under the 1984 Control of Pollution Act, and ordered the authority to pay court costs of £3500.

You do not have to go quite so far to stop river or lake or indeed any inland water pollution. Contact the water company whose area the water is in and lodge a complaint. If you do not get a satisfactory answer, you can then go to the new **National Rivers Authority**, the regulatory body that makes sure water companies keep rivers and lakes clean. Or, call your local environmental health officer and get his backing if you think public health is at risk. Local councils can take private companies or water companies to court under the Control of Pollution Act and compel them to clean up rivers.

Complaints about **land pollution**, such as car dumping or litter strewn around, are usually dealt with by the **local council's environment department** (sometimes under the **planning department**). All land in the United Kingdom falls under some local authority or other, apart, that is, from a few exceptions. These are: **national parks**, which each have their own board of management, **crown commission land**, managed by the crown commissioners, and **admiralty land**, the land around naval ports. The last two still have **crown immunity** which means they cannot be prosecuted under the Control of Pollution or indeed any other Act. But they will deal seriously with complaints if you write to them. Find their address from your local council.

Your council can also put you in touch with **national park boards** who can be prosecuted under the Act. Write to them with your complaint, if necessary with environmental health officer backing. If you don't have any success, you can then take up your complaint with the relevant local ombudsman for the area where the national park is.

For help with any major complaint about pollution or spoiling of the countryside, contact the major pressure groups working in this area. They include the **Council for National Parks** and the **Council for the Protection of Rural England**. Or, contact the **Nature Conservancy Council**, a governmental body.

Noise pollution

Sometimes noise pollution is caused by local council activity or is the council's responsibility (see p. 155). But one area where councils have no power to act is noise from aircraft.

Aircraft noise was specifically excluded when the Control of

Pollution Act was passed in the mid-1980s. And that is a great pity for the thousands of people who live under the flightpaths of civil or military aircraft. All the areas around the major airports – and many areas around smaller airports as well – have spawned local action groups which complain regularly about aircraft noise: your local library should have their addresses. But what can you do yourself?

If the noise is coming from **civil** aircraft, contact the relevant airport. Most UK airports have **consultative committees** which will look into any complaints about noise, and can tell you about any compensation you may be entitled to claim.

If the noise is a result of **military** aircraft, British or American, ring the airfield first. You can then complain directly to the **Ministry of Defence**. At the Ministry, there is an independent civilian organisation which looks into all complaints about military aircraft and airports, not just noise but also low-flying or flying at unsocial hours, and any breaches of Ministry regulations. You can get a leaflet outlining your rights from the **Secretariat (Air Staff), 2b, Ministry of Defence, Whitehall, London SW1**. It will tell you how you can apply for compensation.

What you will need to do to press any aircraft noise complaint is to log the time, date, place and any other details you can find out about an incident that annoys or disturbs you.

Noise pollution from **major roads** like motorways is the responsibility of the **Department of Transport** (or the Welsh, Scottish, or Northern Ireland Offices). The Department has the power to offer you compensation or insulation grants, although these are usually settled when the road is first completed.

One person found that her complaint about transport noise received a sympathetic ear but it was a complaint not about roads but about **rail**, or, to be more specific, about a railway station.

Anita Bowler kept being woken up by train announcements at her station which is near her Surrey home. She took British Rail to the local magistrates court and the court ruled that these announcements were indeed noise pollution. British Rail was ordered

to stop – and Anita now gets a lie-in each morning. There have not been any reports of passengers missing their train as a result!

So if you are disturbed by railway noise, complain to British Rail and remind them of Anita's case.

Complaints about roads

By far the most complaints we receive at *You and Yours* about roads are not about noise nor really about pollution, but about **plans** to build a new road or extend an old one. One complaint we received was from mobile home residents in Staffordshire.

The Department of Transport had published plans for a new orbital motorway around the West Midlands conurbation, plans which would mean the new road going straight through the residents' site. Unfortunately for the residents, the Department did not seem to know they were there at all, as residents' committee chairman Robert Owen explained:

'We've lived here, 300 of us, since the 1950s but the Department seemed to have no knowledge of us. How they missed us I just don't know. We're on all the maps and if they come up to see us, they'd find all these beautiful homes, some with trees and flowers around them, some even with fountains and waterfalls. We were appalled'.

And so was their local councillor who complained on their behalf to the region's Department of Transport officials. The officials apologised for the mistake, and reassured the mobile home residents that they now knew about them, and would take their views into account.

So, if a road is planned for your area, and it has not taken into account your land or home, contact the Department through your local councillor.

What happens when the government or the council wants a new road or by-pass is that it publishes the plans which are usually available in local libraries or direct from the appropriate government department. These are then looked into by an **official inquiry** set up by the Department of Transport to consider the road and any objections to it. If an inquiry agrees to the road, compensation will be paid to the people affected. Remember, though, that the government publishes far more plans for roads than roads that are eventually built. And the whole process is one of political bartering. The more fuss complainers make against the proposed road and the more support they seem to be getting from local councils, influential people like MPs or television stars and pressure groups, the more likely the government will back down, even before any inquiry.

So, if a new road is planned and it is going to affect your home or neighbourhood, get busy and form or join a local action group. If the road is a major one, you might be able to hold up any decision until a new government gets in, a government which might have different priorities. Sometimes you can get the project altered or scrapped pretty quickly indeed. What you cannot do is claim any compensation for the decline in your property value before the road plan has been 'formally approved': another incentive to get organised straight away.

And the more imaginative you can be with your protests, the more likely you are to attract media attention to your cause.

Anne Tribe, from Bedfordshire, discovered that a planned new by-pass was going to go straight through her home. She composed a song which expressed her worries and concerns – and sent it directly to Peter Bottomley, the Minister who was then responsible for roads. With lines like, 'I'm a poor houseowner who lives down Ampthill Road, and now that we're the main A5 we've such a traffic load', Anne's song was not the kind which would storm even her local hit-parade. But it did produce a response from Mr Bottomley in the form of a minsterial poem: 'I thank you for your letter, a superbly written song. I have to say in my reply, that we've done nothing wrong'. (Again, not the kind of poem that would qualify for any collection of English verse.) At least, though, Anne made the Minister aware of her concerns – and as important, her unusual style of complaining resulted in wide media coverage which highlighted local concern about the proposed new road.

Parliamentary ombudsman

There is another person you can complain to about the behaviour of the Department of Transport, the Department of Environment, *or indeed any other government department*: the **Parliamentary Ombudsman**, more correctly known as the **Parliamentary Commissioner for Administration** (in Northern Ireland, the **Commissioner for Complaints**).

This ombudsman, like his local government equivalents, cannot investigate complaints about policy or legislation, but he can look into complaints of maladministration by civil servants. You must, however, first raise your complaint with the government department involved and then make your complaint to the ombudsman *through your MP* within a year of the incident taking place. The ombudsman received 700 complaints in 1988 and 90 per cent of the complaints he investigated were 'wholly or partly justified'. He can order the government department to put things right and pay compensation.

New government action

The new interest that has developed over the last few years in the environment and all things 'green' has led to government promises of a new **Environment Bill**. As this book was being prepared for publication, it was as yet unclear what will be included in this new Bill, but it does seem certain to include new powers for government and local councils to control all kinds of pollution – and new opportunities for us all to complain if our local environment is being threatened.

NEIGHBOURS

Are you regularly woken up in the night by pop music blaring from the house next door? Or by the screams of children or the arguments of adults? Does your next-door neighbour's pet continually foul on your property? Or does their prize tree threaten to block out your view or light? If so, you are in good company.

One in three of us find our neighbours irritating, and over 53 000 people were so upset in 1988 they complained to their local council, double the number only 10 years ago. Dogs and noise were the most common complaints or, as in the case of **John Darrington** from Dorset, both at once:

'I live in a small secluded close and the lady next door lets her dog out every night. He doesn't come back on his own so virtually every night at around 12.30 a.m., she goes out looking for him, calling his name every few minutes or so. Other dogs then join in the cacophany and other people in the street open their windows and ask her to be quiet, to cut the noise down. In the morning, any comments we make go straight over her head. We say 'we didn't get any sleep last night', and she says, 'That's funny, neither did I'.

What can people like John do? We will look at noise problems a few page on, but first, here are the general steps you can take:

How to complain about neighbours

1   First, talk to your neighbours about the complaint. Or if this feels too threatening, write to them or ask another neighbour or friend to talk to them instead.

2   Find out if other neighbours feel the same way either by knocking on their doors, or asking your residents or tenants association. If your complaint is a reasonable one, it will probably affect other people as well.

3   Then contact your local council. For most complaints about your neighbours, the **environmental health officer** is the person to seek out.

4   Ask at the CAB if there is a **neighbour mediation group** in your area. Or contact a solicitor to write to your neighbours asking them to desist.

5   As a last resort, use legal action to stop them.

This is all very well in theory, but in practice, following these suggestions can take more than a little courage.

Research done at Aston University suggests that the average complainant is 57 years old and female, the average offender is 25 years old and male. And there is often a clash of cultures as well: young people's taste in music, for example, or their bedtime hours are usually quite different from their older neighbours. Complaining directly to your neighbour or about them to some official can feel extremely threatening. After all, they know where you live and could take retaliatory action, such as turning the music up louder or worse, much worse. At least, that's the fear. But is it true in practice?

Research done by Nick Yapp, author of *Law and Your Neighbours*, suggests not. At least not most of the time. Retaliation or reprisals by neighbours happen less often than you might imagine. Of course, there are exceptions, particularly in some inner-city boroughs whose black and Asian residents have experienced horrific racial attacks, some of them from their neighbours. In these situations, get advice from your local CAB and council straight away.

In most cases where you are worried about abuse or violence if you complain, however, you do have one weapon up your sleeve: they might know where you live, but you know where they live, too. If, for example, you have complained about your neighbour's behaviour and you start getting abusive phone calls or anonymous letters, that is pretty strong circumstantial evidence you could take to the police. The police will normally not get involved in a neighbour dispute *unless there is likely to be a 'breach of the peace' (for example, threats of violence) or some other form of criminal action.* Harassment certainly counts as criminal, and if this starts happening to you after you have complained, get in touch with the police at once.

Nine out of 10 cases, though, will never come remotely near that. And people are often surprised how the annoying neighbour can become very reasonable and apologetic if you complain directly to them. Even the youngster whose hi-fi seems to make him (and you) permanently deaf. Even the army-type whose idea of a good summer evening is to practise clay-pigeon shooting in his back garden. So try and talk and, above all, don't give up.

Noise

Mary Laker from Yorkshire found that she could hear in her Victorian terrace house every television programme her neighbours put on.

Ann Jones was disturbed by the couple next door having noisy, violent rows.

For Edna Dale from the West Country, it was the sound of her neighbour's pet birds in his aviary: 'I usually like birdsong but not all the time'. What can you do about your neighbour's noise?

The key thing to remember about noise is that it must be **reasonable**. Your neighbours are entitled to make a reasonable amount of noise; you are entitled to a reasonable amount of quiet. Noise becomes unreasonable if it interferes with your enjoyment and privacy, especially if it is late at night or very early in the morning, and when the noise is continuous, not just occasional.

If your neighbour will not turn the noise down, contact your local council environmental health officer. He will know, for example, if there are any by-laws about noise in your area and know of other complaints as well. If the noise is taking place during office hours, his officers can come around and hear it for themselves. Or, if it is at night or at weekends, he can lend you monitoring equipment to get a precise measurement of the noise.

What he can also do is write to the neighbour with a 'notice to desist'. He can then prosecute them in court if they do not stop. Obviously he will be more interested in your case if he thinks other neighbours are being disturbed as well, but do pop into your local office or phone for advice if you think you have a valid complaint.

If the environmental health officer will not help, you can take court action yourself, either by alleging 'nuisance' and asking a judge for an injunction against your neighbours, or by bringing a private prosecution against your neighbours under the Control of Pollution Act. Beware, however. Both these legal actions are expensive, and you will need strong, independent evidence to succeed. Write to the **Noise Abatement Society** for advice.

What you can do quite easily is to pay a solicitor to write to the person threatening court action if they do not turn the noise down. It is an old lawyer's trick: solicitor's letters usually frighten people even if you have no intention of going to court.

And if the noise comes from a council tenant, the council could evict a persistent offender, under the 1985 Housing Act. **Leicester City Council recently used these powers to evict one of their tenants who consistently disregarded warnings about playing loud music.**

Pets

Kathleen Stevens from Somerset has a problem with cats. Not her cats – she doesn't have any – but the cats next door, all six of them. They like Kathleen's garden very much. Too much.

'I landscaped the garden and put wire nettings all around the plants and the shrubs, but the cats still keep coming in and playing with the netting and fouling everywhere. If I leave my conservatory door open, they even come in there and wet on my vegetable trays. I mentioned it to their owner and she said, "Yes I know, it's an awful problem". But it still keeps happening'.

What Kathleen can do is to formally warn her neighbour, by letter, that the cats are damaging her property. Then she can take the neighbour to court for compensation which could be considerable if her plants and flowers are expensive.

This applies to other pets, too, including dogs. If the dog is dangerous as well, contact your local council and ask them to prosecute under the **1871 Dogs Act**. Get other neighbours to support you with this. If pets make an unreasonable amount of noise, contact your environmental health officer. And tell the officer, too, if you think they are being kept in unsanitary conditions: they could be at risk to human health and he should act fast. If you suspect cruelty, call the **RSPCA**.

With all the recent publicity about attacks by breeds of dogs like rottweilers and pit-bull terriers, the government has promised to update the 1871 Act to give local councils more powers over dangerous dogs: at present, fines under the Act are restricted to £1 a day! The government has also promised to impose a duty on councils to round up stray dogs and to clear up dog fouling on public streets. This should give people far more opportunities to press home complaints about dogs.

Children

Evelyn Thomas, from Lancashire, rang *You and Yours* **about a particular problem she was faced concerning her neighbour's children. 'They were always playing out the back, football mostly, and I got extremely fed up. Then one day, the football came into my garden. I wanted to keep the ball to stop them playing. Could I?'**

Well, no she could not. But what she could do is leave the ball where it came over: if the children clamber over her fence to get it, they are trespassing. And, if the football smashed one of her windows, she could then sue the children's parents for compensation.

When children are causing a hazard by playing in the street, ring the police and ask them to have a quiet word to stop what could be a nasty accident.

Finally, if you suspect a child is being maltreated, contact your local social services department or the **NSPCC**. None of us likes to interfere with other people's private lives, but a child's health or life may be at risk if you don't act.

Right to light and privacy

One person's delightful tree is often another person's blot on the landscape as **Sally Wright** discovered at her home in Buckinghamshire. **Her next door neighbour's eucalyptus grew 10 feet tall, blocking out the light which used to come into Sally's home. What could she do?**

Surprisingly, not very much. There is no automatic right to light, although you can earn such a right if you have enjoyed the light for 20 years or if you have made a private contract with your neighbour before he started blocking your light out. The law concerning light is, however, quite complicated. The best thing for people in Sally's position to do is to try and persuade their neighbour to trim the tree, if necessary, by threatening to grow a tree in your garden to block out their light! If this does not work, contact a solicitor, but make sure he knows all about light laws before asking him to act for you. One option he could advise is to take out an injunction alleging nuisance in the High Court against anybody who blocks out your light. This is an expensive option but it could be worth it if you have a good case.

If your light is being threatened not by a new tree but by a new building, you can register an objection to the building at the planning stages. If this is not successful, make sure the building conforms to building regulations. Again, take advice from a solicitor – and move quickly if you suspect a new building is being planned that could block out your light or view.

You have even fewer rights when it comes to protecting your privacy: you cannot gain any right to privacy by enjoying an unlooked-over garden or patio for 20 years. Therefore, if a neighbour has built a new conservatory overlooking your garden, there is very little you can do as long as the conservatory has not contravened any planning requirements. The neighbour cannot, however, complain about anything you might care to do in your garden which he can now see.

Overhanging trees and plants

If your neighbour's tree starts overhanging your garden, you are entitled to cut the overhanging part down – but you must give it back to your neighbour: you can't keep any fruit. But you cannot cut it down if there is a tree preservation order on the tree: check with the **Development Control Office** at your council.

And if your neighbour's plants cause you damage, it is possible to prosecute the neighbours under the **1959 Weeds Act**. Contact the environmental health department for advice.

Boundary disputes

After noise, children and pets, the most common complaints about neighbours are about land, what's yours, what's your neighbours, what they can do on their land that may affect you. **Marie Kay** from South London wrote to *You and Yours* about what happened to her after the 1987 hurricane:

'The storm blew down many of the trees in my gar-

den and also the wire fence that separated my garden from my neighbours. Well, it took quite some time to clear up all the wood and I just left the fence on the ground. One day I came out to find that my neighbour had built a new fence connected to some trees that had not been blown down, and this fence seemed to make the garden much narrower. I measured the garden and found I had lost some 10 feet due to the new fence. And a surveyor measured it for me as well and confirmed this'.

Marie has a pretty good case if she goes to court to get her land back. What you should do if a neighbour tries to claim any of your land by putting up a new fence is to check with the title deeds of your property and confirm that you have lost land by using an expert to measure it for you. Then ask the neighbour to pull the fence down. If he refuses, pull it down yourself and give it back: he has trespassed on your property.

If this does not resolve things, go to court to get an order restraining your neighbour from entering your land. But where there is any dispute about land, try and sort it out soon. Other people can eventually claim ownership or use of land if nothing is done about it.

There is not, by the way, any law compelling you or your neighbours to build a fence to demarcate your land, as long as the deeds of your house do not require one although obviously, a fence can help. Make sure you get it at the edge of your land though: if you are short, your neighbours could eventually claim the land on the other side of their fence as theirs. If too long, you are trespassing on their land. The ownership of a fence is traditionally determined by which land the fence's support stands on.

Planning and building disputes

Helen Weir from Somerset had no problem with fences. Her complaint was about her neighbour's new line of work. He had built an extension in his garden and started a car-repair business which was like a 'constant sub-machine gun. He started at 7.30 in the morning, Saturdays and Sundays as well, and you could hear

**the constant noise, particularly in the summer, even
with our windows closed'.**

Helen is on strong ground, for it looks like her neighbour
has not got **planning permission** for 'change of use': councils
very rarely allow people to open up a business at home, particularly if the business involves hard, manual work. If the
neighbour has not got planning permission, he will have to stop.

The same applies to anybody building an extension or an
entire new home near your property: they will almost always
need planning permission. In Scotland and Northern Ireland,
people who are planning new buildings have to tell their neighbours before requesting planning permission from their local
council. In England and Wales, local councils should tell adjoining neighbours about any new building that is being proposed
before they have granted planning permission. (If they do not,
complain to your **local ombudsman**.) If a new building is
being planned in a conservation area, this has to be advertised in
the local paper.

Once you hear about a new building which you think may
affect your quality of life, write to the council's planning department and register your objection. You may find it useful to find
out about the council's local plan which outlines their priorities
for new buildings in their area. You could also involve other
people who may be affected or ask your local councillor to take
up your case. But act quickly: once planning permission has
been approved by the local council's planning committee (and
the council must have good reasons to refuse permission), that is
normally the end of the matter.

For major building work involving demolition of other
houses, there will almost certainly be a public inquiry in which
you can make your views known. Once formal approval for this
kind of work is granted, you can serve a **blight notice** on your
local authority if the value of your house has gone down: this
compels the council to buy your house at the market price your
home would have fetched without the new building. The council
will give you advice about this.

If you can't get planning permission refused for a new building or extension, check whether the actual building is built
according to the proper **building regulations** – these are

quite different from planning laws. Your local council will help.

Most building work does need planning permission: check with your council's planning department if you are unsure. But some additions to property do not need it, as publican **Keith Lynch** found out.

Keith's neighbour, Stephen Wilcock, is a sculptor by profession and Stephen's latest project was a statue of the risen Christ which he thought would fit nicely into his garden in a small Lancashire hamlet. It certainly fitted in, the finished statue was only a couple of feet wide. But it was also 16 feet high with very large arms outstretched, as Stephen explained 'just like the bible'. Neighbour Keith, however, was not impressed: 'it's monstrous. We live in an area of outstanding natural beauty and there's nothing natural about a lump of concrete. It's a blot on the landscape'.

Unfortunately for Keith, there was nothing he could do, as his local council confirmed. The statue did not need planning permission because it was portable, at least in theory. It was not attached to the ground and the size of the statue was irrelevant. In law it was no different from a garden gnome, at least as far as the planning authorities were concerned!

Parking

Contrary to public perception, and contrary to all the notices that exist in virtually every street in the land, there is no right to park your vehicle – or to prevent other people parking their vehicles – on a public street. If, however, someone parks on a public street causing you damage or obstructing your use of the road you can sue them or get a court injunction to stop them.

One *You and Yours* listener rang to tell us about her neighbour who put dustbins out on the street to save parking space for their *six* cars. Even if it was just one car, you can take any dustbin away – or ask the police to do so – and there's nothing your neighbour can do. The applies to a 'no parking' notice: it has no legal basis to stop you parking there unless it has been put there by the police or council.

But what happens if someone parks on your own land and not on a public street? **The vicar of St Luke's Church in**

Southsea, the Rev. Smithson, decided to do something about motorists who were parking on his church's land not to visit the Lord, but to call in at the shopping centre nearby. He clamped their cars and then charged the motorists £5 to remove the clamp.

Was this legal? The law is unclear. Certainly you could claim damages from a motorist who parks his car on your land for trespass and loss of use. But if you damaged the car or stopped a motorist driving it away he could claim from you for the damage or loss of use. And you cannot 'fine' the motorist at all – only the police can do this. You can, however, ask for an administration or rent charge from the motorist for the use of your land!

It's all very unclear. Until some court case is brought by a motorist for private clamping, it will probably keep carrying on. Police clamping and clamping by companies authorised by the police are, of course, quite legal.

Ownership of land

People who live in Scotland and Northern Ireland have an absolute right to find out who owns any land – just contact the **Scottish** or **Northern Ireland Land Registry**. But residents of England and Wales do not, or at least not at the moment – unless they are trying to find out the freeholder of their lease (see Chapter 7).

All this will, however, soon change. The **1988 Land Registration Act** extends the Scottish and Northern Irish right to find out land ownership to England and Wales. It will come into effect sometime in 1990. When it does, you can just write to the land registry about any piece of registered land and they will tell you who owns it.

HEALTH AND WELL-BEING

When *You and Yours* recently commissioned a major survey into the quality of life in the United Kingdom today, four out of 10 people told us that their health was the most important thing in their life. Only 'family' scored more.

Perhaps this has always been true, but certainly we were surprised. The strength of support for the health services surprised us as well as how informed people were about their rights as patients, and how likely they were to complain if things went wrong.

This really is a major change from 40 or even 20 years ago. Doctors, nurses and other health staff are still held in high regard, but they are no longer seen as knowing automatically what is best, no longer perceived as professionals who never do anything wrong, as people about whom patients have no right to complain. Here are some examples of health complaints we have featured recently on the programme:

- **A woman who was prescribed pain-killing drugs by her GP for 'abdominal pain'. She was, in fact, pregnant and had to have a termination because the drugs would have damaged the baby.**
- **One woman was awarded £85 000 damages in court against a doctor who misdiagnosed her husband's heart attack as 'chest pains'.**
- **A family whose mother was admitted to hospital and died – and they were not told until they popped in to visit her some five hours later.**

And it is not just complaints about the NHS that come into the *You and Yours* office. As private health insurance, private medicine and alternative treatments become more popular, they too are producing more dissatisfied customers. Social services staff have always had a 'bad press' for doing what is sometimes an impossible job. But as they take more responsibility for patients and their families in the community or in residential homes, complaints about their behaviour and practice are mounting up, too.

This is not such a bad thing. The more complaints we all make when things go wrong with the health care we receive, the more likely health professionals will provide a service that suits patients' interests rather then their own.

GENERAL PRACTITIONERS (GPs)

In the NHS, GPs act as the 'gatekeeper' to other health services. With a few exceptions, such as family planning, accidents and emergencies and some mental health services, you have to visit your GP before getting specialist help.

GPs are not directly employed by the NHS. They contract their services to local NHS bodies called **family practitioner committees (FPC)**: each area has a committee which regulates and controls GP activities. Some GPs offer both an NHS and a private service, and a few GPs *only* offer private consultations. To complain about *private* treatment from a GP, see the section on private doctors (p. 194).

Getting or changing your GP

If you have moved house, you can contact your local FPC: it will allocate you a GP in the area. The address is in the phone book.

But it is better to ask neighbours or friends in the area to recommend a GP and then go and ask him if he will take you on. The GP will then tell the local committee. There is, by the way, no obligation on any GP to accept you as a patient but the FPC is obliged to find you a GP who will take you on.

If you are dissatisfied with your GP, simply write to the FPC and say that you want to change. You do not have to give any reason. You could also ask another GP to take you on – although this will be unlikely if he is in the same practice – and the new GP will sort it out with the FPC. The same right, however, applies also to GPs: they can get rid of you simply by informing the FPC who will then let you know.

What your GP has to offer you

GPs are obliged to:

♦   Diagnose your problem and treat it or send you to a specialist for diagnosis and treatment. They can, by the way, refer you to any specialist or hospital they want or you request: it does not *have* to be in your area or your part of the country. Very few hospitals, however, will accept you for NHS treatment if you live outside their 'catchment area'. If a GP refers you to a specialist who is not a doctor, a nurse, for example, or an alternative practitioner like an acupuncturist, the GP should make sure they are competent. Otherwise, you can sue the GP for negligence if anything goes badly wrong.

♦ Offer surgery times when you can visit, some of which must be outside working hours. And offer, too, a visiting service for emergencies which they or a deputy must attend if your health is at risk.

♦ Provide some other services as well such as ante-natal care and community nursing. This does depend on how large the practice is.

GPs are not obliged to refer you to a consultant if they think your problem does not merit it. Although if they do not refer you and you get worse, they are responsible for any unnecessary suffering caused. Most GPs will, however, refer you to a consultant if you request it. If your GP refuses, try another GP in the same practice.

GPs also have to take full responsibility for any drugs they prescribe, as in the following examples.

A motorist was prescribed hay-fever tablets by his GP. He was not told by the GP that the tablets would make him drowsy, or that he should not drive after taking them. He drove his car soon after taking the tablets and his driving was so impaired that he was involved in an incident which lost him his licence. The GP was at fault for not pointing out the effect the tablets would have, and the motorist sued the GP for compensation.

The second case was even more serious. It was sent to *You and Yours* by a woman on behalf of her niece:

'I've just had a very distressing and disturbing phone call from my niece who is married and on the pill – and now finds she is pregnant. She had been on a

course of antibiotics but she was not warned by the GP who prescribed them that their effect would cancel the protection offered by the pill. When she was taking the antibiotics, she started feeling nauseous and had abdominal pains. The GP gave her some pain-killing drugs, but her symptoms got worse and she went down to the hospital where she saw a doctor. He told her she was pregnant and suggested a scan to see if there were any physical deformities in the foetus because the pain-killing drugs should not have been given to a pregnant woman. The doctor suggested she should consider a termination and he told her this would have to be done privately as the consultant in her area would not do one on the NHS. My niece has not got much money and the cost will be £325. Can you imagine how deeply upset she is by all this? What can she do?'

What she *can* do is sue the GP who in this case does seem to be clearly guilty of negligence. Taking a doctor to court, however, is complicated – see p. 192 for how to do it.

If your complaint is less serious – you have not, for example, suffered any great loss as a result of your GP's action or inaction but are just dissatisfied with the service – here's what to do:

♦ If you think your GP has not provided you with **proper service**, for example, he did not refer you on to a specialist when you thought he should have, or he or a deputy did not come out at night when you needed to see a doctor, or the surgery is dirty and unkempt, write to your local **FPC** (in Scotland and Northern Ireland, **area health boards**). They will get the GP's side of the story. The committee can then decide to conduct a formal hearing where you and your GP will put your cases. Some FPCs allow you to have an advisor at the hearing as well, but neither you nor the GP is allowed any legal representation.

You must contact the FPC within eight weeks of your complaint (or have a very good reason, like illness, if any later); this limit will soon be increased to 13 weeks. If your complaint is upheld, you cannot get any compensation, but the FPC can recommend the doctor be admonished, fined or, in very extreme cases, removed from the FPC list. Over 1000 people complain to FPCs about their GPs every year.

♦ If you do not like the **manner** with which your GP dealt with you, for example, if he was rude to you, you can also try your FPC. Some FPCs have an informal complaints procedure to deal with this kind of complaint.

♦ If you are not satisfied with the committee's decision, you can then appeal direct to the Secretary of State at the **Department of Health** (or **Scottish** or **Northern Ireland Office**). You can also appeal directly to the Secretary if the FPC decides not to take up your complaint or if you are out of time.

♦ If you feel your GP is guilty of **serious professional misconduct**, such as being drunk or indecently assaulting you, complain to the **General Medical Council**. Every doctor, including GPs, needs a licence from the Council to practise medicine. That licence can be withdrawn if the GP is found guilty. The Council will almost certainly refer your complaint to their **professional conduct committee**, which will investigate and probably ask you to swear an oath in front of a solicitor that your complaint is true.

Be careful, though: if your allegation turns out to be false, and malicious, the GP could then sue you for libel – and you could end up paying both damages and his legal costs. So, take advice before making this kind of complaint.

As this book goes to press, the General Medical Council has announced its intention of widening its powers to look into complaints, not just about serious professional misconduct, but also about less serious examples of professional misconduct. This should happen in the next few years.

None of these methods of complaining, however, will provide you with compensation for loss or injury as a result of a GP's decision.

♦ If you or your family has suffered as a result of GP **negligence**, you will have to take the GP to court for compensation. See p. 192 for how to do this but be warned – medical negligence cases are long and costly. Raise your complaint with the FPC first. You can then use their decision as evidence in any legal action.

♦ Finally, there are the **Health Service Commissioners**, one each for England, Scotland and Wales (in Northern Ireland, the **Commissioner for Complaints**). Their powers are, however, pretty restricted. They cannot look into any complaints about clinical judgements, or into the *subject matter* of a complaint to an FPC, or into any case which may involve legal action. But you can get in touch with them if you think the way an FPC handled your complaint was unfair or if you have suffered hardship or injustice due to poor administration of a GP's service.

If all this sounds a long, complicated process with little chance of getting anything out of it, take heart. There are a number of organisations who will give you help and at least convince you that you are not alone.

Who can help?

Every health authority and family practitioner committee is monitored by a local **community health council (CHC)**. These councils are the statutory bodies which represent the consumer in the NHS. They have the power to inspect GP surgeries and hospitals, to make recommendations about health care in their area and to take up patients' complaints. So, before making any kind of complaint about NHS care, including about your GP, contact your local CHC: get the address from a CAB, your GP's surgery, or from the phone book under 'Community'.

There are also two national pressure groups which can give you advice about patients' rights, the **Patients Association** and the **College of Health**.

If you have a specific medical problem, there are also many self-help and specialist groups that can give advice, some of which have local or regional groups. Your CHC can put you in touch with these. The College of Health has also compiled a list of these groups.

These organisations can also help you with complaints about NHS hospital care and staff including hospital doctors.

NHS HOSPITALS

Paula Peck had to have a Caesarean operation for the birth of her child. Complications developed:

'I came round and found myself on several life-support machines. Apparently what had happened was that while I was under anaesthetic, my womb became infected. My new son swallowed some of the infection and it also got up my windpipe to my lung which collapsed and put pressure on my heart. I only found this out later because at the time no one would tell me what had happened. The only comment I got was from a registrar who said it was lucky I was in an NHS hospital as the drugs used on me cost a fortune.'

Lack of information was also the complaint of **Kathleen Doverton**, not about herself but about her mother, who had been taken into a hospital in the West Midlands:

'I went in to visit her thinking that she might be coming out soon. As I opened the curtain around her bed, I saw that she had passed away. No one had prepared me for it at all. So I went down a corridor and found a young nurse, who said, "Oh yes, she passed away at 3 p.m. this afternoon." Well, when I visited, it was 7.30 in the evening. I was in such a shock because I was expecting my mother to come home. It took me a few days to think about what had happened and I then thought I should have been informed by someone, the sister or the nurse.'

Complaints about lack of information provided in hospitals are, with the length of waiting lists, the most common grievances patients have with NHS hospital care.

More seriously and, mercifully, more rarely, complaints emerge about the **clinical judgement** of hospital doctors where lack of care or the wrong medical decision results in complications or sometimes death.

How you complain about hospital treatment depends on whose fault it was, and how serious the complaint is.

How to complain about hospital doctors

In hospital, you will be treated usually by a range of doctors, some from different specialities. You may be seen by junior doctors, for example, a **house officer** or a **registrar**. Or by a (more senior) **senior registrar**, but you will almost always be under a **consultant**, even if you never see him!

If your complaint is about the **manner** with which you are dealt with, bring it up with the consultant, in writing if necessary. You should get an explanation and an apology. If your complaint is about **serious professional misconduct**, contact the **General Medical Council** (see p. 183).

If the medical care you received at the hospital was deficient, say, if you were not given certain drugs when you think you should have been, if your illness was misdiagnosed, or if you were kept in pain with no reason given, write to your consultant. It might be better to get advice from your local CHC first.

If you do not receive an adequate reply, you can then contact the health authority's **district general manager** or **regional medical officer** and ask for the matter to be referred for **independent professional review**. If such a review is granted, two consultants of the same discipline as your own consultant but from a different hospital will consider your complaint and your hospital notes and see if they would have acted differently. They can then provide you with an explanation and, occasionally, an apology.

What some hospitals do before granting you an independent review is to try to find out if you have any intention of pursuing a law case for damages and compensation. Be noncommittal if they ask you about this. There is nothing to stop you taking the doctor to court for compensation after a review. If the review finding is in your favour, you will have some backing for your court case.

If you have suffered injury or loss due to **negligence** by a hospital doctor, you can sue for compensation (see p. 192). As all hospital doctors are employed (or in the case of consultants 'engaged') by a **health authority**, sue the authority as well. Present government intentions are that in future patients may only be able to sue the authority which employs the doctor and not the doctor as well.

Finally, with all but the least serious complaints about hospital doctors, contact your local CHC for advice and support. And, as with GPs, you can take your case to the Health Service Commissioners (see p. 184).

Complaints about other hospital staff

Apart from doctors, there are a wide number of other people with whom you come into contact in hospital, from nurses to physiotherapists, psychologists to porters. For less serious complaints like rudeness, try to have a word with their immediate boss: unpleasantness from a student nurse, for example, should be reported to the ward sister. If you are an in-patient, by the way, it is best to do this with tact: hospital staff will not take kindly to unfair complaints and will label you a troublesome patient. You should still get proper medical treatment but you may miss the kind touch or word!

More serious complaints should be raised with the **unit general manager**, the manager responsible for the hospital.

If you still do not have any luck, you can then contact the health authority's **district general manager**, who will certainly want to hear of any serious complaints about staff in any of the hospitals in his area. It is, however, best to get advice from your local CHC first.

Complaints about negligence of hospital staff have to be dealt with by the courts (see p. 192), and you cannot sue individual nurses, physiotherapists or other staff: you have to sue the health authority that employs them.

Finally, complaints about misconduct by hospital **professionals** (basically anybody who gives you treatment) can be made to their appropriate disciplinary organisation, for example, the **National Boards of England, Scotland, Wales or Northern Ireland** for nurses, health visitors and midwives; the **Council for Professions Supplementary to Medicine**, for occupational and physio-therapists.

Complaints about hospital services

You did not get a cup of tea in the morning; the ward was dirty and unswept; you tripped over some building work: all these kinds of complaint are the responsibility of the hospital's **unit**

general manager. Contact him with your complaint. Some hospitals now have a **complaints procedure** and a **complaints officer**. If these exist, use them first.

If your complaint seems more than a 'one-off', for example, if the wards *never* seem to be swept properly, you can write to the **district general manager** or to the **chairman of the Regional Health Authority** responsible for the hospital. If you then are not lucky, you can ask the Secretary of State for Health or his Scottish or Northern Ireland equivalent to look into the matter. To have any chance of succeeding here, however, you will need backing, such as complaints from other patients or your local CHC.

Second opinions

You do not have an *automatic* right to a second opinion on the NHS from another consultant about your illness. Most consultants will, however, arrange for you to be seen by another consultant at the same hospital if you ask them. This may not be worth the trouble involved since the second consultant is unlikely to say anything different from the first.

What you could consider doing is asking the consultant, or going back to your GP and asking him, to refer you to a consultant who specialises in your illness or condition. For example, if you or a member of your family has been diagnosed as suffering from cancer and you are unhappy with either the diagnosis or the treatment offered, you could ask the original consultant or your GP to refer you to a cancer specialist, such as an oncologist.

The difficulty you will face is that you will need to convince them a specialist opinion might reveal something different from the first consultant's opinion. Seeing a specialist consultant may involve you in several trips to a major teaching hospital which might be many miles away from your home – and that's if he agrees to see you. Finally, if a specialist suggests a different range of treatment from the first consultant, you may have to carry on visiting his hospital for the treatment since it may not be on offer at your local hospital.

If you are refused a second, specialist opinion, you can see a specialist privately. This may not cost as much as you think if your original consultant agrees to send the specialist all the notes about your case. You then only pay for an hour or two's consultation which is unlikely to cost more than £100. If this specialist decides a different form of treatment is advisable, you can ask for this treatment to be provided on the NHS: most private specialists are also NHS consultants.

Getting a specialist opinion will take effort and time but it may well be worth it. And most, but not all, GPs and consultants will be quite prepared to pass your notes on to another doctor, even if they think it is all a waste of time. More help and advice can be provided by one of the national organisations which specialise in particular illnesses or diseases – ask your CHC for the names and addresses.

Visiting rights in hospitals

All NHS hospitals have to provide convenient times for family and friends to visit patients in hospital. You have no right to visit outside these times but ask the ward sister for permission if you need to. If, for example, a member of your family is dying, the ward sister will almost always allow this. Similarly, you do not have any right to stay in a hospital if your child is a patient but most hospitals will arrange this if you want it. Let a sister know right away. For a small fee, NHS patients in many hospitals can rent a private room: treatment is still on the NHS.

Waiting lists

Donald Green, from Birmingham, injured his shoulder at work. Physiotherapy didn't do it much good, so he was referred to his local hospital where he was told there was an 'indefinite wait for treatment'. 'I couldn't put any pressure on the shoulder', Donald told *You and Yours*. 'If anybody touched it, I would want to murder them.'

Donald decided he couldn't afford to take time off work if the pain was too bad, so he went back to his GP and asked to 'go private'. Within a week, he had seen the same surgeon but this time privately and not on the NHS, and he received the same treatment he would have had to wait for on the NHS. 'Within a week, the pain had gone and the shoulder cleared up. I got a

**letter from the hospital three years later saying they
still couldn't give me an appointment for my "injured
shoulder"!'**

Donald's experience is by no means unusual. The only difference between him and many other patients is that he could
afford to get his treatment done privately. His health authority,
like many others, made a distinction between **acute** and
chronic conditions.

Acute illnesses are those which threaten life and have to be
treated as emergencies. If a hospital refuses you treatment for
such an illness, they are guilty of negligence. But many other
conditions such as back and shoulder pain do not put patients'
lives at risk, even though they make life miserable and
depressing. Health authorities therefore ration treatment and
put you on a waiting list which may be many years long.

They very rarely forget about you, which is why Donald got
his letter three years later. So do let them know if you no longer
require treatment. But what can you do if you have been told
there is a long wait for treatment and you cannot, or do not want
to, get private treatment?

*You can take advantage of the fact that different health
authorities around the country have very different waiting lists.*

Your GP can refer you to another hospital in another region
where the waiting list is much shorter. Bear in mind, however,
hospitals outside the area where you live do not have to treat
you, and you will have to pay all your travelling expenses.

It is also possible, at least in theory, for you to be treated on
the NHS in another Common Market country. We have not
heard at *You and Yours* of anyone who has done this. It could be
worth trying, as some countries like West Germany can do certain kinds of operation very quickly indeed. One problem is that
you may be refused this option if the operation is *available* in the
UK even if there is a long wait for it.

Consent to treatment

With one or two exceptions, all treatment in hospital is voluntary: doctors cannot compel you to have it. What happens is that
a doctor diagnoses what he thinks is wrong with you, often after
a period of observation, and then offers you treatment. You do

not have to accept any treatment offered, but if you don't the doctor may discharge you.

For some forms of treatment you may be asked to sign a patient consent form: this form does not take away any legal rights you have if, say, an operation is done negligently. The form is only valid if the doctor has set out all the pros and cons of the treatment he suggests, so make sure you discuss these with the doctor before you give consent and ask about any side effects.

The main exceptions to patient consent are if you are unconscious or temporarily incapable (for example, as a result of consuming alcohol) of consenting to what a doctor thinks is essential treatment.

Patient consent is also needed for you to take part in a research programme, such as testing a new drug, and for students to be present when a consultant sees you. Many doctors will assume you do not mind about this, but if you do, object: they still have to treat you. Bear in mind, though, medical students are the consultants of the future and they have to learn 'on the job' somehow.

Mental health

Nearly all patients in psychiatric wards or hospitals are voluntary patients and have the same rights to turn down treatment as any other patient, although they will probably be discharged if they do so. A very small number of patients are there under a mental health order, usually called a 'section', and regulated by the **1983 Mental Health Act.**

There are only two reasons why you can be detained in hospital under a mental health section: your life is at risk or other people's lives may be at risk through your actions. The Act lays down a number of conditions about how these two reasons are to be judged. In most cases, a social worker and a doctor, who are both registered under the Act, must sign the order detaining you.

The hospital cannot keep you indefinitely, and you can appeal to an independent **mental health tribunal** within a certain number of days or, more rarely, months, depending on which 'section' of the Act you have been detained under. The hospital must inform you of this right. The best thing to do is to take advice from a local branch of the **National Association for Mental Health (MIND)** before appealing: they can often arrange representation at a tribunal.

The rights of people with **mental handicaps** are, in principle, no different from any other patient. In practice, though, there are real problems with patient consent to treatment and in the ability of people with mental handicaps to care for themselves. Complaints about the treatment and care should be brought up with the health authority, but take advice from **Mencap** or the **Campaign for People with Mental Handicap.**

Complaints about community services

These are straightforward: the only difficulty is working out who is responsible! All community services are run either as part of a **GP surgery**, a **hospital** or **health authority** or by the local **social services**. If you have any complaints about a district nurse, a health visitor, a day centre or a community mental health centre, for example, find out if they are employed by a GP, a hospital or the social services. Then make your complaint to the appropriate organisation.

TAKING LEGAL ACTION FOR MEDICAL NEGLIGENCE

If a GP refused to come and visit you and you then had to be admitted to a hospital for an emergency operation, if a member of your family died on the operating table as a result of a surgeon's incompetence or if you slipped on a dirty hospital floor and broke your leg you can sue the doctor and/or the health authority for negligence. Newspapers regularly report on cases where people *have* won hundreds of thousands of pounds when they went to court for compensation in cases of medical negligence. If you read these stories, though, you usually find that they have taken several years, years in which people have had to put up with an appalling situation while their case is being prepared. That's the rub.

Taking a doctor or a health authority to court is a long and potentially costly process. This is because you have to prove not only that you or your family suffered by their mistake, but also that the mistake was something that could have been avoided, that someone behaved **negligently**. You also have to prove not only that the doctor acted wrongly, but that any other competent doctor would not have acted that way.

In virtually every case of a medical accident, this is extremely difficult to prove. Medicine is not an exact science and all doctors or health authorities have to show in court is that, in the circumstances, their judgement was understandable, and understandable not by you or the public but by a 'responsible body of medical opinion', that is other doctors!

That is by no means all. Proving your case means employing a skilled solicitor and barrister and getting expert opinion from other doctors. All this costs a lot of money, although you may qualify for legal aid (see p. 287).

Don't, however, be put off by all this. As the newspaper reports testify, if you have a solid case, you can win the kind of money that will compensate you for all the suffering you or your family have had to put up with. You will need, though, a solicitor who **specialises** in medical negligence. Most high-street solicitors do not have the experience necessary to fight your case.

Get in touch with **Action for Victims of Medical Accidents**, a pressure group which can tell you about such solicitors, and give you general advice and their opinion about whether your situation is worth the long and difficult effort to get to court – and how much you are likely to get if you win. The group reckons that up to 30 000 people could win claims for medical negligence at any one time.

One thing you should not worry about if you take a doctor to court, however, is getting the money if you win. All doctors have to have medical insurance – and the insurance pays, not them.

COMPLAINTS ABOUT PRIVATE HEALTH TREATMENT

All health care not provided by GPs, health authorities or local council social services departments is 'private'. It is paid for directly or through private medical insurance schemes like BUPA, Private Patients Plan (PPP) and several others. As with any private service, you have the right to get your money back if the cost is unreasonable or the service was poor. The difficulty with health complaints is in proving this. Private doctors or health practitioners very rarely promise to make you better – and certainly don't put it down in writing.

There are also far fewer ways of complaining about private treatment compared with the complaints procedures open to NHS patients. Often the only option is to use the courts.

Private doctors

There is nothing to stop any qualified doctor setting up a private practice as long as he or she is registered with the General Medical Council. Many NHS hospital consultants also see private patients, often in 'private beds' in the same hospital, occasionally in their own private clinic or hospital instead. Some GPs also have private patients as well as NHS ones.

You can complain to the General Medical Council if the doctor you have consulted privately seems guilty of **serious professional misconduct** (see p. 186). You will have to sue the doctor if you have suffered because of **negligence**. You cannot sue the health authority, even if you were treated in a 'private bed' in an NHS hospital, nor can you sue any private health insurance which may be covering the doctor's bill. The legal procedure is the same as it is with NHS doctors (see p. 192).

Private medical insurance

Fred Hills, from Greater Manchester, had been insured with PPP for 18 years. The company where he worked paid his premiums but, some years after he retired, the company stopped doing this and negotiated with PPP for former employees like Fred to be offered a health plan they could pay for themselves. Fred takes up the story:

'PPP offered me a Masterplan costing £42 month. Well, that was far too much. My premium had started

off at £2 a month and then gradually increased to £32 which I could hardly afford, let alone £42. So I said, have they got anything cheaper? And they said I could take out a Retirement Plan, especially designed for older people. When I was filling out the form, they asked me what treatment I had had in the last five years and I said I had been taking tablets for angina, had some arthritic treatment and occasionally my war wound needed seeing to. They said, well, those won't be covered.'

Since he had never made a claim in 18 years with PPP, Fred felt aggrieved: all the benefits of his PPP insurance seemed to be wiped out by this new plan. So, he made a fuss, visiting PPP headquarters and contacting us at *You and Yours*. After we featured his case, PPP agreed to treat Fred as a special case and to let him have the Retirement Plan without any exclusions.

Before taking out a private health insurance plan, consider carefully what will be included and excluded, and what will happen to the premiums or exclusions after you retire.

If you have any complaint about the cover offered or how your claim is met, take action as you would against any other insurance company (see p. 137). It is always best with medical insurance to make sure all the treatment a doctor offers you will be covered and what will happen in any emergency.

Alternative medicine

Alternative, or complementary, medicine covers a multitude of practices. Some like homeopathy, osteopathy and acupuncture are well established and occasionally offered on the NHS. Others like aromatherapy, reflexology and numerology are very much a minority taste.

Most people who visit alternative practitioners feel it has been worthwhile, if only because they have had the time to talk about their problem in depth. Some particular kinds of problems like chronic back pain, for example, seem to respond better to alternative medical treatments like acupuncture or osteopathy than to conventional medical methods. Some GPs or consultants offer these treatments themselves. (If they do this, by the

way, you have the same rights against the doctor as with any
other treatment he offers.)

In all branches of the alternative medicine tree, however,
there are incompetent, rogue and dangerous practitioners. The
difficulty is that there is nothing stopping these people offering
their services to a sometimes unsuspecting public.

**Nazir, a student from the West Midlands, sought
help for pain in his shoulders and neck from a woman
who described herself as a homeopath: 'I paid £40 and
she listened to my problems and asked what I could do
and couldn't do. She then got out a piece of string
upon which there was a golden ring and started moving it all over my body. When I asked her what she was
doing, she said she was "divining". I asked what that
was, and she said that through my water content she
could work out what was wrong with me. She then
came out with the statement that the only way to
"unperforate or restore my aura" was for me to clutch
two magnets, one in each hand. I did this and, after a
minute, she said my aura was restored. Well, at that
stage thousands of ducks started quacking in my head,
quack, quack, quack. I've had no faith in homeopathic
medicine since then.'**

Nazir's experience may not be typical of alternative medicine, but he is by no means alone. And complaining about bad or
dangerous practice is difficult. There are two main problems:

1   There are not any organisations with power to regulate and con-
    trol practitioners, no General Medical Council, FPC or health
    authority to which you can take your complaints and which can
    discipline the practitioner. Of course, each form of alternative
    medicine usually has its own national organisation with its own
    code of practice and training procedures. These organisations
    vary widely, and there is nothing to stop anybody calling them-
    selves an acupuncturist, a homeopath, a psychotherapist or any-
    thing else in the alternative medicine field. Nobody, however,
    can call themselves a medical doctor without being registered
    with the General Medical Council.

    You *can* complain to any national organisation your alterna-
    tive practitioner may be registered with but while most of these

organisations will offer you some kind of advice and help in exposing a charlatan, there is little they can do apart from removing the practitioner's membership.

2   If you have suffered because of treatment, you can take an alternative practitioner to court for negligence. This is usually much easier to prove than against a doctor, but the problem is that very few alternative practitioners have indemnity insurance against any such claim. You might be awarded compensation by the courts but the practitioner might not be able to pay up and there will be no insurance scheme or organisation to back him.

The best thing to do, then, is to try to ensure you have a trustworthy alternative practitioner in the first place. Check out their membership of any national body and check out that body, too: what is their training, do they offer indemnity insurance and so on. The **Council for Complementary and Alternative Medicine** can help you. And get references or recommendations from other people who have used the practitioner.

COMPLAINTS ABOUT OPTICIANS

Anybody can now sell you a basic pair of glasses but only a qualified **optometrist** or an **ophthalmic medical practitioner** can test your eyes for glasses and write prescriptions. This test and prescription is subsidised by the NHS, although you now have to pay some of it, too (currently £10). You do not have to buy glasses from them after they have tested you: you can take the prescription elsewhere. You can complain to your local Family Practitioner Committee (FPC) about any NHS treatment.

All optometrists and ophthalmic medical practitioners must be registered with the **General Optical Council**. You can complain to the Council about any professional misconduct. Most opticians are members of trade organisations like the **Association of Optometrists (AOP)** and the Association of British Dispensing Opticians. The AOP will look into any complaints about its members.

If you are dissatisfied with non-NHS glasses, you have the

same rights as you have when you buy any other goods, under the Sale of Goods Act (see Chapter 5). NHS treatment for eyes at specialist eye units or hospitals falls under the same rules as other hospital treatment.

COMPLAINTS ABOUT DENTISTS

Dentists are much like GPs: they have to be registered with the **General Dental Council** to practise, and most of them have contracts with local **FPCs** to offer NHS treatment. The main difference is that most dentists do a lot of private work as well, so check first if your treatment is 'on the NHS'. If it is, you will have to pay at least some of its cost but you can complain to the FPC about poor service or bad treatment.

You should complain to the General Dental Council in cases of negligence or misconduct during NHS or private work. Neither the Council nor the FPC, however, will offer you any compensation for suffering as a result of a dentist's negligence. You will have to take the dentist to court for compensation and that is as difficult as it is for doctors. The procedure is the same (see p. 192).

COMPLAINTS ABOUT PHARMACISTS

To dispense drugs on prescription, a pharmacist has to be qualified with the **Pharmaceutical Society of Great Britain** (or their sister organisation in Northern Ireland), and has to be licensed with a local FPC. To complain about professional misconduct, contact the Society. To complain about the service offered, go to the FPC.

If you are concerned about the quality of the drugs that the pharmacist has supplied, contact your local CHC. Pharmacists have to ensure the drugs they make up meet the standards of the various **Medicine Acts**: they can be prosecuted if the drugs do not.

SOCIAL SERVICES

Many of the 'caring' services offered in the community are provided not by NHS hospitals, clinics or GPs, but by local social services departments. These are part of county, borough or metropolitan councils in England and Wales, regional councils and health and social services boards in Scotland and Northern Ireland.

It is sometimes difficult to know whether a health authority or a local council's social services department is responsible for a service. Psychiatric day *centres*, for example, are usually run by social services, while psychiatric day *hospitals* are controlled by health authorities, even if both seem to offer the same activities!

Generally, anything that takes place in a hospital is health authority run, any service provided in the community which involves doctors or nurses also falls under the NHS and other community services, like children's and residential homes and day centres, are run by social services. If in doubt, just ask and they will soon tell you!

All this matters little, until you want to complain. If social services are responsible for a service which you think is badly done or not done at all, here's what to do:

1   Write to the **area director** of social services, the person responsible for the services in your council area. You can get his name from the council. If you do not receive a satisfactory reply, then write to the **director of social services** for the entire council and then the **chief executive** of the council.

2   Or, you can bring the matter up with your local councillor or the chairman of the council's social services committee. If it is a serious complaint, you can ask your MP to intervene, and your local CAB can help.

3   You also have the right to go to the local ombudsman (see p. 158), if your complaint is one of maladministration.

4   If social services are threatening to take your child into care, consult a solicitor, preferably one who specialises in these cases, **straight away**.

Under various Acts of Parliament, councils must provide a range of social services help for adults and children in their area. These include:

- protection and control of delinquent children, for example, in approved schools;
- care for children in need of protection due to their family circumstances, such as children at risk of abuse;
- services for the disabled, mentally ill and the mentally handicapped, which may include employment training schemes and day centres;
- care for the elderly infirm both at home and in residential homes.

These statutory obligations on council social services departments do not mean they have to run the services themselves but they have to make sure they are provided and that standards are maintained. Local councils will soon assume responsibility for financing all 'community care' for the elderly, mentally ill, mentally handicapped and the disabled, due to the government's decision to implement recommendations by the Griffiths Committee.

If these duties are not being met, complain as outlined above. But if you still don't have any luck, you can then do one of three things:

1 Complain to the appropriate Secretary of State that your local council is not meeting its statutory duties.

2 Take your council to court for failing in its duty to you or your family for care or protection.

3 Lobby councillors to make them promise to provide the services you require in their next election manifesto.

To succeed with any of these methods of complaining, however, you will need backing from local or national pressure groups.

Residential homes

All **residential homes** have to be registered with the local council, which has a duty to inspect every home in their area twice a year. **Nursing homes** have to meet higher standards of care than residential homes and have to be registered with the local district health authority. Some homes are run by local councils or health authorities but most are privately owned.

If you are dissatisfied with the standards of a residential home, complain to social services who can take away the home's registration. To complain about nursing homes, contact the general manager of the district health authority. For both kinds of home, you can also get in touch with the **Registered Nursing Homes Association** which carries out regular inspections of their members and potential members. The Association can also provide you with a list of homes in your area.

Further information can be provided by local branches of **Age Concern**. This pressure group recommends anybody who is considering a home for themselves or a family member to have a good look around and to try a 'trial stay' before committing themselves. They also suggest asking the home owner or manager to show you their registration documents. Prices vary considerably, so shop around.

How much you can claim from a local council or from state benefits if you live in a residential or nursing home is currently being reviewed under the government's 'community care' policy. For up-to-date information, contact **Age Concern**.

Sheltered housing and staying at home

Local councils also have a duty to arrange sheltered housing for people in need, and many councils are able to do this. The main legal requirement for housing to be able to be called 'sheltered' is that there is a warden on the premises and on call, day and night. Private sheltered housing is now becoming increasingly common either for rent or more usually for purchase. Before you buy, check carefully all the service charges you will be expected to meet.

If you want to stay at home but need financial help or other forms of care, your local council will soon have more powers, and resources, to help you do this. Get in touch with your local social services department. Ask, too, if there is a **housing agency** which offers advice on re-mortgaging and house repairs and how you can get these done cheaply.

FUNERAL SERVICES

In 1989, the Office of Fair Trading with the help of *You and Yours* published a report on the funeral business. While the report did not specifically examine the costs involved in providing a funeral, it did note that the average price had increased some 20 per cent above inflation over the past 10 years. And the Office concluded that while most people were satisfied with the funeral company which they chose to bury their loved ones, a small minority had grievances, people like *You and Yours* listeners **Margaret Fairchild and Alan Duncan:**

Margaret used what she thought was an old-established firm to bury her mother in East Anglia:

'I then discovered that it had been taken over by a large company and I was very disappointed by their service. For example, we wanted to see mother in the chapel of rest and we were given a time to view but there were no flowers there and she had obviously been embalmed with no attempt to make her pretty. It was an horrendous thing to see. She looked as if she had been jammed into what was a too small coffin. You need to take your leave from people who have died but that picture of mother has always stayed in my mind.'

Alan Duncan organised his late wife's funeral in Scotland, a funeral which turned out to be 'a farce'. 'After the service we asked the funeral director to drive slowly to the cemetery because many people had come down from the Hebrides and might lose their way. That was ignored and after 800 yards, my funeral car collided with the one in front with my wife's coffin in it. They then drove through the cemetery gates at nearly 20 m.p.h. At the graveside, they told the minister to hurry up because there was another funeral taking place straight away. So most of the other mourners missed the service completely.'

Like Alan and Margaret, one in 10 people were unhappy with some aspect of an undertaker's service, according to the Office's report. This is particularly disturbing since people rarely shop around for the best deal and are often at their most vulnerable at this time in their lives.

Only one in four of the people the Office of Fair Trading interviewed reported that their funeral firm displayed a price-list, even though this is required under the **National Association of Funeral Directors'** code of conduct.

The report has been taken seriously by the **National Association of Funeral Directors**, and hopefully things will get better. In the meantime, here's what to do if you are organising a funeral.

1   Shop around if you feel able to, or ask someone to do it for you. Prices vary considerably. Check if the company is a member of the National Association of Funeral Directors, and ask for a quote, or at least an estimate, for every item involved in the service. A reputable firm will provide this.

2   If an Association member has let you down, complain to the Association: it can provide you with details of the code of conduct and the arbitration scheme which you can use to claim compensation instead of taking the firm to court. This scheme is approved by the Office of Fair Trading and is independent.

3   If the firm is not a member of the Association, you will have to take them to court for some or all of your money back, or for compensation. You could, though, deduct a 'reasonable' amount for the bad service you experienced and let them take you to court instead. But do get evidence of this, from other mourners, for example, and the priest or minister involved.

LEISURE

Fifteen-year-old Tomontra Mangrum was looking forward to her date with handsome basketball player Marlon Shadd. She put flowers in her specially cut hair and bought new shoes. She then waited for Marlon to turn up. And waited. And waited. Marlon didn't show.

Tomontra, however, certainly wasn't going to behave as young girls and boys have done through the ages when their dates changed their minds: claim they weren't all that interested anyway and spend a night at home with Mum and Dad. *Tomontra decided to take Marlon to court for damages* to cover the cost of the flowers, hair-do and new shoes. According to Marlon. 'She didn't believe me when I told her I had fractured my ankle.' He settled out of court, agreeing to pay Tomontra £51.

Fortunately for teenage boys here, all this took place recently in Florida: there is not, as yet, any precedent in Britain for somebody suing a date for not turning up.

In recent years, however, the British have become almost as good as Americans at complaining about things that go wrong when they were meant to be enjoying themselves. The local cinema, dance-hall and even the vicar can no longer get away with providing poor service, at least if the post-bag to *You and Yours* is anything to go by. In fact, anything people pay for in their leisure activities is fair game for complaining, even if the complaints sometimes seem as bizarre as Tomontra's.

PUBS AND WINE BARS

A pub or a wine bar can refuse to serve you without giving any reason at all, as long as their decision is not based on your sex or race – that would be against the sex or race discrimination acts (see Chapter 16). But if they just do not like you, that's OK, for them if not for you.

If you do get refused or thrown out of a pub or wine bar, check who is the owner. If it is a **free house**, then there is very little you can do since it was probably the owner who escorted you to the door. But if it is a **tied house**, that is, one owned by a brewery, write and complain to the customer service department at the brewery's head office. Write to them, too, if you have any general complaints about opening hours or the pub's or wine bar's style. In these competitive times when pubs are becoming 'targeted leisure concepts', breweries always want to hear from their customers.

Complaints about pub noise should be made to the **police**: they can ask for the licence each pub manager needs, to be withdrawn. You can also complain yourself to the local **Licensing Justices** if the pub is consistently unruly or stays open after licence hours. The Justices hold licensing sessions six to eight times a year, and at any of these sessions they can withdraw a publican's licence. You have to give 21 days' notice but you can go along to the session in person and argue your case.

If you think your drink is being watered down, contact trading standards officers. And, one final point: it is illegal for pubs to operate a 'slate' where regulars drink on credit. **One pub manager in Wiltshire was recently fined £250 for doing so – and also lost his job.**

CINEMAS AND THEATRES

If you are fed up with your local **cinema** choosing to show cartoons, say, rather than 'art films', or horror movies rather than Oscar Award-winning material, don't take it out on the local manager: he is just following head office orders. Write instead to the **director of programme booking** of whichever company owns the cinema. The most you will probably get is an explanation of 'what the public wants', but it will at least get them thinking that not everyone conforms to their market research.

Complaints about anything other than choice of film, such as dirty seats or poor service, should be made to the cinema manager and then, if you don't have any luck, the area manager. You will probably get offered free tickets to make up for your spoilt night out.

All films shown in public cinemas and all videos for sale or rent have to be licensed by the **British Board of Film Cen-**

sors. Write to the Board if you feel a certificate is misleading. Also, local councils sometimes decide not to allow a film to be shown in their area, or to increase the age restriction from, say, '15' to '18' (they rarely do it the other way around). You do not have any *right* to challenge any local decision but if it annoys you, let them know.

Theatres, unlike cinemas, do not have to get any board or council approval for their productions, although they have to be licensed both for entertainment and to be able to sell drink. All you can really do to complain about the price of tickets, choice of production or general state of commercial theatres is to let the manager and then his board of directors know. For subsidised theatres like the National Theatre and the Barbican, in London, and the regional equivalents, you could also let the sponsoring body know about your complaints. These are usually the Arts Council, local councils, regional Arts Council committees and, occasionally, private companies.

SPORTS CENTRES AND HEALTH CLUBS

Julie Carter, a *You and Yours* **reporter, decided to take a whirlpool bath in her local health club. She had just had her hair cut and streaked blonde for her wedding, and she thought the bath would provide just the relaxation she needed. It certainly did – until the next morning:**

'I combed my hair and noticed that the bottom two or three inches had gone bright green, and I mean green, as green as grass, from the chemicals in the whirlpool.'

Julie complained to the manager of the club, who advised her to wash her hair with a peroxide shampoo and offered to do this at their salon if she wanted:

'But I didn't want that at all. I wanted blonde streaks in my hair, not all of it blonde. And, I wanted only *my* hairdresser to touch it before I got married. My hairdresser was very reluctant to put any more bleach on my hair and in the end she cut off the green bits.'

So, Julie got married, but not with the hairstyle she wanted. Could she claim damages from the club?

Probably not, because the management claimed they were just following local council guidelines for disinfecting the baths and that they had put warning notices up in the club advising customers to wear hats. Julie said she didn't see the notices. These notices, however, would have had to point out the exact nature of any risk and, anyway, could not exclude liability for personal injury or death (see below). So if you use a health or private sports club, do check that they meet local environmental health office regulations and ask about any possible effects their facilities or cleaning agents might have on your body or health. If you suspect the 'health club' is about as healthy as a garden shed, contact environmental health officials.

If, by the way, you hurt yourself on a club's equipment, you can sue the club for negligence, even if there are large notices up saying that 'liability is limited'. Clubs, pubs and any other leisure activity centres, even car parks, cannot get away with any disclaimer if their negligence causes injury. This is because of a very useful law called the **1977 Unfair Contracts Terms Act**, which controls 'exclusion' clauses in all kinds of contracts.

All this applies, too, to **sports centres** and **swimming baths**, both private and council run. They all have a general 'duty to care' for your health and safety which they cannot limit by large notices. They also have a duty to care for your possessions if they assume responsibility for them. If, however, the club provides you with, say, lockers to protect your clothes and you don't use them, and your clothes are stolen, the club will probably have carried out this duty to any court's satisfaction.

Local council sports centres and baths are also like any other council-run activity: you have the same right to complain as with other council services if the centre is badly run or offers poor value for money. See Chapter 10 for how to complain: the relevant council department is usually called arts and recreation.

And, as with all other local council complaints, you can take your complaint to the **local ombudsman** if you are dissatisfied with the council response. One man did this recently about a council's Turkish baths in London:

He enjoyed his bath very much, but he did not enjoy what he thought were the prying eyes of female attendants when he was undressing. After complaining about his lack of privacy several times, he had a row with one attendant. The council subsequently banned the man from the baths. The local ombudsman decided the council had not given the man the proper right to explain his side of the story, so he ordered the council to allow the man back, but on the condition that the man behaved properly in future.

If you have a similar complaint and want to involve this ombudsman, see p. 158.

PRIVATE FUNCTIONS AND ACCIDENTS

Private individuals – even your friends, family or neighbours – have legal duties to look after your safety. Their premises must be safe and they are liable if you suffer because of their negligent behaviour, even if you have just popped in for a cup of tea or to have a few drinks.

In one recent court case, a teenage girl was awarded £20 000 damages for the burns she suffered when she attended a friend's birthday party. A teapot fell off a table and showered her with hot tea causing permanent scarring. The court decided that the friend's mother was responsible. Fortunately for the mother, her household insurance included a personal liability clause, so she was covered. Make sure your household insurance covers you if you invite friends around, particularly for children's birthday parties.

To claim damages for any accident, you must show that someone behaved negligently. David Neild's daughter, Joanne, had a terrible accident at a girl guides' function held in a school near her Yorkshire home. A 29-foot overhead lighting bar fell on Joanne, almost killing her, and she had to have an operation to remove fragments of the bar from her brain. She took a year to recover. David wanted to sue for compensation, but the problem was that no one, neither the school, the manufacturers, nor the girl guide leader, had acted negligently. Each had taken reasonable care. It was just an 'act of God' (or more likely, his satanic rival).

Much less seriously, Jack Plowright was taken to court for damages that occurred to his dancing partner when they took the floor for a quick-step on holiday. The quick-step turned into a quick fall after Jack tripped on the shiny floor and fell on top of his partner, hurting her leg. Jack sent her a get-well card when he got back from the holiday but eventually received back, not a thank-you, but a court summons claiming, Jack told *You and Yours*, 'I had been dancing in a dangerous and boisterous manner without due regard to my partner's safety. I was very annoyed and upset. I'd been dancing for 50 years and most people like my dancing.'

The judge seemed to like Jack's dancing, too. He threw the case out and Jack's dancing reputation remained intact. But think carefully before you try to emulate Fred Astaire with a partner who thinks she's Ginger Rogers. You could end up in court!

DATING AND WEDDING AGENCIES

Wendy Richings, from Surrey, did not write to us at *You and Yours* about any dancing problems. What she did tell us about was her problem with men or rather with a particular kind of man, accountants.

After breaking up with her boyfriend, Wendy enrolled with a dating agency to introduce her to new male friends: 'They sent me an application form which requested my salary, profession and education, and also asked me if there were any kinds of people I would not want to meet. I put on the form that I didn't want to meet anyone involved in the City or finance, and I told them I definitely didn't want to meet accountants because I had worked with accountants for eight years and found that they did tend to talk about their work to the exclusion of anything else.'

The first date the agency arranged was, they said, 'very sporty, very nice'. He was also an accountant. When Wendy protested, the agency said they were always getting comments like this, but this man was different. Wendy, somewhat reluctantly, agreed to meet him:

'It was a disaster and very embarrassing. He kept talking about his job and we had nothing in common. If they had asked me which person I would definitely not like to meet, he would have been an ideal candidate.'

Wendy was so put off that she tried to claim her money back but the agency refused. The agency pointed out it had promised to introduce her to a range of men over a two-year period and still intended to.

And the agency was right: it could still make amends. There was nothing Wendy could do to get her money back. She just had to rely on the agency introducing her to different kinds of men in the future – or, as one accountants' professional association pointed out on *You and Yours*, change her view of accountants: 'Most of us are very nice indeed and certainly not boring.'

If you are dissatisfied with the service provided by a dating agency or a wedding bureau, try and bring your complaint up quickly and give the agency time to make amends. Your only recourse then is to take the agency to court for not providing the service you paid for. However, as in Wendy's experience, you will only win if the agency has quite clearly fallen down or ripped you off.

PETS

There is not a 'national health service' for pets: anything a vet does has to be paid for, and their bills, even for a check-up or routine injection, are often considerable, as **Theodore Sinclair** found out when she took her cat, Tizzer, to a local vet near her Birmingham home. Tizzer had started limping badly as Theodore's daughter, Gloria, explained:

'**I said to the vet that if the cost was high, we would rather the cat was put down because my parents couldn't afford a huge bill. I left Tizzer at the vet's and kept phoning to find out how much it would cost, but the vet was never available. When I did eventually get through, the vet said the cat had a broken pelvis and had been operated on, and it would all cost £84.13 less my £13 deposit.**

'**My parents said they couldn't pay that, and I went back to the vet to sign a consent form to put the cat down. Well, then the vet said I would have to pay the bill first and they would keep the cat alive until I paid and charge me a holding charge as well.**'

The vet was quite within his legal rights, but fortunately a local cat charity heard about Theodore's situation and offered to pay the bill. The vet was embarrassed by the publicity and gave the cat back, free of charge.

The case does illustrate, however, the general point about dealing with vets and then complaining about their service. If you feel you have got a bad deal, the only recourse to get your money back is to take the vet to court claiming, for example, that he has broken the Supply of Goods and Services Act, a law which applies as much to vets as it does to builders (see p. 110).

The **British Veterinary Association** will, however, provide you with help and advice about any problem you have with a vet, particularly if the vet is a member, as most are. Also, all vets have to be registered with the **Royal College of Veterinary Surgeons**. This organisation can strike off a vet from practising in cases of serious professional misconduct.

If you think a vet or a pet shop is guilty of cruelty to animals, contact the **RSPCA**. Many animals are not allowed to be sold over the counter and the RSPCA can investigate if you are suspicious. They will also know of local schemes or charities which can help you pay some or all of a vet's bill if you cannot afford it.

COMPLAINTS ABOUT CHURCHES

People may not go to church as they once did but one thing about religion remains much the same: the number of complaints received about vicars, priests, ministers and bishops is very small indeed. When *You and Yours* contacted both the Church of England Information Service and the Catholic Information Service about the kind of complaints they receive, they both had to think very hard before recalling any at all. The same also seems true of other churches and religions in the United Kingdom – if their members do not like what is on offer, they tend to stop going. What can you do, however, if you are dissatisfied with the service or vicar, priest or minister and still want to remain part of the church?

The only thing you can do is to bring up your complaint with the person in charge (or rather his earthly representative).

The Church of England and its sister churches in the rest of the United Kingdom, for example, give bishops the right to intervene in local disputes with a vicar. It would have to be a pretty extreme complaint, though, for the bishop to get rid of a vicar since each vicar has a freehold on his church until he is 70 years old. But if you can get enough support together, it is possible for a bishop to arrange a quiet move elsewhere. If you are dissatisfied with Church of England services, you can complain to the **Parochial Church Committee** at the Bishopric: this Committee is responsible for services in the diocese. Any evidence of serious criminal action by vicars will mean instant dismissal by their bishop.

Complaints about other churches and religions follow a similar pattern.

ADVERTISEMENTS

We are all, by now, immune to the glossy claims made by a poster advertising a 'space-age' new car, a TV ad saying that one brand of margarine 'convinced three million Australian housewives it was the *only* thing to put on sliced bread', or a radio jingle extolling the 'caring' virtues of a bank. We're all immune to these claims, aren't we?

Well, if we were, the ads would not exist. Companies would not spend money on advertising the wonderful qualities of their products if they did not have good evidence that the ads work, that despite our scepticism about an advertisement's claims, at least some of us will go out and buy the product.

But what can you do if you are offended by an ad?

The **1968 Trade Descriptions Act** makes it a criminal offence to falsely or misleadingly describe any goods or services that are for sale. This includes, for example, a duvet described as 'made of feathers' when it is, in fact, made of synthetic fibres. Or a 'meat' pasty made out of soya beans. Contact your local trading standards department if you think a trader has broken this law: they can prosecute and the court can award you compensation.

Poster, **magazine** and **newspaper ads** are also regulated by the **Advertising Standards Authority** to which you can complain if you think an ad is not 'legal, decent, truthful and honest'. The Authority will investigate and, if they agree with you, put pressure on the company to stop using the ad. This pressure is 'voluntary': the Authority has no legal power to compel a company to withdraw its ad, but most companies will comply. Most newspapers and magazines have agreed not to carry any ad if requested not to by the Authority.

You can also complain to the **Office of Fair Trading** if you think an ad is likely to mislead people. The Office now has the power under the EEC-inspired **Control of Misleading Advertisement Regulations** to seek a court injunction to compel a company to withdraw an advertisement. They used this power recently to ban ads for a slimming product which was felt to seriously mislead readers of a Sunday paper. 'Seriously', though, is the operative word: don't bother to contact the Office if you have just a minor complaint, and you must normally have contacted either trading standards officers or the Advertising Standards Authority before approaching the Office.

Finally, if you have bought a product as a result of an ad which you think was misleading, you may be able to claim your money back under the **1967 Misrepresentation Act**.

TV and radio ads are regulated by the **Independent Broadcasting Authority (IBA)**. The IBA has developed various codes about the advertising, for example, of drink and children's toys. Write to it if you are bothered by any ad on commercial radio or television. All ads on the media have to be approved by the IBA before they get shown or aired, and the IBA takes complaints very seriously indeed.

The **Securities Investment Board** will look into any complaints about **investment** advertisements.

NEWSPAPERS AND MAGAZINES

Elizabeth Crawley, a partner in a hypnotherapy business in Lincolnshire, discovered one Sunday her company was of interest to 10 million people. Or at least the editor of one Sunday paper thought it was, because he had printed a story about the business in a very prominent way. A little bit too prominently for Elizabeth, though. And, a little bit too salacious. 'Sex fantasy in the garden' did not quite come up to Elizabeth's image of her work. In fact, she was amazed and horrified at how the paper had described her business.

Ronald Wright had a similar experience with newspapers. His work involves painting portraits of star actors and actresses and he gave an interview to a paper about this. The resulting story was not exactly what he had in mind:

'The printed that one star had offered to pose in the nude and had thrown me out when I said all I wanted to do was sketch her face. Another star was reported as saying that unless I removed the lines of her face, she would have me beaten up. Both stories were completely fictitious. But when I asked a solicitor about suing them for libel, he said that unless I had lots of money, it would be a waste of time.'

The solicitor was probably right. The major difficulty with taking a newspaper, or, indeed, any other medium like radio and television, to court for libel is that you will almost certainly get involved in a long, complicated and costly case, a case which you have no guarantee you will win.

Libel law is difficult and uncertain: newspapers, magazines and other media all have access to specialist lawyers and will almost certainly contest your claim. And, there is no legal aid for libel, you risk ruin if you lose.

Of course, some people do win – and get enormous settlements. But it is a lottery which depends on how a judge and a jury weigh your case. So, be warned.

If you do think a newspaper has libelled you, *do not contact the paper* but take legal advice first from a solicitor who has experience of libel cases. If you have – and can afford – a good solicitor, you may be able to get an out-of-court settlement, but it will be a struggle. It is probably not worth bothering taking a small publication to court as, even if you win, it may end up with them being unable even to meet your costs, let alone pay the award. You can take the printer, wholesaler or newsagent that sells the publication to court instead, but such cases are rare and there are not very many precedents for your lawyer to quote.

There are, however, alternatives to suing for libel if you feel a paper has misrepresented you or printed something which is not true. You could write to the editor asking for a correction – and some papers will print this even if they feel they have not been at fault, although probably not with the prominence of the original piece. If the editor refuses to print your letter, you can then report the newspaper to the **Press Council**.

This Council will investigate your complaint. If it finds in your favour, it can instruct a newspaper or magazine to print the finding. You will need, however, witnesses to give evidence for you, and you must agree not to take action for libel before the Council will consider your complaint. (It is unclear, though, whether any agreement not to go to court after a Press Council verdict is legally binding. Some lawyes think it cannot take away your right to sue but nobody has tested this right in court, to our knowledge.)

One thing you can do is to lodge a complaint with the Council and then write to the editor saying that you will withdraw the complaint if he prints a correction. Despite the Press Council's limited powers, most editors do not like risking a judgement against them: it makes them look silly in front of their competitors and owners. You cannot, by the way, get any compensation from the Press Council even if they uphold your complaint.

There is not any law which protects people's privacy, although, of course, reporters have no greater rights than any other person to stop you or come on to your property if you do not want them to. If you feel you are being harassed by reporters, you could get a court injunction to stop them.

TELEVISION AND RADIO

If you feel you have been **libelled** by a television or radio programme, you will have to take the broadcasting company to court in exactly the same way as for newspapers and magazines. (Even though words are usually spoken in broadcasting, they still count as a libel and not as a slander: slander only applies to everyday conversation.)

It is just as difficult and hazardous to take a broadcasting company to court as it is a newspaper company and just as costly – but some people do succeed. Consult a lawyer who specialises in libel before considering any action.

Most complaints about television and radio are not, however, about being libelled, nor about people's privacy being violated. What seems to incense viewers and listeners most are bad language, violence, sex and repeats. If you have a complaint about a television or radio programme, here's what to do.

BBC television and radio programmes

For any BBC1 or BBC2 television programme, you can ring or write to the **BBC Television Information Office** at Television Centre, Wood Lane, London W12. Just ring the switchboard (01-743-8000) and ask to be put through. The office receives calls between 8.30 a.m. and closedown, every day. All calls and letters get entered in the duty log and then get circulated to programme controllers and programme production teams. Your comments will be noted – but it is unlikely that you will get a reply, unless you specifically ask for one.

BBC national radio (Radios 1, 2, 3 and 4) has a similar system at Broadcasting House in London – as does the BBC World Service at Bush House. The **BBC Radio Information Office** (01-580-4468) is open from 7.30 a.m. to 11 p.m., every day. To complain about BBC local radio programmes, contact the **station manager** or the **programme organiser** at the station.

The best way to press home a complaint about a BBC programme is, however, to write to the **producer** (not the presenter or reporter). Ring the general switchboard, ask for the programme's office and ask who the producer was of a specific episode. Then write to him by name and say what you felt was wrong with the programme, whether it was unfair or biased, or badly researched or presented. If you want to make sure of a reply, although most producers will reply to letters of complaint as a matter of course, send a copy of the letter to the producer's boss, usually the programme's **editor** or the programme's **head of department**.

If you are dissatisfied with the producer's response, you can then write to the **BBC director general** or the **BBC Board of Governors**. Let them know that you have tried to raise the matter with the production team but did not have a satisfactory response. The director general is responsible for all BBC programmes: television, national and local radio and the World Service.

You can also pursue your complaint by writing to an independent organisation called the **Broadcasting Complaints Commission**. This works in a similar way to the Press Council (see p. 216), except it can only deal with complaints from people who have been contacted or interviewed or mentioned on a programme and who feel they have been unfairly or unjustly treated or that their privacy has been infringed. It cannot deal with any complaints about the quality of a programme, nor look at a complaint if there is any court action pending. The Commission will investigate a complaint or make a judgement, which the BBC programme has to broadcast on air. It cannot, however, award any compensation.

There is now another organisation that has been set up by the government especially to deal with matters of taste and decency: the **Broadcasting Standards Council**. As this book was being prepared for publication, this Council was working out a code of practice for radio and television programmes. It intends to deal with viewer and listener complaints but it is not yet clear how it will deal with them and what power it will have.

And for any kind of complaint or opinion, you could also try and get your views across directly to other listeners and viewers. BBC local radio stations have phone-in and access programmes. BBC national radio also has *Feedback* and *The Radio Programme*, both of which actively encourage listener correspondence. On BBC television, there is the long-running *Points of View* and the newer *Network* and *Open Air*.

If your complaint is one about the **poor reception** of TV or radio programmes, check first with the shop from which you bought the set that it is working properly. If it is not your set, you can then contact the television company's **head of engineering** to see if they will investigate. For radio programmes, the BBC has a special **radio investigation service** at Broadcasting House in London which looks into listeners' complaints.

Independent television and radio

To complain about programmes on the independent television and radio channels, write to or phone the company responsible.

Channel Four and **TV-am** are organised centrally and you should contact their **duty officers** in London.

ITV programmes are transmitted by 15 **regional** companies. In Manchester, for example, **Granada** broadcasts ITV programmes, and in the Midlands, **Central** does. Almost all of the ITV companies now have complaints procedures and special complaints officers; and these people should be your first point of contact. Central Television has gone one further recently and appointed its own **ombudsman** to deal with viewers' complaints about taste and sensitivity: the company intends to screen criticisms of programmes which this ombudsman decides are valid. It is too early to say how effective this will be, but several other ITV companies are expected to follow Central's initiative.

Complaints about independent local radio stations are made

in much the same way as BBC local radio: contact the **station manager** or **programme organiser**.

If you cannot resolve your complaint with the independent television or radio company, get in touch with the **Independent Broadcasting Authority (IBA)**. This is the organisation which regulates Channel Four, TV-am, ITV and independent local radio stations. The IBA, by the way, looks likely to be replaced soon by two organisations: the **Radio Authority** and the **Independent Television Commission**.

You can also pursue your complaint with the **Broadcasting Complaints Commission** or the **Broadcasting Standards Council** in the same way as with BBC programmes (see p. 218). And Channel Four's *Right to Reply* programme provides direct access to other viewers if you have criticisms of any independent TV programmes.

Cable and Satellite television

Cable television is provided by independent companies which link subscribers to their channels via an underground cable. **Satellite** television works by subscribers purchasing a satellite dish (and sometimes a decoder) which receives signals from a TV company via a satellite in space. To confuse matters, some satellite channels are also provided on cable.

At present, **Sky Television** is the only satellite television company operating from the UK, although it looks likely to be joined soon by others including **BSB**. You have the same rights to sue for libel or complain to the Broadcasting Complaints Commission or the Broadcasting Standards Council as with any other television company. At the moment there is not a regulatory organisation which controls Sky although the **IBA** will have some control over BSB. Check with your local council about any planning permission you might need before installing a satellite dish.

All cable television companies come under the **Cable Authority** and you can complain to it if you are not satisfied with how your cable company has dealt with you.

Future changes in broadcasting

It looks likely that the next few years will produce several significant changes in how broadcasting is run in the United Kingdom. More national and community radio stations are on their way, and possibly a fifth television channel as well. One probable change that will affect complaints is the government's proposal to merge the Cable Authority and the IBA into a new body, the **Independent Television Commission**. It is too early to say how much regulatory power this proposed Commission will have.

LIBRARIES

If you have borrowed a book from a **library**, contact the chief librarian with any complaints you may have about the book or indeed about the library service. Most libraries are run by county, metropolitan or borough councils (regional councils in Scotland), and you can pursue your complaint in the same way as any other local council complaint (see Chapter 10: the relevant council department and committee is usually called arts and recreation.) Councils are obliged to provide some form of library service: if they do not, you could get in touch with the government's **Office of Arts and Libraries**.

BOOKS

If a book is badly printed, return it to the bookseller or publisher. You have the same rights under the Sale of Goods Act with books as with any other item, and the bookseller must give you your money back. But publishers will also be usually co-operative if you have bought a new book of theirs which turns out to be damaged. **One** *You and Yours* **listener, Edward Philpott-Kent from North London, wrote to us saying he had no problems getting an Oxford University Press journal, which had several pages missing, replaced by writing direct to OUP.**

If you feel a book has been badly written or is factually inaccurate, write to the author at the publisher's address, which has to be in the front of the book along with any bibliographical information. And send a copy of your letter to the author's editor at the same address. You may be able to influence the author or publisher in future editions or in other books, and you may get involved in correspondence which could prove satisfying. For example, if you feel *this* book is unfair, write to me, **David Berry, c/o BBC Books**, Woodlands, 80 Wood Lane, London W12 0TT.

TRAVEL AND TRANSPORT

Next to builders, plumbers and double-glazing specialists, complaints about travel and transport come out top in letters to *You and Yours*. When we asked listeners to phone in with *any* experience they had of complaining, one in three chose to comment about package holidays, most of which were emphatically not the holiday of a lifetime or, indeed, a welcome two weeks away.

British Rail, local buses, airports and taxis also seem to provoke more than their fair share of complaints, and as for 'timeshare' apartments, well, it is undoubtedly true that there are many satisfied customers but there also seem to be many dissatisfied ones.

AIR

Scheduled flights are those offered by the major national and international carriers, which sell you a ticket and guarantee you a seat on a flight leaving at a precise time. **Charter** flights are those offered by smaller companies in conjunction with an arranged package holiday, although all that may be arranged is a 'room' in a boarding house that no one expects you to stay in. Charter airlines have to have an **Air Travel Operator's Licence (ATOL)**: if the company goes bust, you can then get a refund.

How to complain about scheduled flights

1   If you are on board, tell the cabin staff and, if necessary, ask for a complaints form which will get sent to the airline's customer relations department.

2   If you are at the airport, ask to speak to the company's representative and then, if not satisfied, write to the customer relations department. Some airlines, like British Airways, have introduced a novel way of making complaints at major airports: they have a video booth where you can go in and record your complaint.

3   You can then contact the **Air Transport Users Committee**, the passengers' watchdog, which will attempt to mediate

between you and the company. Although this committee does not have any power to order compensation, it can refer serious complaints to the **Civil Aviation Authority (CAA)**, the organisation which regulates air travel in the United Kingdom. Most airlines are understandably reluctant to have any customer dissatisfaction brought to the attention of that authority – they could lose their right to offer certain routes – so, there is an incentive on airlines to settle matters.

Partly because of all this, most complaints about scheduled airlines are dealt with satisfactorily. Indeed, most of these airlines have laid-down procedures for dealing with the different types of complaints that do arise.

If your flight is **delayed**, you will be offered meals and an overnight hotel stay if appropriate. It is unlikely you will be able to claim any other form of compensation unless the delay was the fault of the airline rather than, say, air congestion or the weather.

If your seat has been **double-booked** and you are, to use the new terminology, 'bumped', you will almost certainly be offered compensation to cover hotel bills and inconvenience. If the compensation offered seems too small, haggle with the representative or make a claim as soon as you can to the customer relations department of the airline and send them copies of receipts.

If your **luggage** doesn't turn up at your destination when you do, most airlines will have special forms for you to fill in. Delayed luggage will usually be delivered to you. If your luggage is lost or damaged, you can claim for replacement or compensation.

How to complain about charter flights

Unlike scheduled flights, the opportunities for complaining about charter flights are more restricted: there certainly are not any video booths in airports, and it is difficult enough even finding a company rep who has the power to help you. If the problem does emerge at the airport, bring it up with any airline rep you can find and ask to speak to the airline's duty manager.

The most common complaints are about **delays**. These have become almost routine in Britain's major airports during the holiday season. Each charter company has its own way of dealing with delays but most will follow the scheduled airlines' procedures: meal vouchers and then an overnight hotel stay. Some will, however, offer an overnight stay after eight hours, some after 10 hours, and some will say there aren't any hotels available!

The best way to complain is to get together with other passengers and organise a delegation to speak to the duty manager to press your complaints. Managers have considerable discretion and they can organise something if they see a lot of their passengers who are not only dissatisfied but want action.

For other kinds of complaints, contact the customer services department of the company. You could also write to the holiday company which charters the airline (technically, you have a contract with them, not the airline), and to the **Air Transport Users Committee** (see above).

How to complain about airports

If your complaint is with the airport rather than with the airline, for example the services provided or the information given out about flights, go the airport's information desk. You will be given a complaints form to fill in and eventually you will receive a reply. If you are not satisfied with this, you can then complain to the airport's manager and, if still no luck, to the **airport's consultative committee**. Most airports now have such a committee to deal with complaints. Most British airports, by the way, are not privately run.

To complain about airport noise or other forms of airport pollution, see p. 163.

RAIL

David Lindsay went to King's Cross station to see off a young friend on the train to Cambridge. They arrived 40 minutes early which, in the end, didn't help them at all, as David recalls:

'We spent half an hour asking platform staff what platform the train was going from but they just didn't

know. We then went to the information desk where a young girl also said she didn't know. Finally, we found an official who said there was a train leaving in two minutes from Platform 8 – and that we should get in one of the last four coaches, which my friend did with a lot of other passengers as well when we told them. Twenty minutes later, the train was still on the platform and a porter came around and told us, very brusquely, that the train to Cambridge was the first four coaches and had already left. He pointed to another train but he wasn't sure if it was going to Cambridge or Peterborough. That would be announced when we were on our way!'

Fortunately for David's friend, the train did end up going to Cambridge. But when they went to catch the same train three weeks later, they were again told the wrong platform and the wrong time and 'we were forced to make a 100-yard dash to get on the train just as it was pulling out. It was intolerable.'

David brought up his complaint with the British Rail area manager and eventually received a reply admitting they had let down passengers badly. The problem, the manager said, was that everything was in complete disarray due to engineering work running three hours late which meant that 'all our trains were in the wrong place at the wrong time'. Should they not have told this to passengers? Well, yes, they should, the manager replied, 'but our experience has been that it is just best to keep apologising and say nothing at all. Sometimes this doesn't go down very well with the passengers.'

Too right, it doesn't, but at least David forced an explanation from BR and an admission that passengers should be told the reasons why trains get delayed in future.

In fact, providing proper information to travellers about train delays is one of the features of BR's **code of practice**, which you can buy for £1 at major stations. Armed with the code, here's how to make a complaint about BR:

1   Contact the manager in charge of the service: the **station manager**, for example, for badly-kept stations or rude or unhelpful staff, or the **area manager** for inter-city trains or for suburban trains and so on. Ask any BR staff for the appropriate manager's name and address.

2   If your complaint is unresolved, write to your regional **Transport Users Consultative Committee (TUCC)**. This group of people is empowered by government to represent train passengers. They can mediate between you and BR in any claim for compensation.

3   If your complaint is a serious one and has cost you money, you can then opt for **arbitration** under the BR code of practice. Arbitration is an alternative to court action and is run independently of BR. You must apply within three months of your last letter from BR and the most you can claim is £500. The fee of £10 is refundable if you win. Take advice from the TUCC.

4   For amounts more than £500 or for any cases involving injury, you will have to take BR to court. Injury cases, however, are usually agreed out of court by BR: you will be offered a settlement which is usually quite reasonable.

In Northern Ireland, by the way, trains are not run by BR but by the **Northern Ireland Railway Company**. And the **Northern Ireland Consumer Council** performs the role of the TUCCs.

Fare prices

There is very little you can do, unfortunately, about BR fares since the TUCCs don't have any power to intervene over fare increases. But do let your regional TUCC know if BR have increased a fare without it being publicly announced.

Train delays

BR's 'conditions of carriage' allow it to delay or cancel a train without prior notice and with no liability to passengers. These conditions, however, do clash a little with BR's code of practice. Certainly, passengers have no right to claim compensation if a train is delayed or cancelled due to conditions outside BR's control, for example, bad weather.

But what about that old excuse 'staff shortages'? It is a debatable point. One thing's for sure: if a train arrives too late for you to catch your normal bus home from the station, you should be able to claim the cost of a taxi. Take one, get a receipt and then press your claim with the area manager.

But what if, as sometimes happens, BR announces an 'unavoidable change' in your journey? **This happened to a judge recently and he and his colleagues decided to sit tight on the train until BR promised to stop an express train to pick them up. BR agreed. So it's worth making a fuss and getting other passengers on your side.**

Overcrowding

Margaret Parker, a 79-year-old pensioner from Newcastle, boarded a train from Cheltenham to take her back to the North East. The journey was not a pleasant one:

'I couldn't get on the train at first. I had to be squeezed in because there was so much luggage and then I couldn't move at all. I was left sandwiched in a corner with two large cases on each side. Well, I thought that would just be for a while but no, at the next stop, more people got on. I was there from 11 a.m. to 6 p.m. in the evening when the train finally reached Newcastle. It was absolutely awful because I just couldn't breathe: I ended up sitting on the toilet seat.'

Instead of just accepting that overcrowding is one of the occasional hazards of 'letting the train take the strain', Margaret complained to her regional TUCC – and she eventually won £25 which was roughly the cost of her fare. Commenting on the case on *You and Yours*, the TUCC said that getting compensation was very unusual for overcrowding. 'The most common situations where compensation has been awarded are lateness, rudeness and the state of the train. The highest award made has been £500 after a man was wrong-

**fully arrested by a ticket inspector who thought he was
evading his fare.'**

This means Margaret's case has set a precedent – and
one you might be able to use in the future if you have suffered a
painful journey owing to overcrowding. Also note there are
agreed limits about how many passengers are allowed on each
train: let your regional TUCC know if any train you use regularly seems to be dangerously overcrowded.

Food

Complaints about food on BR are dealt with on p. 72. Many
restaurants, take-away bars and cafés on stations are now fran-
chised out by BR, so if you have complaints about these, take
them up with the company concerned or contact the station's
catering manager and tell him what you think.

Complaints about the Underground

The London Underground is run not by BR (apart, that is, from
the Waterloo and City line) but by **London Regional Transport (LRT)**. They operate under similar conditions to BR
and complaints should be made in the same way. Write to the
public relations office and it will pass on your complaint to the
appropriate person. The **London Regional Passengers
Committee** (the area's TUCC) can also take up your complaints.

Other city metro lines like the Newcastle Metro are run
jointly by BR and the local council. The council is usually
responsible for stations, BR for services. Complaints about
stations run by councils should be made in the same way as any
council complaint (see Chapter 10).

Some suburban and some rural rail stations in different
parts of the country are also operated by local councils and not
British Rail.

BOATS

Perhaps because most of the journeys people make by boat are
short hops across the Channel or the Irish Sea, there is not a

passenger watchdog committee to take up customer complaints. The only methods of complaining about boat travel are to the ferry company itself or by taking legal action for compensation.

If you are on a ship and are disturbed by other passengers' rowdiness or noise, or if you feel the catering or cabin standards are below par, take it up with the ship's **purser**: ask for him at the information desk. Most ferry companies now have complaint forms which you can fill in. After your journey, write to the company's customer relations department and ask for compensation for a ruined journey: you are unlikely to be offered a refund but you may get a free ticket for future travel, and the complaint will encourage them to review their standards.

Each ferry company has a responsibility to get you to your destination with reasonable safety and efficiency. If, for example, your car is damaged during the journey, the company can only get out of this responsibility if it was due to circumstances outside their control, such as a bad storm at sea. Get good legal advice before you try and sue. If you are worried about the safety standards or procedures on board, contact the **Health and Safety Executive**.

COACHES AND BUSES

Coaches and buses outside London (and soon in London itself) have had their services 'deregulated'. This means that as long as the companies conform to basic safety rules, they can offer any route they want at any price they choose.

Many councils, however, subsidise local bus routes, and if there are not any bus routes in your area, you can write to the council's **transport co-ordinating officer** suggesting he could encourage (and subsidise) a new route. Get some evidence of 'social need' for a new bus service and, if the officer refuses your request, complain to your councillor or council transport sub-committee. You could also get support from your neighbours and write a joint letter to local bus companies suggesting they consider a new service.

You can also complain to the transport co-ordinating officer about the **quality** of the bus service in your area, but it is best to contact the bus operator first.

In London, go direct to the public relations office of **LRT**: your complaint will be forwarded to the appropriate person. If you are not satisfied, contact the **London Regional Passenger Committee**, the consumer watchdog organisation for all public transport in London.

There are also a number of national organisations which can help you with your complaints. The **Bus and Coach Council** is the trade association for the industry and could mediate between you and a bus or coach operator. They also have a scheme for getting your money back if you book a coach ticket and the coach operator subsequently goes bust.

If you are concerned about safety, contact the government's local **traffic commissioner** via your local council. All buses and coaches have to be registered with him.

By using some or all of these methods, you can usually embarrass a bus company enough into providing the service that you want.

Paul Morris, however, wasn't able to do this. He boarded a bus in Birmingham to go and visit a friend in hospital who was a teddy bear enthusiast. Paul took with him a three-foot teddy bear under his arm – and was made to pay a full adult fare for the bear as well!

As the bus company told *You and Yours***, 'there are no specific instructions about teddy bears, so it was up to the driver to charge for it like any ordinary luggage'. We have not, though, heard of any more bears being charged since then, so maybe Paul's complaint was worth it after all.**

TAXIS

All London taxis have to be registered with the **Public Carriage Office**: London **minicabs** do not have to be registered, although they do have to have an operator's licence from their local borough council. Outside London, local councils register taxis and have the power to license minicabs.

Within London, taxis have to accept any journey within the Metropolitan Police District that is not more than six miles or one hour's travel from the pick-up point, and any journey to Heathrow Airport. They do not, however, have to stop for you, even if their 'vacant' light is on, unless they are parked in an authorised taxi-rank. All journeys inside the six-mile limit are metered, but outside this district taxis can charge what they want: it is best to agree the fare before you get in.

To complain about a taxi-driver, take down the taxi number and registration plate and, if possible, the driver's number. Make a note of the date and time and complain to the **Public Carriage Office** in London, the local council elsewhere. Complaints about minicabs should be made to your local council.

Most complaints about London cab drivers are about being refused a journey, even though it was within the six-mile limit. **This happened recently to Harry Feigen, who is not only a taxi-driver himself but secretary of the taxi-drivers' association. His advice? Get into the taxi first before stating your destination, and if the driver refuses remind him that he has to take you within the six-mile limit, and ask him to drive you to the nearest police station to make a complaint.**

HOLIDAYS

As this book goes to press, the government has speculated about the need for a **travel industry ombudsman** to whom customers can complain if they have not been able to get satisfaction or compensation for a lousy holiday. And not before time, as letters that come into *You and Yours* testify. Here are some:

♦ **One London listener took a seven-day holiday to Lanzarote which cost over £800 for her and her family. She found out that the electricity was turned off for 12 hours each day in her hotel. After several letters of complaint to the tour company, she eventually received £40. 'What was £40 after a ruined holiday?' she told us.**

♦ **An East Anglian couple went to Malta, only to discover their food and accommodation were 'well below standard'. When they returned home, the tour operator 'refuted everything we said and just stonewalled. We knew another couple on the holiday who were so disgusted they transferred to another hotel but we didn't take their address, so it was just our unsupported word.'**

♦ **A Birmingham listener wrote about her motor-rail holiday in France, where the company lost the keys to her car on the way home. She came home as a foot passenger on the ferry, leaving her husband behind to sort it out – and he lost a day's work. They applied for compensation, getting a solicitor to draft the letter and got £165 'after being very, very persistent'.**

If all this sounds as if the travel industry is not the most popular trade when it comes to dealing with complaints, well, that's true, at least if our experience at *You and Yours* is anything to go by. Undoubtedly, we do not hear from very many satisfied holidaymakers on the programme – and there are millions of these each year. Undoubtedly, too, there are things that can go wrong on holidays that are not the fault of travel companies: the weather, for example, or foreign customs being different from those in Britain, or some customers' unrealistic expectations about the kind of holiday a cheap package will actually buy.

But that said, there does seem to be a mismatch between the number of complaints holidaymakers have and the amount of compensation complainers eventually receive. Of the 13 000-odd complaints the **Association of British Travels Agents (ABTA)** receives every year, only a minority go to their final complaining stage of arbitration where the customer usually wins. Many people's experience of making complaints about holidays is of letters being unanswered, various fob-offs being tried out and then some kind of derisory payment being offered. So be prepared to be very persistent with your complaint – read the general rules for complaining outlined in Chapter 3 for tips.

How to complain about holidays

Even though you may have arranged your holiday with a travel agent, your contract is, in most cases, with a **tour operator** or **company**. You complain to them and not the agent. Here's how to do it:

1   Complain to the company's representative at your holiday destination and ask them to put things right. They are in constant touch with the company's headquarters back home and have the discretion to put things right or offer you an alternative. Give them 24 hours and if nothing is done, write down your complaint and get them to telex it back to the UK. If they make you an offer which is still not quite right, accept it but also write them a note saying that this is 'under protest' and that you are 'reserving your legal rights'. Keep a copy of this note.

   If nothing is done, one ploy that is sometimes successful is to ring the newsroom of a British tabloid newspaper; they will always accept 'reverse charges' calls. Summer is a 'slow news' time and 'British holidaymakers slam tour company' always makes a good story. Even if they do not print your comments, they may alert the tour operator to what is going on and that alone can bring action.

2   Get evidence of your complaint by taking photographs, keeping a record of what was wrong and when you complained, and the names and addresses of other holidaymakers who agree with you. Keep all this safe and don't hand it over to the rep: just tell them you have it.

3   When you return home, write to the tour company with your complaint, sending copies of any evidence you have and ask for compensation. If they do not reply within four weeks, write again, giving them another fortnight before you will take legal action. Send all your letters recorded delivery, and keep copies. Since many tour companies will try and prevaricate when they get a complaint, it is important for you to set them reasonable deadlines – and then stick to them. A solicitor's letter, if you can afford it, can often do wonders.

4   You then have two options if you have not received satisfaction:

(a) If the company is a member of **ABTA** (and most are), you can write to ABTA and ask it to investigate your complaint. What it will try to do is to conciliate between you and the company to reach a settlement. If this does not work, you can then ask ABTA to refer the matter to independent **arbitration**. Arbitration for claims under £2000 will cost you £23, with an additional £7.45 for any other members of your family who also want compensation, and you can claim up to £1500 per person. But the tour operator must agree to the arbitration as well, and once your arbitration has started you cannot then go to court if you are dissatisfied with the decision.

(b) Or, you can take the company to court. Generally, if you have a pretty strong case and the amount claimed is under the limit for a Small Claims Court case, this is a better option since courts tend to award you more than an arbitrator. If you have paid for your holiday by credit card, and the amount is over £100, you can claim from the credit card company instead (see p. 48).

What you can claim for

Most complaints to ABTA are about 'general dissatisfaction' with a holiday. But to get compensation in court or from an arbitrator, you will have to be more specific. Basically you can claim for **loss of value**, the difference between what you paid for and what you received. An example of this complaint would be a poorer quality hotel than you were led to expect. Another point for compensation would be for **loss of enjoyment**, for example the hotel being noisy or dirty or not having proper facilities. You can also claim for **out-of-pocket expenses**.

ABTA has now introduced a new code of conduct which will give increased opportunities for holidaymakers to press their complaints. From 1 May 1990, ABTA members will be responsible under this new code for all promises made in their brochures and responsible, too, for the actions of anybody they employ for your holiday. This will include foreign hoteliers and guides, for example. The new code also makes it much easier to press a claim of negligence for any injury you may have suffered as part of your holiday. If you are injured in an accident in the hotel pool due to the pool being unkept or dirty, for example, you will be able to press your claim in the UK against the tour company that booked you into the hotel instead of having to take court action against the hotelier in a foreign court.

Promises not kept

Peggy Bailey, from Suffolk, went on a combined walking and sightseeing holiday in southern Spain which specified certain places of interest in the itinerary. 'But the first few days were disappointing as some of these visits did not take place, and the promised coach transport was not available', she told *You and Yours***.**

'Although things did improve, there was still some continuing dissatisfaction which the tour leader did not seem able to put right. One of our number with considerable legal knowledge drafted a letter to the company which all the group signed. When I got home, I reiterated the criticism in another letter but also told them of the many enjoyable aspects of my holiday. The result was a handsome apology from the company, and a refund of £50. I hope to use them again.'

Members of the **Cirencester Youth Football Club** were not so lucky –and have no intention of using their (non-ABTA) travel company again. **They arranged a seven-day coach tour of Italy, Yugoslavia, Austria and Germany, including four football matches. They ended up playing just one game and not against any home side but against another visiting football team from Scandinavia! And that was not the only problem.**

The coach got lost several times and their final overnight stay in a youth hostel in Germany did not happen as the hostel said they had no confirmation of their booking.

The problem with the team claiming compensation from the company was that it was unclear how much the company was at fault: the company claimed that the weather was 'too hot' for the arranged matches, a claim disputed by the team, and that, in any case, the

**contract for the football tour did not lay down any
condition that said football matches must actually be
played!**

So, if you want a specific requirement from your holiday,
make sure to get this in writing and if it doesn't happen, you can
then sue the company for breach of contract.

You can also sue a tour company if the holiday does not live
up to the description put in its brochure, a description which
could be in writing or by a photograph. The brochure may have
some small print which tries to absolve the company of any
liability, but this small print is only legally acceptable if it is a
'reasonable' exclusion: consult your local trading standards
department if you are uncertain about this. Also contact your
local trading standards department if you think a tour company
has deliberately misled you by the brochure description: the
officers can prosecute.

Cancellation and surcharges

If your holiday is cancelled, you will almost certainly be offered
your money back or an alternative. But consider, too, pressing
the company for compensation, such as any out-of-pocket
expenses you may have incurred.

If you are **surcharged**, you will have to pay the extra (apart
from the first two per cent), unless the company has promised
'no surcharges'. If the surcharge amounts to more than 10 per
cent of your holiday's cost, you can cancel without losing your
deposit. All surcharges must be due to circumstances outside the
company's control, such as rising fuel costs.

If an ABTA firm goes bust, there is a 'bond' scheme which
protects your holiday by getting another ABTA firm to take it
over or by offering you money back.

Holiday insurance

If you have an accident on holiday and it is the result of the tour
operator's incompetence or negligence, you can sue the operator
for compensation and for your medical bills. But it is far easier
to claim off your holiday insurance. Unfortunately, these insur-
ances do not cover everything, as **Mark Porter** discovered.

Mark went on holiday to Corfu and took out the

holiday insurance his tour company recommended as 'for real peace of mind'. Mark was strolling down a pavement after a meal when a truck swerved out of control and knocked down him and two friends. He spent the night in hospital and then flew back to England, all paid for by the insurance company. But it then took him over a year to completely recover, a year when he had to give up his job and claim invalidity benefit and a year in which he had considerable medical problems as a result of the accident. All this, however, was not covered by the insurance because the personal accident clause only covered loss of limbs or eyes. So Mark received no compensation at all, and such clauses are not the exception, but the rule.

Make sure you check out exactly what is covered when you take out insurance, and see if the policy will cover you for accident compensation. It is far easier to do this than to sue any person responsible for an accident in another country. If you are self-employed, make sure you take out a policy which covers you for loss of earnings if you are injured on holiday.

Complaints about travel agents

Many things that go wrong on holiday are the fault of a travel company and not of the travel agent who arranged the deal. Occasionally, though, travel agents can be at fault, as **Jacqueline Flanagan** discovered.

'I went into my local travel agent and asked him to arrange the cheapest flight to Dublin. It didn't matter when I went, I just wanted the cheapest. He told me this was an Apex flight and I paid £69 for a single ticket. But I then discovered that you could get a return flight for this amount, so I was going to end up paying twice that amount. He didn't do his job properly. What could I do?'

What Jacqueline could do is to sue the agent for breach of contract. They are obliged, as any expert is, to provide you with the best advice and if you ask for the cheapest ticket, they should find this out for you. Jacqueline could take them to court for the money she lost. If this happens to you, write to the agent and point this out, threatening to take them to court. You should then get a refund. Agents are also usually members of ABTA so you could take your complaint to ABTA instead of going to court.

Complaints about hotels

Hotels are usually part of a package holiday and your contract is not with the hotel-keeper but with the travel company who booked you into the hotel. If you have booked into a British hotel by yourself, not as part of a package tour, you have the same rights against the hotelier as with any provider of a service (see p. 110).

Many hotels in Britain and abroad are run by large companies, so consider also taking your complaint to the customer relations department at the company's head office if the hotel manager does not deal with it adequately. Tell the manager you intend to do this.

All British hotels are obliged by law to offer you a room if you have booked or if they have rooms free unless they have grounds for suspecting you can't pay or if you look generally disreputable.

To complain about hotels abroad which you have booked yourself, your best bet is to contact the local office of the country's tourist board or the tourist police. In all the major holiday destinations, tourist boards license and control hotels: they will be more than happy to hear about any of their hotels which are not offering a good deal.

Timeshares

Strictly, a 'timeshare' is not a holiday contract at all but rather a property contract, so always make sure you consult a solicitor who has experience in dealing with timeshares or property abroad before you buy. And never buy on the spur of the moment, despite all the incentives offered. Be very careful of 'free gift' offers or 'specially arranged' discounts.

There is a **Timeshare Developers Association** which can deal with complaints about their members and also has a code of conduct and an arbitration scheme. If this Association cannot resolve your complaint, you can opt for arbitration which, unusually, does not require the timeshare company's agreement as well. This will cost you £115 which is refundable if you win but you cannot then take legal action. Many timeshare companies are not members of the Association so check this out before committing yourself.

At the moment, the Office of Fair Trading is investigating the marketing methods of timeshare companies since many of their techniques do not appear to fall under existing consumer laws. This should lead to greater controls in the future.

CHAPTER FOURTEEN

EDUCATION

In the last decade, there have been more changes in how the education services are organised than at any time since the war. New education acts have given parents greater choice in state schools, a greater role for school governors and the opportunity for state schools to 'opt out' of local education authority control. In the pipeline, too, there are government proposals to reorganise higher education, particularly to switch over from student grants to loans. Whatever the *educational* merits of these changes, they have certainly given parents more rights over their children's education – and more chances to complain.

STATE SCHOOLS

State schools are run by local education authorities who are responsible to the Secretary of State at the Department of Education and Science (in England) or the Northern Ireland, Scottish or Welsh Offices. Each authority must provide a state school place for children from the age of five to 16. Every parent also has the responsibility to ensure their children receive an education during these years, either by making sure the children attend a state or private school, or by convincing the education authority that they, the parents, are making some kind of alternative provision such as private tutors.

With all the opportunities there are now for parents and schools to 'opt out' of state schooling, most parents still use local education authority schools. A recent Consumers' Association poll indicated that 90 per cent of people are, in general, satisfied with state school services. In particular circumstances, however, complaints do arise.

Choice of school

Your local education authority will allocate your child to a school, usually the nearest one to you. But you do not have to accept this allocation. Under the **1988 Education Reform Act**, you can decide on a different school outside your immediate local area, and this school must take your child unless it is full. You may, however, have to pay all transport costs if you do this. Local education authorities have to pay transport costs if you live more than three miles (two miles for under-eights) from the school to which they allocate your child.

How can you decide about schools? Perhaps the best way is to ask friends and neighbours, and you can also ask schools for their prospectus: every school must provide one. If a local education authority refuses you the school of your choice, you can appeal. If this fails, you can then appeal to the Department of Education and Science (in England), the Welsh Office, the Northern Ireland Office or the local sheriff in Scotland.

Complaints about schools

Jacqui Torrance complained to *You and Yours* **that her daughter's school was not stretching her daughter very much. Margaret Stephen's complaint was that her boy's homework was too easy. For Jean, it was concern that her son's teacher seemed to single him out for ridicule and humiliate him. And Lorey Garcher complained that there wasn't any proper supervision for her children at break.**

These are just four of the many complaints we have heard about state schools. But what is the best way to make complaints? The general procedure is this:

1   Contact your child's form teacher and talk to him about the complaint.

2   If you feel nothing is being done – or your complaint is about the teacher himself – make an appointment to see the head or deputy. They do not have to agree to see you but most will.

3   You can then bring the matter up with a school governor (school councils in Scotland). Governors now have additional responsibilities under recent education acts, including attending selection meetings to appoint teachers and offering advice on discipline. The school will tell you how to contact a governor.

4   Or, you can get in touch with the school's **Parent Teachers Association (PTA)** if there is one.

5   If nothing is done about your complaint, you can then bring it up with the Chief Education Officer of your education authority or

with the chair of the education committee who will not be an officer but an elected councillor.

6   If you still feel your complaint is not being taken seriously, you then have three options: you can complain to the local ombudsman (see p. 158); you can report your worries to the local education inspectors (HMIs: they inspect schools for the government. While they cannot enter into any individual correspondence, they might start up an inquiry to see if standards have slipped); finally, you have the right of appeal to the appropriate Secretary of State. Your complaint will need to be pretty serious, though, to interest a government minister, and you will need backing from other parents for him to consider taking action.

Who can help you?

Each school now has to provide a written prospectus laying out what it offers pupils and you can compare this with what you think is actually going on. And there is a national organisation that can provide you with advice: the **Advisory Centre for Education (ACE)**.

The best thing, though, is to try and get the school on your side by not getting angry with teachers. Remain reasoned and calm and make them feel your complaint is one that you, as well as they, want to help sort out.

You will certainly get a lot of support from teachers if your complaint is about the lack of resources in the school, for example, lack of books or too few school trips. To complain about resources, lobby your local education authority or councillor. If you feel the authority is not meeting its statutory requirements for a proper education, contact the appropriate Secretary of State.

Many parents are also concerned about **teaching styles** at schools which do not seem to conform to their idea of a basic education. In a recent edition of *You and Yours*, parents contacted us about the way reading and writing were taught to their children at school. **Jo Armistead, from Yorkshire, for example, disagreed with the textbooks used for her children. And Dean Nixon, from Staffordshire, felt he** was not given any information from the school about how his children should use the reading materials provided.

In the end, the head teacher has the ultimate power to decide how his school should teach pupils, although schools will soon have to conform to the new **national curriculum** which attempts to lay down standards all schoolchildren will have to reach at certain ages. Each school, by the way, now has to have some kind of procedure to deal with complaints by parents about how they are teaching this new curriculum and about the school's collective worship.

The best way for parents to bring up worries about the general style and content of their children's education is through the **PTA**. Some associations have **year-groups**, where parents of children in the same class can get together with the class teacher to talk about problems.

School reports

Carol Hall was annoyed with her head teacher at the primary school her three young sons were attending. The head announced that there would no longer be annual written reports, partly because they took up too much staff time. For Carol and her husband, this meant 'we could no longer sit down and discuss how our sons were doing, and compare the progress they were making over the years'. The head, though, was quite within his rights.

There is no obligation on a school to provide a report about your child at the moment. But the government intends parents will soon have the right to receive an annual report on their child's progress in national curriculum subjects. And in the next few years, many schools will start providing a 'record of achievement' for every pupil before they leave school, although this is unlikely to be a compulsory requirement on schools.

Special needs

If your child develops a problem with learning at school, you have the right to ask for an **assessment**. This is an informal but confidential procedure and the aim is to identify any problems that can be sorted out.

You can, however, press for a more formal **statement**, which will mean your child is seen by a number of experts who specialise in learning and behavioural difficulties. This statement will lay down obligations on your local education authority to provide, for example, special lessons or a special class for your child. It is reviewed every year. But take advice before you do this, as any statement might also insist that your child is educated separately from his peers – and you will not be able to do anything about it. Contact **ACE** for help. If an assessment or a statement is refused, you can appeal to the education authority for one; if it refuses, to the appropriate Secretary of State.

Opting out

The **1988 Education Reform Act** has given parents the chance to decide whether they would prefer their children's school to go 'independent', that is, to opt out from local education authority control. As a result, the school's governors have control of their own finance and are answerable only to the Secretary of State. All secondary schools and all primary schools with over 300 pupils are compiling an up-to-date list of their pupils' parents to give them this vote, as this book goes to press. If a majority vote for opting out, then the school must go independent. It is too early to say how this will affect parents' ability to complain about a school which decides to opt out: presumably all serious complaints will have to be made directly to the appropriate government department rather than the local education authority.

PRIVATE SCHOOLS

All private ('fee-paying') schools with more than five pupils must be registered with the Department of Education and Science or the Scottish or Northern Ireland Office. If you are concerned about the school premises or the teachers' behaviour towards your children, you can complain to the appropriate Secretary of State.

One organisation that can help you with any information about private schools, or assisted places in these schools, is the **Independent Schools Information Service**. Many private schools are part of the **Independent Schools Joint Council** which will want to hear about any decline in standards of their members. But try and bring up complaints with the school's head or governors first.

Unlike state schools, you have the right to take a private school's managers or governors to court for breach of contract if they fail to provide the education you have paid for. Take legal advice before you do this.

RELIGIOUS SCHOOLS

Some state schools are run by religious organisations and fall under the category known as **voluntary schools**. This is particularly true of Catholic schools, but also true of some Church of England, Jewish and other religions' schools. You have the same rights to complain to the local education authority about these schools as with any other state school. But you can also complain to the appropriate religious body if the school seems to be falling down on its religious teaching or standards. In Catholic schools, for example, complain to the bishop in whose diocese the school is.

SCHOOL EXAMS

Whether your child's school is state-run, private or voluntary, one of their most important tasks will be preparing and entering their pupils for the public examinations, the GCSE and A levels, which are run by independent examining boards. Every year these examination results produce a large number of complaints from pupils and parents who are dissatisfied with the marks and grades awarded. A bad mark can, after all, seriously affect a young person's future, especially if it is undeserved, **as Gillian Davies from London discovered:**

Gillian's 17-year-old daughter failed the old O

level maths and this 'threw into question all sorts of things that she might do next. Well, we found a crammer for her to study at so she could sit the exam again. It cost £400 but then, three days before she was due to re-sit the exam, we got a telephone call from her old school saying that she had, in fact, passed after all: they had regraded her.'

Gillian's daughter was one of 200 pupils who had been 'failed' when, in fact, they had passed: the local examination board decided to reassess the exam after teacher concern. Gillian's daughter and husband were delighted but Gillian herself was horrified. 'My daughter had done an unnecessary course which cost us a lot of money. And she would very probably have stayed on to the sixth form. I was so upset I wrote to the examining board.'

Unfortunately, there was very little that could be done. You cannot claim compensation for a wrong examination mark unless you can prove the examining board acted negligently, a very difficult thing to prove indeed. Also, what most people forget is that the official examination results are *not* the same as the results which are first sent to the school. The result only becomes official and binding when the certificates are issued, some six weeks after the results first go to schools in August. This is to allow examining boards to deal with complaints about individual results or, as in Gillian's daughter's case, results of an entire class. But what can you do if the exam result is lower than you expected it to be?

You can appeal to the examining board for a **simple clerical check** that the exam results corresponded to what the board expected. You can also ask the board for a **re-mark**: this will cost you about £14 and usually takes about four weeks. Another option is to ask for a **re-mark and a report**: this will take longer and costs vary from board to board.

It is possible for you to appeal direct to the board, but if your child has been entered by a school, the board will usually expect your appeal to come via the school's head teacher, so you will need his support: most heads will support you if they think there has been a marked difference between the anticipated mark and the end result. Get the head to tell the board if a university or polytechnic place depends on the exam result: the board will then try to re-mark quicker and tell the college directly if they suspect any revision of grade is likely.

If your child was not feeling very well during the examination, you will not be able to get the paper marked with this in mind. Tell the teacher or invigilator who is supervising the exam, however, and get a note from them which can be presented in explanation for a low grade.

Other queries or complaints about GCSEs or A levels should be made to the **schools liaison officer** of the examination board.

Sandy Lincoln, a mature student from Surrey, discovered that her A level English examination (set by the AEB board) and GCSE Chinese exam (set by the Midlands board) had been arranged at the same time on the same day in two centres 20 miles from each other. She was only told the dates and times one week before and thought that this would mean two years of studying for one of the subjects would be wasted. But when she contacted the schools liaison officer of the Midlands board he quickly came up with a solution which enabled her to take both exams. And she passed both as well.

UNIVERSITIES AND POLYTECHNICS

Complaining about universities and polytechnics is much more difficult than complaining about school education since they are not under any direct local education authority or government control. They are essentially self-regulating, self-managing institutions, and the government is unlikely to look at anything other than extremely serious complaints. It is better to bring up any complaint you may have about the quality of teaching or the resources provided with the head of department and then the governing body. The students' union or the **National Union of Students (NUS)** may be able to help as well.

Private universities and colleges now have to be licensed by the appropriate government department, and the government will be interested in hearing any complaints you have about these institutions.

If your child gets a place on a degree course at a UK university or polytechnic, he is, subject to eligibility, entitled, at present, to an award or grant from your local education authority, although the amount may depend on your circumstances. Awards and grants cover fees and basic living expenses. Some education authorities also offer grants for other courses, but this does vary.

Complaints about grants should be made to your education authority: the NUS may be able to help with the complaint. It seems very likely that a proportion of awards or grants will soon become loans, if present government intentions are followed through.

YOUR WORK

YOUR COMPLAINTS ABOUT WORK

There is one major problem about making a complaint at work: unlike most other kinds of complaint, here you have something you might lose if you complain: your job. Of course, it rarely comes to this and, in most jobs, you *are* protected against 'unfair dismissal'.

But there are all kinds of ways in which employers can make life very difficult for the complaining worker. Your promotion prospects may be blown, for example, or the conditions or status of your job may be subtly changed. So, if you are thinking of making a complaint about your work, be very careful. Consider whether the complaint is worth the trouble and do not run the risk of losing your employer's goodwill for something that may not in the end be worth very much.

Present a complaint to your boss as a common problem, a problem that you as well as he need to resolve. This approach at least gives him room to manoeuvre, and even if the complaint remains unresolved, you may get credit for thinking about what's best for the company rather than what's just best for you.

Before you make a complaint about your work, find out if other people are affected as well. If they are, see if they will back you up either by going with you to talk to your boss or by allowing you to say that other employees feel the same way.

Take advice from a **trade union**: if you have a serious complaint, their help may be invaluable and could save you from being victimised. Exhaust all informal methods of complaining before putting anything in writing. A quiet chat with your boss when he is in a relaxed mood may (but only 'may') work wonders.

COMPLAINTS ABOUT YOU

If you have been employed in a full-time (18 hours or more a week) job for 13 weeks, you are entitled to a written contract which lays down the conditions and obligations of your job. Ask the personnel officer for one if you have not been given it. This contract should also tell you how you can bring up grievances and what the disciplinary procedure is for complaints about your work.

These procedures differ slightly from company to company but this is roughly what should happen if your work is proving unsatisfactory:

1   You will be given an oral warning: your boss will tell you what's wrong.

2   If he feels you have not taken heed of this, he will then give you a written warning. This may happen straight away for a serious breach of your contract or of company rules.

3   If your behaviour persists, you will then be given another written warning, saying that you are likely to be dismissed if nothing is done.

4   You can then be dismissed.

Provided you have been in full-time employment for more than 13 weeks, your employer cannot dismiss you instantly unless you have committed a serious and blatant breach of company disciplinary rules.

WHAT TO DO IF YOU ARE DISMISSED

First check that all the procedures outlined above have been followed. Also, make sure that you have been given a written letter stating the reasons why you have been dismissed.

If you feel you have a case for 'unfair dismissal' or 'constructive dismissal' (where your employer has forced you to resign), consult a Citizens Advice Bureau (CAB), trade union or a solicitor who specialises in employment law, perhaps via a local law centre. You will almost certainly need legal advice and help to win your case.

You or your advisor can then apply to have your case heard by an industrial tribunal. You have to do this within 42 days of your dismissal and you can only go to a tribunal if you have been employed for at least two years apart, that is, from cases of sex and race discrimination and equal pay where there are not any qualifying times. The tribunal will consider not just the reasons for your dismissal but also whether the correct dismissal procedures have been followed.

You can apply for a tribunal by going along to your local job centre, unemployment office or CAB and asking for the appropriate form. This should be sent to the **Central Office of Industrial Tribunals**, which will refer your case to **ACAS** to see if a settlement between you and your employer can be worked out.

Industrial tribunals are held locally and are more informal than the County Court: basically you make your case and call witnesses and your employer does the same. Tribunals are, however, binding on both parties and you can only appeal on a point of law (to an **Employment Appeal Tribunal**).

Tribunals can hear cases such as dismissal, redundancy and refusal of maternity rights or trade union membership. And they can also deal with cases of discrimination at work and equal pay (see Chapter 16). Tribunals *cannot* deal with any wages that may be owing to you or any cases of injury at work: you will have to take your employer to court for these.

If you win at a tribunal, you will be offered either your job back or compensation. It is best to press for reinstatement since you can then bargain for more compensation than a tribunal would normally have offered you, and for extras like a good reference or redundancy terms.

One advantage of pressing for a tribunal is that it is bad publicity for a company, even if they win, and many companies choose to settle before your case comes up, sometimes as late as the morning of the tribunal hearing. Also, you will not have to pay either the cost of the tribunal or your employer's costs unless the tribunal decides your case was brought frivolously and your employer has nothing at all to answer.

The disadvantages are that *you* may suffer from the publicity as well: industrial tribunals are usually reported in the local press and a future employer may not want to employ someone who knows their legal rights well enough to use a tribunal. Also, you cannot get legal aid: this means you will have to pay any legal costs you may incur for a solicitor or other legal advisor, even if you win.

Many solicitors and law centres, however, will help you, often for a low charge, if you have a good case. And there is a scheme in London called the **Free Representation Unit (FRU)**, which provides trainee barristers to represent people at tribunals free of charge (see p. 288). **Michael Underwood, a spot welder, used the FRU when he was unfairly dismissed from a job he had done for many years. His trainee barrister won Michael a large award.**

HEALTH AND SAFETY

Although the laws governing health and safety at work in the United Kingdom are amongst the best and oldest-established in the world, the actual safety record in this country has got worse over the last two decades. The TUC, for example, estimate that 700 people are killed and 178 000 injured every year as a result of their work. Environmental health officers put these figures even higher since 60 per cent of work injuries are not even reported.

The new industries of the last decade are also producing new hazards. Cases of repetitive strain injury and stress brought on by VDU screens are showing an alarming increase. Each new form of work seems to bring with it both benefits to the workforce and also new kinds of strain and injury.

All companies who employ more than five workers must have a written policy on health and safety which is open to inspection by employees or their representatives. In addition, the companies must meet the health and safety regulations that apply to their industry in, for example, the various **Factory Acts**. The responsibility for enforcing these regulations lies with **environmental health officers** (for businesses like shops), and the **Health and Safety Executive** (for most industrial and commercial premises).

If you are concerned about conditions at work which you think may affect your health or safety or that of others, find out who is the person responsible (usually the 'safety officer') and raise your complaint with him. Your trade union will almost certainly be interested as well, and may want to bring it up with your employer.

If nothing seems to be done, you could then report your employer to the local environmental health department or the Health and Safety Executive. Each has the power of inspection and can instruct your employer to put things right or prosecute him. Each will treat your complaint with confidence and not give your name to your employer if you do not want this.

If you have been injured at work or been forced to retire early due to your working conditions, you can press for compensation, by taking your employer to court if necessary. The difficulty with court action is that you have to prove that your injury or illness was *due to or exacerbated by your work*: this can prove tricky and many employers contest these cases.

You will also need expert medical evidence and most doctors are extremely reluctant to say with certainty what the cause of an illness or injury was, especially if it is long-developed. The best thing to do is to get your trade union to act for you or join a trade union if you think you have such a claim.

Your trade union will also tell you if you are entitled to claim for industrial disablement benefit if you have been forced to take early retirement. Some CABs have expertise in this area as well.

PAY

In most situations, your pay is negotiated between you, or your union representative, and your employer: it is a private contract and it is up to both of you to agree an amount for the work that is done. If you do the work agreed and you do not get paid your full wages or fees, you will have to take your employer to court for breach of contract.

An employer, by the way, cannot deduct a proportion of your wages for things like breakages or not meeting sales targets *unless you have agreed to this happening before you did the work*. All deductions must be reasonable and not more than 10 per cent of your basic wage.

But what happens if your employer pays you too much? **The 2500 employees of Knowsley Council in Merseyside were the happy recipients of this when the council**

**paid them all double one December. When they
returned to work after Christmas, however, the council had discovered its mistake (which had cost it
almost £2 million) and proposed not to pay the
employees at all in January to get the money back. Was
the council entitled to do this?**

Yes, they were. The council could argue it had discovered
the mistake before employees would have spent all the money
and most employees would have realised a mistake had been
made.

To keep extra money your employer pays you by mistake,
you must meet three conditions:

1   The employer's mistake must be one of fact (like human or
    computer error) and not one of law. If your employer pays you
    too much maternity pay, for example, that is a mistake of fact.
    If, however, he does not deduct enough tax from you, that is a
    mistake of law and you will have to pay it back.

    and

2   The mistake must not be your fault, for example, by you giving
    your employer wrong information.

    and

3   You must have spent the money in good faith without realising
    the mistake before the employer demands the money back.

    It is difficult to prove all these three conditions and the best
advice is once you realise a mistake has been made to pay the
money back.

The danger if you do not give the money back is that your
employer may get you prosecuted for theft, as well as demand
the money back. **Wendy Roberts was paid an extra
£18 500 by her employer and then was charged with
theft when the mistake was discovered. The court,
however, found her not guilty because she said she
thought the money was compensation for an accident
that had happened to her at work. She had not acted
dishonestly because she thought the money was right-
fully hers.**

PART-TIME WORKERS AND SELF-EMPLOYED WORKERS

Your rights as a part-time worker, for example, over maternity pay, unfair dismissal and union membership differ from full-time employees. If you work fewer than 18 hours a week, you have to be employed for five years before you qualify for the same rights as a full-time worker. If you work fewer than eight hours a week, you do not have any employment rights and you can never qualify for them, irrespective of how many years you work.

If you are self-employed, you do not have any specific employment rights but merely the general rights of anyone providing a service for someone else. This is so, even if you work mainly for one person: if he breaks your contract, you will have to take him to court to get your money.

DISCRIMINATION

Have you ever been turned down for a job because you were the wrong sex? Have you ever been refused a drink in a pub because the landlord did not like your colour? And what about being refused entry into a cinema or theatre because of your disability? Or not being considered for an interview because you were over 40?

All these situations are examples of discrimination. At *You and Yours* we have also heard cases of discrimination because of sexual preference, religious beliefs and even someone's weight. They all seem unfair but are they all illegal? Surprisingly not.

It is not a **criminal** offence to discriminate against anybody: you cannot be sent to jail, for example, if you prefer employing women to men, white people to black people, able-bodied to the disabled and so on. But it is a **civil** offence if you discriminate against someone on grounds of sex or race, although most other forms of discrimination are legally (if not morally) acceptable, and there is, unfortunately, very little you can do to challenge these, at least in law. But let's look first at the two situations that you can challenge, sex and race discrimination.

SEX DISCRIMINATION

The **1975 Sex Discrimination Act** states you cannot be discriminated against on the grounds of your sex at work, in public services like health and leisure and in most commercial situations, for example, being refused a drink in a pub. There are some exceptions but not very many: the Act does not apply in Northern Ireland (although there is legislation there which is broadly similar), and the armed forces and religious orders are also exempt. So, too, are some pension and insurance schemes provided the company has actuarial data backing the discriminatory price. No longer exempt, however, are the traditional heavy manual jobs like coal-mining.

The Act applies not just to being refused a job on the grounds of your sex, for example, but also to not being considered seriously for a job or not making the shortlist for interviews because of your sex. It also applies to men as well as women, as the airline company **Dan Air** found out three years ago.

The company decided its cabin staff should only be women and their recruitment procedures were designed not to consider male applicants. Dan Air defended this decision first on the grounds of 'customer preference', and then because of 'their worry' that potential male staff might be homosexual and, so they claimed, put customers at risk of AIDS.

Dan Air were forced to change this policy and consider men as well as women for new cabin jobs as a result of an investigation by the **Equal Opportunities Commission (EOC)**, the government body set up to enforce sex discrimination laws. This is the organisation you should go to for help in any situation where you feel you have been discriminated against due to your sex.

The EOC can give you advice and may also take up your case, either by doing their own investigation and serving a 'non-discrimination notice' on a person or organisation breaking the Act, or by backing individuals in court or tribunal action. You can take court action under the Act yourself, although it is far better to get EOC support since it will pay legal costs if you lose and have considerably more expertise than you.

Work

If you have been discriminated against at work because of your sex, you have not been promoted when you were the best candidate, for example, or you have been forced out of your job because of sexual harassment, you can take your employer to an **industrial tribunal**. How these tribunals work is explained in Chapter 15 – but note that, unlike other cases, you do not have to be employed for any length of time before you apply. Get EOC advice: if it cannot provide representation for you at a tribunal hearing, it will put you in touch with a solicitor who specialises in this area.

As well as the Sex Discrimination Act, the EOC also enforces the **1970 Equal Pay Act**, which came into effect in 1975. This Act applies not just to getting the same pay for the same job but also to equal pay for jobs of the same status. It has recently been complemented by tougher European Community regulations which now apply in the UK.

Again, if you think you are not getting equal pay with other workers of a different sex, the EOC can help you take your case to an industrial tribunal. You must do this within six months of accepting the job – or three months if it is a training post.

You can also use these acts to press a case of discrimination at a tribunal if you have suffered at work as a result of being married, for example, or if you are a married woman who was passed over for promotion in favour of a single woman or man.

Education

Parents in Glamorgan were concerned that their children's schools were breaking the Sex Discrimination Act. It seemed the local education authority was hardly encouraging boys to try out domestic science or girls technical drawing.

The parents asked the EOC to investigate, and the Commission found that six Glamorgan schools were breaking the Act, not intentionally but by default. Two primary schools, for example, separated the boys and girls for craft and needlework classes; two mixed secondary schools did not let the girls and boys know they had a choice between craft and design and home economics: the boys all did the former, the girls the latter; and two single-sex secondary schools did not give girls the chance to do design or boys the chance to do home economics.

This was the first case of a school's *curriculum* being challenged by the EOC – and indicates the priority the Commission gives to equal opportunities for girls and boys in schools. If you feel your child is suffering due to tacit discrimination at school, contact the EOC.

Advertising

Sexist advertising is a cause of annoyance for many women and some men all over the UK. The **Advertising Standards Authority** regularly gets complaints about the way women are used in advertising and about how women are portrayed as 'dumb housewives' or 'pin-ups' for selling certain products.

It is possible for the EOC to issue a non-discrimination notice about adverts – but this power is mainly used as a warning against recruitment advertising in ads, for example, that specify the sex of desirable applicants. (You can *encourage* either men or women to apply; you cannot *exclude* either men or women.)

For other kinds of adverts, the best thing to do is to make your feelings known both to the **Advertising Standards Authority** (or the **Independent Broadcasting Authority** if the ad is on television or radio) *and* to the company selling its product. You may not get any immediate satisfaction – but your views will be noted by the companies concerned, and over the last few years there have been changes in how women and men have been portrayed in adverts, partly due to complaints received from the public.

RACE DISCRIMINATION

The situation in terms of race discrimination is almost exactly the same as in sex discrimination: basically it is not allowed. The **1976 Race Relations Act**, like the Sex Discrimination Act, does not make it a criminal offence to discriminate against somebody on the grounds of their race, but it recognises that it is a serious infringement of a person's legal rights. And in the same way as the EOC is empowered to investigate sex discrimination, the **Commission for Racial Equality (CRE)** tries to stop racial discrimination by using the courts if necessary.

Unlike the EOC, however, the CRE is helped by local offices around the country, usually known as **Community Relations Councils (CRCs)**. Although independent of local councils, CRCs work closely with them: your council will give you their address.

If you have experienced any example of discrimination due to your race, contact your local CRC. If your complaint is a serious one and you have suffered loss or injury as a result, it will put you in touch with the Commission which can investigate and prosecute or advise you how to bring a case to court yourself. Also many urban councils have **race relations committees** which can provide advice, particularly about discrimination in council services like housing, and tell you what you can do about racial harassment.

If you have experienced race discrimination in employment or in not being shortlisted for a job, you can bring your case to an industrial tribunal – the CRE will give you support. You should usually do this within three months of the discrimination taking place. For other examples of race discrimination, you will have to bring your case to the County Court. Again, get specialist help to do this. Both the courts and industrial tribunals can award you compensation, not just for any material loss you may have faced, such as being dismissed from a job, but also for 'injury to feelings' as a result of the discrimination.

Just as with the Sex Discrimination Act, there are very few exceptions allowed under the Race Relations Act: the two main ones are religious orders and private clubs. The armed forces are not exempt.

Although the Act does not cover discrimination due to **religious belief**, if you think you are being discriminated against not on the basis of your religion but on your colour, you should have a case. For example, if you are refused a job because your employer does not want to employ Sikhs, Moslems or Hindus, it would be very difficult for the employer to show that he is not, after all, discriminating on the basis of colour not religion.

Almost all the cases brought under the Race Relations Act have been about discrimination against black or Asian people: that, after all, is the main reason why the Act was first introduced since these people suffer far more from racial discrimination than their fellow whites. But the Act does apply to *any* kind of race discrimination, against white people as well as black. The CRE, for example, did intervene after a complaint by **Gordon McDonagh. He applied for a job with Leicester City Council as a gardener and did not get an interview despite his experience. He re-applied under the name of Patel and was granted one. The council was trying to encourage more Asian people to take council jobs but the way they did this, by not granting Gordon an interview because his name clearly indicated he was not Asian, was not allowed under the Race Relations Act.**

OTHER FORMS OF DISCRIMINATION

Most people would agree that the Sex Discrimination Act, the Equal Pay Act and the Race Relations Act have contributed substantially to getting rid of sex and race discrimination, even if they do not appear to have affected racial or sexual prejudice very much. There is, after all, little the law can do to change people's attitudes to other people, as opposed to outlawing certain kinds of behaviour. But the law gives you no opportunity to challenge other forms of discrimination, except in very specific cases. Take these two examples:

Forty-eight-year-old Jenny Mather went to several employment agencies to find a new job. Despite being highly qualified, it was not a happy experience:

'On several occasions I was told the employer specifically asked for applicants between 30 and 40 years old or between 25 and 35 years. One woman who ran an agency, who was herself over 50, said she had terrible problems placing people over 35 and that I might as well not bother. The general attitude seems to be that older people do not have the stamina, are not adaptable, cannot learn new skills and won't get on with other employees, which is all absolute nonsense.'

Liza Costas Paraskevas also felt she had been discriminated against when she went for a job with a bank – although not because of her age (she was only 24), but because of her weight. She was offered a job by the bank subject to a routine medical. But she was then told she could have the job only if she lost two of her 13 stones. Liza was quite happy with her weight, and did not feel that the bank's medical reasons for refusing her the job were fair. It did not refuse to accept people who smoked, a much greater health hazard.

At *You and Yours* we have received many similar stories of job and other forms of discrimination against older people and fat people. But there is not very much they can do, at the moment. There is no law against employers discriminating on the basis of age or weight, as long as they do not have different standards for men and women or for black and white people.

The same applies to disability. Although there is a government requirement on companies with more than 20 employees to try and ensure the workforce consists of three per cent disabled people, there is not an enforcement agency making sure this happens. This 'requirement' is widely ignored since it is not an offence not to meet it.

If you are **dismissed** from your job because you are too old, overweight or disabled, you may be able to bring a case of unfair dismissal to an industrial tribunal (see p. 254). But you would not have a case if, for example, you were over your company's retirement age.

If you become unable to do your job due to disability, get help from your trade union or local law centre: you should at least be able to bargain for a different type of job or an early retirement package. It is very unlikely that illnesses such as AIDS count towards 'being unable to do your job'. The **British Medical Association**, for example, has recently warned employers that it will help employees with AIDS or the HIV virus to take their companies to court if they are sacked simply because of this.

In Northern Ireland, the new Fair Employment (Northern Ireland) Act has created a **Fair Employment Tribunal**, which can deal with complaints about job discrimination with particular reference to religious beliefs.

These are, however, small, albeit important, exceptions. With most forms of discrimination apart from those based on sex and race, there is little recourse to law. The only thing you can do is make a fuss: contact the local or national media with your case, appeal to people's sense of fair play, write to the managing director of any company which has discriminated against you and embarrass the company to face up to its prejudices. Above all, get together with other people in your situation and press for change.

In many American states, pressure groups have succeeded in getting several anti-discrimination laws on the statute book. In California, for example, companies are not allowed to discriminate on the basis of health or disability, age, religion or sexual preference. These laws are the direct result of lobbying, and laws that groups in Britain like **Age Concern** want to see here too.

USING THE LAW

Whether we complain about goods we buy from shops, services we receive at home, professionals who exploit our trust or bureaucrats whose idea of a quiet life is not to bother to take into account our wishes, the final card we all have is using the law.

A quiet word may work wonders; a stiff letter may embarrass companies to give us redress; trading standards officers, Citizens Advice Bureau (CAB) workers, professional and trade associations, councillors and MPs may take up our case but, in the end, almost all complaints that cannot be resolved by negotiation need to be sorted out by the courts.

Here is the good news:

♦ There are quite a number of organisations which will help you if you decide to take someone to court. They are indicated in the appropriate chapters in this book.

♦ Suing someone in court does not have to be difficult or expensive. In this chapter, various schemes to help you use the law cheaply and easily will be outlined.

♦ Often the threat of legal action will make someone cave in without the need to go to court.

And here is the bad news:

♦ The law is actually quite complicated and specialist legal advice can be expensive. If you are claiming a large amount in a case which requires expert testimony, your costs could be very high indeed.

♦ You are never certain you will win a case, although, of course, some legal actions stand a much better chance than others.

♦ There is a difference between winning a law case and being awarded compensation by a court, and actually getting the money. That is why it is always best to sue established firms rather than fly-by-nights, people who have some kind of insurance backing rather than self-employed entrepreneurs.

Now all this is not meant to put you off using the law to enforce your complaint. But it is important to re-emphasise that taking legal action should always be held in reserve, a final option, and then only considered if you can cope with the worst scenario (losing your case and having to pay all the costs), and have a pretty good chance of getting the best (all legal costs and the compensation you deserve, and it all paid straight away).

With these provisos, here's how you can stand a better chance of winning your case rather than losing it.

THE LAW ITSELF

On p. 26 we explained that the law is divided between **civil** and **criminal** law. Basically, civil law covers private disputes between individuals or companies, and criminal law covers actions by individuals that society has deemed unacceptable.

Most complaints we have as consumers will be **civil** ones, so we will have to take legal action ourselves through the civil courts: the Small Claims and County Courts, the High Court and, if necessary, the Court of Appeal.

Civil cases are heard by judges or registrars, and they decide between the **plaintiff** (the person who is bringing the case) and the **defendant**. Nobody is found guilty – and no criminal record results. The case is decided on the 'balance of probabilities', usually just by a judge, very rarely by a jury.

If the case is found for the plaintiff, the judge can either order the defendant to stop the action the plaintiff complained about and/or pay compensation. If the defendant refuses to pay – or doesn't bother – the plaintiff will have to go back to court for an enforcement order. If this still does not produce the money, the court can order a bailiff in.

Criminal cases are almost always brought by law enforcement officers like the police, trading standards or environmental health officers and some others. In the police's case, they do not prosecute themselves but rather refer the case to the **Crown Prosecution Service**. The case starts in a Magistrates Court and then, if necessary, is referred to the Crown Court to be heard by a jury. Guilt must be established 'beyond reasonable doubt', a more difficult decision to reach than 'balance of probabilities', and the judge has the power to either fine someone or imprison them.

Criminal courts can also make awards to people who have lost out by a criminal action. If someone throws a brick through your window and is prosecuted, for example, the judge can decide to order him to pay you for a new window.

But most situations where people have lost money owing to someone's criminal actions will be less clear cut, and there are often limits on the amount of compensation awarded. You may have to sue someone for compensation or damages in the civil courts after they have been found guilty in the criminal courts. For example, a supermarket may be fined in the criminal court for selling mouldy food. But if that food caused you food poisoning, and your claim for compensation is complex, you will almost certainly have to bring a civil suit afterwards. The great advantage you have, though, is you can use the criminal court decision as evidence for your case.

There are two main kinds of civil law that affect us in our daily lives: laws concerning **contracts** and laws concerning **torts** (an old French word meaning 'wrong'). Basically, contract law covers agreements between people to do things which involve payment. Tort law covers hurt, injury, nuisance, inconvenience or financial loss as a result of someone being negligent or not exercising proper care. For example, when you sue a trader for bad service, you are alleging a breach of contract. When you sue a council for a pavement injury, you are alleging a breach of tort.

Most contracts and torts are enshrined in what is known as **common law**. This is the law that has grown up over the years as a result of judges' decisions and is based on **precedent**, decisions that have been made in the past. Decisions made by higher courts are **binding** on lower ones. You would not, for example, be able to persuade the County Court to contradict a judgement from the Court of Appeal or the House of Lords (the final arbiter) unless the circumstances were very different. That is why lawyers are always quoting other court judgements.

In some kinds of contracts and torts, Parliament has made **specific** laws by Act, Order or Regulation. These are known as **statute** law and usually extend rights at common law. The Sale of Goods Act and the Supply of Goods and Services Act are examples of statute law. They lay down the specific conditions that certain contracts, like buying an item in a shop or asking a builder to do work for you, must meet. You do not *need* to cite a specific statute law to sue someone in court. You can just claim, for example, 'breach of contract'. But it is generally easier for you to prove your case if you can cite the specific statute law.

Finally, some civil disputes are heard not in court but by a tribunal or arbitrator. In most of these situations, the decision made is as binding as any civil court decision: you cannot then go to the County Court if you lose.

When you decide to pursue a complaint through the courts, what you are doing is bringing a civil action to get some kind of redress, usually money or preventing something happening in the future.

When you claim money in a civil court due to a breach of contract or tort, you can claim for **general** and/or **special damages. Special damages** are compensation for things like damaged clothes, money you have lost as a result of your case, and so on. These damages can be easily figured out and are usually agreed by everybody concerned if you win your case. **General damages** cover less quantifiable things like pain, suffering, reduced quality of life, distress and inconvenience, and the judge will make a decision about these after he has listened to arguments from both sides. Since these kind of damages are much more difficult to work out, his decision will always be a somewhat arbitrary one. In all civil cases, you have the right to claim general as well as special damages as long as they are reasonable and you are not trying to profit out of your case.

You can try to sue somebody or get an injunction against somebody for virtually anything, as long as you have a course of action recognised by the law. In the United States, people do all the time. In the UK, though, we are more cautious – and judges do not take kindly to frivolous law suits. In rare cases, they can ban 'vexatious litigants' from using the courts at all.

In most situations, however, there is an extremely effective sanction against using the courts without a good reason based on a good case: money. You could end up paying not just your costs but also those of the defendant and those of the court, and legal costs do not come cheap. Unfortunately, this also deters many people who have a good case from using the courts at all. But do not despair: there is one court that nobody should feel deterred from using: the Small Claims Court.

Scotland and Northern Ireland

The law and the legal system are very similar in Northern Ireland to that of England and Wales. Scotland, however, is another matter. With some exceptions, such as not having a Supply of Goods and Services Act, most English and Welsh law has equivalents in Scotland. Many of the legal procedures are, however, different. The County Court is replaced by the Sheriff's Court, for example, and people bringing civil cases to court are called pursuers, not plaintiffs, and so on. Where it would be misleading not to, we have indicated Scottish legal differences at appropriate points.

USING THE SMALL CLAIMS COURT

One of the great advances there has been in the UK for people who want to get compensation for a breach of contract is the introduction of the **Small Claims Court**. Strictly, it is not a court at all, but merely a **procedure** of the County Court which is open to plaintiffs to sue for damages or compensation of not more than £500. In England, Wales and Northern Ireland the limit is likely to be raised to £1000 sometime in 1990, and in Scotland, where it is part of the Sheriff's Court, the limit is £750. But everybody calls it the Small Claims Court – and we will, too.

What happens in the Small Claims Court is that you, as plaintiff, present your case to the court which serves a summons on your opponent. You both then present evidence to support your cases. The case is heard by a court official, known as a **registrar**. He decides between the two of you: there is no jury involved, no press or outsiders present and everything is very informal. This process is known in legal terms as **arbitration**, although it is not to be confused with the other kinds of arbitration on offer which are an alternative to court action.

You are allowed to have a lawyer who can make your case and, in Scotland, you have the right to ask for someone else to represent you like a CAB worker or other consumer advisor. (You do not have the *right* to do this elsewhere, although some registrars will grant it to you if you ask. But you *will* have this right soon.) The defendant can have a lawyer as well.

Most people who appear before a Small Claims Court, however, do not have any legal representation and the reason for this is not just because it is easy to represent yourself. *It is, and this is the great advantage of the court, because nobody can claim their legal costs.* Your solicitor's costs will not be paid – neither will the defendant's. So if you lose, you will not be landed with a large bill. The only thing you will have to pay, if you lose, is the court fee and any out-of-pocket expenses of the other side.

How to bring a complaint to the Small Claims Court

1 Ask at the County Court for a form requesting 'arbitration'. You have to take action in the court where the defendant lives, has a business or where the problem arose – check with a CAB for the court's address. If you are uncertain how to fill the form in, ask the court officials for help or take the form to a CAB.

2 Return the form to the court with the 'particulars of claim' filled in, the main points of your case in outline and the request for arbitration. You will have to pay the plaint fee, which is on a sliding scale depending on how much you are claiming. The defendant will be ordered to pay you back this fee if you win.

3 The court will then issue a **summons**, with a copy of your 'particulars of claim', to the defendant who will be asked either to pay the amount you are claiming into court or to **dispute** the claim by filling in the form of defence.

4 If the defendant disputes your claim, the court will call you both to a **preliminary review**. The registrar will go through the written and oral evidence you and the defendant intend to present and agree the number of witnesses to be called, whether either of you needs to inspect any documents the other may be presenting as evidence and the date and likely duration of the final hearing.

5 Finally, the hearing itself is where you present your case with

evidence and witnesses and are cross-examined by the defendant. The defendant then does the same and sums up his case. You then sum up, and the registrar makes his decision.

Although all this is in a court of law, it is much more like a business meeting than a case out of Perry Mason. The registrar will certainly discourage any histrionics, there is nobody else present and, if you are representing yourself, the registrar will try and be as helpful as he can without being biased.

6   If you win, the defendant will be asked to pay the award and, in England, Wales and Northern Ireland, he may have to pay 'loss of earnings' and the travel (but not legal) costs of the plaintiff and witnesses. Different registrars interpret these costs very differently. In Scotland, there is an absolute limit on these costs of £75 and no normal expenses will be awarded for amounts claimed under £200.

7   If the defendant does not pay the amount ordered by the court, you have to go back to the court again which can then order a bailiff to seize his property up to the value of the award.

And that should be that. The Small Claims Court is meant to be easy to use and most people who do use it come away satisfied. Over 50 000 people now file actions in the Small Claims Court each year. Here are the answers to some common queries that we get asked at *You and Yours* about going to the Small Claims Court.

'Can I make a claim for someone else?'

Yes, if there is a good reason, such as if someone has died or a person under 18, why that person cannot make a claim. You can also have the right to sue someone handed on to you. All this is explained on the form.

'What happens if the person I'm suing offers a settlement?'

This is one of the great advantages of the court. When a dodgy trader has received your court summons, he starts thinking seriously about paying up. He can offer a settlement at any time before the final hearing but he must pay it into the court and not directly to you, although this may change soon. He must also pay your plaint fee. Before you agree to drop your claim, check that the court has received the money.

Be prepared to bargain all the way up to the final hearing: a first offer is usually just that. But in any correspondence you have after the summons has been sent out, mark your letters 'without prejudice'. This means that any bargaining cannot be referred to in court if you are not satisfied with the final offer.

'What if I can't find the name and address of the person I'm suing?'

You cannot do anything about this, unfortunately. The court cannot help you with tracing a trader. There are some tips on p. 48 but if you cannot serve a summons on a named person at their proper address, your claim falls down.

'What about if I'm sued in the Small Claims Court?'

With most complaints, you will be the plaintiff, the person pursuing someone else through the court. But we have given some examples in this book when the best way to complain is not to pay for the faulty goods or poor service and to tell the trader to sue you.

If they do, and most will not if you have acted reasonably, you become the defendant and they are the plaintiff. But the principles are the same. Try and get the number of witnesses kept low at the pre-trial hearing, so the expenses will be low if you lose and get CAB or legal advice once you know the case against you. If you lose, ask the court for time to pay in instalments if necessary.

'Can I ask for an "order of action" in a Small Claims Court?'

Only in Scotland. The Scottish scheme allows you to ask the court to order the defendant to do something instead of paying you compensation. A builder can be ordered to finish the work, for example, or a council to repair your house. In England, Wales and Northern Ireland, the Small Claims Court can only award **compensation**: you will have to go to the full County Court for any action you may require.

USING THE COUNTY COURT

For any claims over the small claims limit and up to £5000 (possibly to increase soon), you will have to press your case in the full County Court. It is possible to use the Small Claims Court for claims over £500 but only if both parties agree: most defendants will not.

The procedure is roughly the same: you have to get a summons from the court, there is a preliminary and then a full hearing and so on.

The three main differences are: the court hearing will be public and may be reported by the local media; in rare situations, there may be a jury involved to decide the case; and, most importantly, if you lose you will almost certainly have to pay some or all of the other party's legal costs, as well as your own and the court costs.

In other words, unless you have a very good case confirmed by legal advice *and* you are sure that the person you are suing can be traced and has the money to pay up or you are on legal aid (see p. 287), forget County Court action. For example, if you have lost a few thousand pounds as a result of a builder's incompetence, are you sure the builder can pay if you win the court case? Or if your holiday cost £2000 and was a disaster, how sure are you the court will agree with you?

In all County Court cases, you are well advised to get a solicitor to represent you, and if it is a case involving negligence, one who specialises in the area. Do not let this put you off if you have a very good case against an established firm: just be careful.

There is, of course, nothing to stop you taking out a County Court summons in the hope that the defendant will settle before the hearing. Or using it as a tactic, even if you do not intend ever going to court. But you will have to pay court costs once the final hearing has been agreed, unless you can get them paid in an out-of-court settlement.

Claims of over £5000, at the moment, have to be settled by the **High Court**, the next court up. (As this book goes to press, however, the government looks likely to introduce new legislation compelling almost all civil cases to start in the County Court, much like criminal cases starting in the Magistrates

Courts.) All the above provisos apply, except that procedures are more complex and less user-friendly, and the costs of High Court action are even more expensive than those in the County Court. And while you have the right of appeal against any Small Claims, County or High Court action, the costs of an **appeal court** will be even higher – even if you are granted leave to appeal.

One final note of caution about using the County or High Court. If you are offered a formal out-of-court settlement, where the defendant pays the sum he is offering 'into court', and you refuse this, you may have to pay legal costs if the court decides to award you less. A well-publicised case in 1989 illustrated this drawback.

Two sisters, Frances Warby and Ann Chastell, were arrested in a branch of Tesco in 1984 and accused of shoplifting. They were held in a police cell for several hours and then had to face two Magistrates Court hearings, before waiting to go on trial at the local Crown Court. In 1985, the case came to court, and Frances and Ann were acquitted after the prosecution offered no evidence of the shoplifting. The two sisters had protested their innocence all along and were now vindicated.

Frances and Ann then decided to sue Tesco for wrongful arrest, false imprisonment, libel and slander in the civil courts 'in an attempt to clear our names'. Before the case came to the High Court, Tesco offered them £1500 each (without admitting liability) as a paid-into-court full settlement. The sisters refused this, went to court and won their case. But they were awarded only £800 each in damages. Because this was less than the Tesco offer, the judge decided Frances and Ann should pay a substantial part of the legal cost of their case, about £16 000, under rules governing these kind of out-of-court settlement offers. Frances and Ann appealed against his judgement and the Appeal Court increased their damages from £800 to £7500 each. This was above Tesco's offer so they no longer face a large legal bill.

Get good legal advice if you are made a similar offer before your case – otherwise it could cost you far more than the amount you are claiming.

USING THE CRIMINAL COURTS

When a criminal law has been broken, an offender is prosecuted either by the Crown Prosecution Service (with evidence from the police who charge him) or by other law enforcement officers like trading standards or environmental health officers. This all takes place in the criminal courts: Magistrates Courts, Crown Courts and so on.

It is possible in criminal cases for the judge to award compensation. For example, if you have lost money as a result of a misleading description given to you by a builder and the builder is prosecuted in court by a trading standards officer as a result, the judge can order the builder to pay you back the money you lost. Under a recent change in the law designed to encourage the payment of compensation in the criminal courts, the judge must now give reasons if he decides not to do this. It is up to the trading standards officer to bring this up in court – make sure he knows you want compensation and has full details of how much you are claiming. But what if the 'misleading description' was not the only wrong the builder did you?

This happened to a *You and Yours* listener in London. **The listener had lost several thousand pounds not simply because a builder had not done the work he said he had done (a criminal offence), but also because he had done the work badly (a civil dispute). What she did, though, was to ask trading standards officers to prosecute for the misleading description – and the builder was duly fined in court. She then used this court decision as evidence in a civil action which she took in the County Court for all her money back because of his bad workmanship. It worked a treat.**

If you have suffered personal injury as a result of a criminal action, you can also apply to the **Criminal Injuries Compensation Board**. You will have to provide evidence for this – but the case does not have to come to court. Although the usual time limit for applying to the Board is three years, this can be extended in certain circumstances, for example, adults who make a claim as a result of abuse they have suffered when they were children. Compensation Board decisions can take several years to sort out.

One other award you can claim is **bereavement damages** for the loss of one of your family in a disaster of some kind. CABs or local law centres can advise you about claiming both these awards.

But what if trading standards officers, the police or Crown Prosecution Service or other enforcement agencies refuse to prosecute someone you think has committed a criminal offence? It is possible, although quite rare, for a private individual or company to bring what is called a **private prosecution**. Or to do what **Mary Wally**, a nurse from Staffordshire, did recently.

Mary was in her car with her two children and she stopped behind a local driving instructor. His car had two stickers on the back window, stickers which shocked her.

'**They were depicting two sex acts, one straight sex, the other an outline of two people at opposite ends of each other kissing but not on the lips. I was angry because they were being forced on my children and on me. I didn't want my children to see them, what do you say to them? I don't want them to grow up quicker than they need to. This kind of thing spoils life and it will get progressively worse if you turn a blind eye to it.**'

The police wouldn't prosecute the instructor, but Mary managed to persuade the Crown Prosecution Service to take up the case and bring the instructor to court under the Indecent Displays Act, legislation designed to control sex shops. Unfortunately for her, the judge threw it out of court. But at least she had made her point.

You can try and persuade the Crown Prosecution Service to take up your case, too, if you have been offended, not just for indecency or obscenity but for all kinds of possible criminal offences as well. You can bring the case entirely by yourself but costs can be very high if you lose.

ARBITRATION AS AN ALTERNATIVE TO THE COURTS

For some kinds of disputes between you and a trader, there is the option of choosing to go to **arbitration** rather than court action. (This kind of 'arbitration' is not the same as the Small Claims Court procedure which is also known, confusingly, as 'arbitration'.)

Most of the arbitration schemes on offer for consumers are approved by the **Office of Fair Trading** under trade association codes of practice. They are called 'code arbitration' and include new and used cars, furniture, photography and others mentioned throughout the book. Some arbitration schemes are run separately from the Office of Fair Trading. Make sure that these are decided by an independent arbitrator, such as a member of the **Chartered Institute of Arbitrators (CIA)**, the association of professionals who oversee most arbitration cases.

How to use arbitration

1 Check first that the trader you are in dispute with is a member of a trade association. Trade associations will tell you if they offer arbitration and how much it will cost.

2 Apply to the trade association for an arbitration form and a copy of the association's code of conduct. You can also get this from the CIA.

3 Complete the form and send it to the trade association with the arbitration fee, which will be on a sliding scale depending on how much you are claiming. Once you have signed this form, you surrender your right to go to court.

4 You will get a claim form from the CIA which you must fill in and return within 28 days. You must send two copies of any evidence supporting your claim, for example, witnesses' state-

ments, photographs or receipts. Keep a copy yourself, and be as factual as possible. You are called the 'plaintiff'; the trader is the 'recipient'.

5   The CIA then asks the trader to respond to your claim within 28 days. You are then allowed 14 days to respond to the trader's response. The arbitrator ('arbiter' in Scotland) may call for independent evidence. He then makes the award, giving his reasons. He may also get the trader to pay back your arbitration fee if you win. The trader must pay the award and fee within 21 days and the award is legally binding. If the trader does not pay up, you can go to court for an enforcement order.

COURT ACTION OR ARBITRATION?

In almost all forms of arbitration, you have to make a choice between taking a trader to court and using a trade association's arbitration scheme. What's best? There are arguments both ways:

♦   An arbitration scheme does not involve any appearance any-where: a case is usually resolved by documents alone. This means you do not have to go to any hearing. On the other hand, you will not be able to argue your case in person, or cross-examine any witnesses. If your case is very complicated, it may well be better to go to court to explain it all.

♦   Using arbitration is almost always cheaper than using the courts because if you lose, you will not have to pay any costs. However, for some reason, courts tend to make higher awards then arbi-trators. So, if you have a very good case, you may be better off going to court. The great advantage of arbitration, however, is that the limits allowed under the different schemes are higher than those of the Small Claims Court –and sometimes higher than County Court limits. Arbitration is much less risky than using the County or High Court.

On balance, if you have the chance of arbitration, it is prob-ably better to use it, rather than chance the courts.

THE LAW AND CHILDREN

A 15-year-old boy from Derbyshire hit the headlines recently when his attempt to become a stockmarket wizard went disastrously wrong. He lost £200 000. But was he or were his parents liable for this debt? It depends.

Generally, young people under the age of 18 in England, Wales and Northern Ireland cannot have civil laws of contract enforced against them unless what they bought could be regarded as a 'necessity', such as food or clothing. For certain contracts, however, it is now possible to persuade a court to order a young person to repay money owed when they reach 18 years of age. Scottish contract law is a little different. There are some contracts in Scotland which are legally enforceable for and against girls over 12 and boys over 14: the **Scottish Child Law Centre** can give you advice.

Parents are usually not liable in the United Kingdom for any civil debts their children may owe.

Civil laws of tort (where for example someone may claim compensation for an injury due to a young person's negligence) are more complicated. In some torts, children or their parents may be held responsible but there will certainly be a lot of legal argument involved. If you are in this situation, good legal advice is essential. The **Children's Legal Centre** may be able to help.

It can help, too, if your child has been charged with a criminal offence. The age of criminal 'responsibility' varies, depending on the offence: if your child is charged with a serious criminal offence, get good legal advice. For some kinds of fines a criminal court may order parents to pay.

LEGAL REPRESENTATION

When you go to court either as a plaintiff or defendant in a civil case, or as a defendant or, more rarely, as a private prosecutor in a criminal charge, you do not have to be represented by anyone at all. There is no obligation to employ a solicitor or barrister to put your case, although, if you do employ a lawyer, the present rule is that only barristers can represent you in the higher courts. (This may change in the next few years if government proposals get through.)

Certainly there is very little need to employ (and pay for) a lawyer to put your case at a Small Claims Court – and the small claims procedure is designed for this not to be necessary. In the other kinds of civil courts (and, indeed in the criminal courts), however, you can also put your case to the court yourself – and have a friend present to advise you. The friend is known as a 'MacKenzie Man' after a famous case where a defendant asked for this to happen.

But in most civil cases that reach the County Court or High Court – and in all criminal cases where you might lose your liberty – you are well advised to get a lawyer, not just for advice before you go to court but also to represent you. Lawyers, after all, are the experts – and they know how the law and the courts work.

For any case which involves either expert testimony, such as a medical negligence case, or complicated argument about facts or legal precedent, like complicated contracts, a lawyer, preferably one who specialises in these cases, is absolutely essential. But lawyers are expensive. How can you get legal advice without it costing an arm and a leg?

Other legal advisors

In the different chapters of this book, we have outlined various people who can give you an opinion about your legal rights – and sometimes these people know more about particular branches of the law than your local high street solicitor. Many of these are mentioned in Chapter 4, people like CAB workers (for general advice, especially housing and social security), and trading standards officers and consumer advice centres (for general consumer law).

There are also some organisations which will take your case up for you or provide you with free legal advice. For example the Commission for Racial Equality and the Equal Opportunities Commission will help in cases of discrimination. And some pressure groups like Action for Victims of Medical Accidents or the National Association of Mental Health (MIND) offer legal advice in their areas of interest.

Finally, it is always worth checking if there is a law centre near you – contact the **Law Centres Federation** to find out. Law Centres have legal workers and solicitors who can give free advice – although it must be said that they concentrate more on criminal law and public sector law than on straightforward civil disputes, and are geared more to poorer clients than those who are relatively well off.

Consulting a solicitor

If you have a straightforward dispute with a trader who has broken a contract with you or caused you an injury, the people mentioned above can also put you in touch with a local firm of solicitors.

Another way of finding a solicitor is to ask your family or friends whom they recommend, or to pop into a firm of solicitors in your neighbourhood and try one out for an initial interview: you can always change your mind and try someone else. Membership organisations like the AA can also recommend solicitors, and your company or trade union may have access to a solicitor as well.

It is important to feel happy about your solicitor. He is, after all, representing your interests, and you will depend on his advice. Bear in mind, too, you may have to go and see him during office hours, so try to find someone near to your home or work.

And remember you are entering a contract with a solicitor when you get him to do work for you: you pay for his service and he provides expert advice and help. Ask how much he charges and what the likely cost of his services will be to resolve your case. Ask him, too, if there are some aspects of the work you want done that you can do yourself to cut down your bill. And make sure he contacts you if it looks likely his bill is going to be much higher than he originally estimated. If he is reluctant to talk about money, find another solicitor who will. To complain about solicitors' bills or service, see p. 291.

Unless you settle or win your case *and* get awarded legal costs, you will have to pay for all the legal advice and services the solicitor does for you, including any interview that you have with him and any letter he writes to you or on behalf of your interests. How can you get this bill reduced?

♦ **Fixed fee interview** Most solicitors participate in this scheme where you get a 30-minute interview with a solicitor for just £5, much lower than they normally charge. This interview can be about any legal problem and it does not depend on your income or savings: it is open to everyone. You can also use the interview to see if you qualify for the other forms of free legal help, the **legal advice and assistance scheme** (known as the 'green form' scheme) or **legal aid**.

♦ **Green form scheme** This entitles you to two hours' free legal advice from a solicitor (three hours in matrimonial cases and the time can be increased on application from a solicitor), but you only qualify if you have a low income and not many savings: this can be worked out quickly for you by any solicitor. The green form scheme covers all types of legal work, including a solicitor taking advice from a barrister, apart from actually appearing in court. In Scotland it is called the pink form scheme, presumably because the form is pink!

♦ **Legal aid** Legal aid is available for most kinds of civil cases, although there are some important exceptions like libel, and for almost all criminal cases. It is means-tested but a solicitor cannot tell you if you definitely qualify. He can, however, tell you if legal aid is granted in cases like yours. A solicitor will give you a form which you then fill in and send to your local DSS office. The DSS will decide if you *qualify* for legal aid, and, if so, they will send your particulars to the area office of the **Legal Aid Board**, an organisation created in 1989.

This Board will let you know if it thinks you have a reasonable case, and hence whether you can be *awarded* legal aid. If you get through all this, all your legal advice and representation is usually free from any solicitor who agrees to take you on, although sometimes you may be asked to make a limited contribution. If, by the way, you lose your case, you will not have to pay more towards the costs than this contribution. As a (very rough) rule of thumb, you will generally qualify for legal aid, at present, if your income is under £14 000 p.a.

The procedure is different for legal aid in criminal cases. If you are charged with an offence, ask the court straight away for legal aid: it is much more readily granted than civil legal aid.

You do not, by the way, have to accept the solicitor the court may allocate to represent you: you can choose your own. In some criminal cases, you may have to make a contribution to the costs of your defence even if you are on legal aid.

♦ **Accident Legal Aid Service (ALAS)** If you are involved in an accident that causes you injury, you can get free initial legal help from ALAS under a scheme set up by the Law Society in 1987. You have to use a solicitor who is part of the scheme: contact ALAS for local names.

The scheme is not as widely known about as it should be, but more than 6000 people have got free advice under it in the last three years, and two out of three people have gone on to claim damages in the court as a result, people like **Cicely Munroe:**

'I was in Oxford Street in London crossing the road and I was knocked down by a motorbike that didn't stop. I was taken to a hospital with a very badly broken arm and broken foot. Well, the last thing I wanted to do at the time was to take out a law case, but the CAB advised me to use this scheme and everything was done for me. The compensation was very good indeed.'

Three thousand solicitors now participate in ALAS, and have won awards of several thousand pounds for their clients who have been injured in accidents.

♦ **Free Representation Unit (FRU)** Like ALAS, this is not as widely known about as it should be. The FRU is a scheme in London, run by the Bar Council, to provide barrister help for people at **tribunals** (but not in court). Most of the time, the barristers who take on tribunal cases from the unit are trainees – which does not mean to say that they are not any good. For some complicated cases, though, the unit has engaged eminent QCs. All the advice and representation is free and independent of your financial circumstances.

Most of the clients they represent come up before tribunals in London, usually employment or social security tribunals. One or two higher education law departments around the UK, notably Birmingham Polytechnic, offer a similar scheme with free representation by law students under the guidance of their lecturers. These are certainly better than nothing, since you cannot get legal aid for tribunal representation. It might be worth contacting your local university or polytechnic to see if it offers a similar service: it is good practice for their students, after all.

♦ **Contingency fees** Wouldn't it be nice if you could engage a lawyer on the basis that if you don't win your case, you don't have to pay them? Well, actually, there are a lot of problems with these contracts with lawyers, usually known as contingency fee law, 'no win, no fee' or 'speculative action'. They are common in the United States where lawyers offer to take on your case for a percentage, usually from 25 per cent upwards, of the costs awarded if your case is successful. This is one reason why everyone in America seems to be suing everyone else, and one reason, too, why American lawyers earn a lot of money.

This form of contract with lawyers, however, is not allowed in Britain at present, *apart, that is, from Scotland*. There are restrictions there about which kind of cases can qualify for speculative action – contact the Scottish **Law Society** for details. The government has promised to introduce a similar scheme based on fixed legal costs (not on a percentage) in the rest of the United Kingdom, as this book was being prepared for publication. It will be a 'no-win, no-fee' scheme and the Law Society or your local CAB should have details.

Apart from these forms of free or cheap legal advice, you will have to pay for any work done for you by a lawyer. A straightforward solicitor's letter, for example, will cost you anything from £25 upwards, although it might be well worth it if it forces a trader to cough up the few hundred pounds he owes you.

Try and claim your legal costs from whomever you are threatening with legal action, although this is not possible for Small Claims Court action or arbitration disputes. You also might consider **legal insurance**. There are many insurance forms on the market now which cover legal costs for an annual premium, although, like all insurance, you cannot take it out after the action for which you want to claim compensation or damages has happened.

♦ **Specialist solicitors** All family or high street firms of solicitors should have the ability to give legal advice and assistance across the entire range of the law – or at least be able to put you in touch with a solicitor who takes a special interest in your kind of legal case. That's the theory – and it is true for most forms of **contract law**, where you are in dispute with someone who has not delivered their part of your contract and you want damages or compensation.

But it is much less true when it comes to the law of **tort**, where you are generally claiming money due to someone else's negligence. The classic examples are personal injury cases or medical negligence. It is much more difficult to win these kind of cases, and you really need a solicitor who knows his way around and knows, too, what kind of expert evidence is required, how you can get the usual three-year deadline extended and so on. Here's why:

John, a retired railway worker, was determined to sue a health authority for medical negligence as a result of an operation that went wrong on his son. His son was a successful businessman who was treated in hospital for pleurisy – and came out with a mental age of four, a tragic mistake. But was it due to negligence? And could this be proved? John consulted several local solicitors whom he found 'very rough indeed. They all tried and failed to get a settlement. Well, eventually I decided to consult a lawyer who specialises in medical accidents, and he won my case. I got an award of about £500 000. I had 11 years of worry wondering where to go, what to do, was I going to get justice? If I had gone to a specialist solicitor right away, all that might have been unnecessary.'

For cases of medical negligence like John's, **Action for Victims of Medical Accidents** can put you in touch with specialist help. For cases of personal injury, the **ALAS** scheme can help. You can also ask law centres, CABs or national pressure groups to recommend to you solicitors who deal with particular kinds of cases – and have a good record in them. These solicitors may charge you more than your local high street firm but it may well be worth it.

COMPLAINTS ABOUT LAWYERS

Throughout this book, we have indicated at certain points the advantages of going to a solicitor for advice and when to use a solicitor to press home your complaint. Solicitors and barristers, after all, are not only *inclined* to take your side in any dispute, they *have* to: that is what you are paying them for. Sometimes, too, they are better at representing your interests than you are yourself since they do not have to bother with little things like the feelings of people to whom you are complaining.

But lawyers are by no means infallible: they, like any other professional, can do a bad job and not deliver their side of the bargain, or charge you an extortionate amount for what seems like very little indeed. So the final advice about complaining in this book is about the legal experts themselves.

How to complain about solicitors

People are often very surprised when they receive a solicitor's bill – and the surprise is very rarely a pleasurable one. If you think the bill is too high, you can ask for the solicitor to send it to the **Law Society** for what is called a **renumeration certificate**. You must do this promptly and before you pay the bill. There is no charge for the certificate – but the Law Society can increase as well as reduce bills, if they think the solicitor has not charged enough! Renumeration certificates are also not available in Scotland or Northern Ireland, and they only apply to work which does not include a solicitor's appearance in court.

If court work is involved, you can apply to the court involved for the bill to be 'taxed', and it will approve, reduce or increase it. This applies all over the UK, but courts are only *obliged* to look at a bill if you present it within a month of the court action. Cases involving legal aid are taxed automatically.

For other complaints about solicitors, here's what to do:

1 Contact the senior partner of the solicitor's firm. He will particularly want to hear about cases of misbehaviour which put the practice into a bad light. The secretary of your local Law Society may also be able to deal with your complaint informally.

2 Then go to the **Solicitors' Complaints Bureau**. This used to be part of the **Law Society**, but it has now been separated and it received over 17 000 complaints in 1988. The Bureau can look into all kinds of complaints about solicitors, including shoddy work and overcharging, apart from some cases of pure negligence: see 4 below. In Scotland and Northern Ireland, all complaints, apart from claims of negligence, are still dealt with by their respective Law Societies.

3 The Solicitors' Complaints Bureau (or the Scottish or Northern Ireland Law Society) can refer your complaint to the **Solicitors' Disciplinary Tribunal** if there seems to be a case of serious professional misconduct. That tribunal can issue a warning to the solicitor involved – or stop a solicitor practising.

4 What the Tribunal, Bureau or Law Society cannot do is offer or award you any compensation due to **negligence**: you must go to court for that. The Law Society can, however, put you in touch with another solicitor who will take up your case for compensation. And they can provide you with details of the **Solicitors' Arbitration Scheme**, run by the Chartered Institute of Arbitrators. The solicitor must agree to this as well. This scheme will arbitrate between you and your solicitor and can make an award to you. It does, however, cost you £46 and, while this is refundable if the independent arbitrator agrees with you, you will have to pay another £46 if he agrees with your solicitor. That is why it is not used very much!

5 There may be another way you can get money back. If your solicitor has been **dishonest**, the Law Society has a compensation fund. This does not apply if you just got bad advice, but it is useful if a solicitor has disappeared with your money or is tried and disciplined by the disciplinary tribunal.

6 Finally, if you are dissatisfied with how the Solicitors' Complaints Bureau or the Law Society of Scotland or Northern Ireland has dealt with your complaint, you have one final chance of complaining: ask for your complaint to be referred to the **lay observer**. He can review how your complaint has been handled, and, if he is not satisfied, order it to be considered again.

But he has no power to offer you any compensation – you will have to take your solicitor to court for that. There are separate lay observers in England and Wales, Scotland, and Northern Ireland. (Under new legislation proposed as this book was going to press, some details of how you can complain about lawyers may change. For example, lay observers look likely to be replaced by a new legal ombudsman. Check with your CAB or the Law Society.)

Complaints about barristers

It is much more difficult to complain about barristers than solicitors, partly because they are instructed, not by you, but by solicitors and you pay the solicitor for the barrister's service. But mainly because barristers have a legal immunity against being sued for negligence in their work in court. If they fail to get you off a criminal charge, for example, you cannot sue them for poor advocacy. So, if you are thinking of trying to sue a barrister, forget it! If a barrister has, however, been off-hand or rude to you, or broken Bar Council rules like not seeing you in the presence of your solicitor, you could complain first to his Head of Chambers and then, if serious, to the **Bar Council**, which has the power to strike a barrister off. This rarely happens, however.

AND FINALLY . . .

At *You and Yours*, we do hear complaints from our listeners about lawyers and the legal system – although to be fair to our 'learned colleagues', they are way down the list in our league table of complaints, somewhere above ministers of religion but a long way below dodgy builders or incompetent travel companies.

Can we just re-emphasise, though, that if you have a serious complaint about lawyers or indeed any other professional, trader or bureaucrat, or indeed any type of complaint about a private organisation, company, trade body or government or council department, try and pursue it as far as it seems worth it to you. Everybody will benefit if you do. And if your complaint seems one that will affect other people as well, get in touch with us at the programme. Here's our address: *You and Yours*, BBC, Broadcasting House, Portland Place, London WIA IAA. Good luck!

ADDRESSES OF USEFUL ORGANISATIONS

Accident Legal Advice Service
(ALAS)
    c/o The Law Society
    Freepost
    London WC2A 1BR
    01-242 2430
Action for Victims of Medical
Negligence
    Bank Chambers
    1 London Road
    Forest Hill
    London SE23 3TP
    01-291 2793
Advertising Standards Authority
    Brook House
    2–16 Torrington Place
    London WC1E 7HN
    01-580 5555
Advisory Centre for Education
    18 Victoria Park Square
    London E2 9PB
    01-980 4596
Advisory Conciliation and
Arbitration Service (ACAS)
    27 Wilton Street
    London SW1X 7AZ
    01-210 3000
AFBD (Association of Futures,
Brokers and Dealers Ltd)
    Section B
    The 5th floor
    Plantation House
    5/8 Mincing Lane
    London EC3M 3DX

Age Concern
    Bernard Sunley House
    60 Pitcairn Road
    Mitcham, Surrey
    CR4 3LL
    01-640 5431
Air Transport Users Committee
    2nd Floor Kingsway House
    103 Kingsway
    London WC2B 6QX
    01-242 3882
Air Travel Organisers Licence
(ATOL)
    Room T506
    Civil Aviation Authority
    45–59 Kingsway
    London WC2B 6TE
    01-379 7311
ARCUK (Architects' Registration
Council of the UK)
    73 Hallam Street
    London W1N 6EE
    01-580 5861
Association of British Insurers
(ABI)
    Aldermary House
    10–15 Queen Street
    London EC4N 1TT
    01-248 4477
Association of British Travel
Agents (ABTA)
    55–57 Newman Street
    London W1P 4AH
    01-637 2444

Association of Mail Order
Publishers
    1 New Burlington Street
    London W1X 1FD
    01-437 0706
Association of Optometrists
    Bridge House
    233–234 Blackfriars Road
    London SE1 8NW
    01-261 9661

Banking Ombudsman
    Citadel House
    5–11 Fetter Lane
    London EC4A 1BR
    01-583 1395
BBC Radio Information Office
    Broadcasting House
    London W1A 1AA
    01-580 4468
BBC TV Information Officer
    Room 1260
    Television Centre
    Wood Lane
    London W12 8QT
    01-743 8000
BBC World Service Duty Office
    Bush House
    The Strand
    London WC2 B4PH
    01-240 3456
BIBA (British Insurance Brokers'
Association)
    14 Bevis Marks
    London EC3A 7NT
    01-623 9043
British Association of Removal
Firms
    3 Churchill Court
    58 Station Road
    North Harrow
    HA2 7SA
    01-861 3331
British Board of Film Censors
    3 Soho Square
    London W1V 5DE
    01-439 7961

British Direct Marketing
Association
    Grosvenor Gardens House
    35 Grosvenor Gardens
    London SW1W 0BS
    01-630 7322
British Medical Association
    BMA House
    Tavistock Square
    London WC1H 9JP
    01-387 4499
British Rail
    Euston House
    24 Eversholt Street
    London NW1 1DZ
    01-928 5151
British Standards Institution
    2 Park Street
    London W1A 2BS
    01-629 9000
British Veterinary Association
    7 Mansfield Street
    London W1M 0AT
    01-636 6541
Broadcasting Complaints
Commission
    Grosvenor Gardens House
    35–37 Grosvenor Gardens
    London SW1W 0BS
    01-276 0820
Broadcasting Standards Council
    5–8 The Sanctuary
    London SW1P 3JS
    01-233 0544
Building Employers Confederation
    82 New Cavendish Street
    London W1M 8AD
    01-580 5588
Building Society Ombudsman
    Grosvenor Gardens House
    35–37 Grosvenor Gardens
    London SW1X 7AW
    01-931 0044

Cable Authority
    Gillingham House
    38–44 Gillingham Street
    Lodon SW1V 1HU
    01-821 6161

Campaign for people with Mental
Handicaps
    12A Maddox Street
    London W1R 9PL
    01-491 0727
Central Office of Industrial
Tribunals
    2nd Floor
    Bedford House
    16/22 Bedford Street
    Belfast BT2 7NR
    0232 327666
Channel Four
    60 Charlotte Street
    London W1P 2AX
    01-631 4444
Chartered Institute of Arbitrators
    75 Cannon Street
    London EC4N 5BH
    01-236 8761
    SCOTLAND
    Chartered Institute of
    Arbitrators
    50 Wellington Street
    Glasgow G2 6HJ
    041-221 0210
Childrens Legal Centre
    20 Compton Terrace
    London N1 2UN
    01-359 9392
Citizens Advice Bureaux (National
Association)
    Myddelton House
    115–123 Pentonville Road
    London N1 9LZ
    01-833 2181
Civil Aviation Authority
    CAA House
    45–59 Kingsway
    London WC2B 6TE
    01-379 7311
College of Health
    18 Victoria Park Square
    London E2 9PF
    01-980 6263
Commission for Racial Equality
    Elliot House
    10–12 Allington Street
    London SW1E 5EH
    01-828 7022

Commissioner for Complaints
    33 Wellington Place
    Belfast BT1 6HN
    0232 233821
Companies Registration Office
    Companies House
    55–71 City Road
    London EC1Y 1BB
    01-253 9393
    (Personal callers only, no
    correspondence)
Consumers Association
    2 Marylebone Road
    London NW1 4DX
    01-486 5544
Council for Complementary and
Alternative Medicine
    Room 10
    Panther House
    38 Mount Pleasant
    London WC1X 0AP
    01-409 1440
Council for National Parks
    45 Shelton Street
    London WC2H 9HJ
    01-240 3603
Council for Professions
Supplementary to Medicine
    Park House
    184 Kennington Park Road
    London SE11 4BU
    01-582 0866
Council for the Protection of
Rural England
    Warwick House
    25 Buckingham Palace Road
    London SW1W 0PP
    01-235 9481

Data Protection Registrar (Office
of the)
    Springfield House
    Water Lane
    Wilmslow
    Cheshire SK9 5AX
    0625 535777

Department of Education and
Science
    Elizabeth House
    39 York Road
    London SE1 7PH
    01-934 9000
Department of Environment
    2 Marsham Street
    London SW1 3EB
    01-276 3000
Department of Health
    Alexander Fleming House
    Elephant and Castle
    London SE1 6BY
    01-407 5522
Department of Transport
    2 Marsham Street
    London SW1 3EB
    01-276 5170
Design Council
    28 Haymarket
    London SW1
    01-839 8000
Direct Selling Association
    44 Russell Square
    London WC1B 4JP
    01-580 8433
Disability Alliance
    25 Denmark Street
    London WC2H 8NJ
    01-240 0806
Domestic Coal Consumers'
Council
    Dean Bradley House
    52 Horseferry Road
    London SW1P 2AG
    01-233 0583

Electricity Consumers Council
    Brook House
    2–16 Torrington Place
    London WC1E 7LL
    01-636 5703

English National Board for
Nursing, Midwifery and Health
Visiting
    170 Tottenham Court Road
    London W1P 0HA
    01-388 3131
Equal Opportunities Commission
    Overseas House
    Quay Street
    Manchester M3 3HN
    061-833 9244
European Commission for Human
Rights
    BP431
    R6–67006
    Strasbourg CEDEX 614961
    France
    01033 88

FIMBRA (Financial
Intermediaries, Managers and
Brokers Regulatory Association)
    Marsh Wall
    London E14 9RW
    01-538 8860
Free Representation Unit (FRU)
    13 Gray's Inn Square
    London WC1R 5JP
    01-831 0692
Friends of the Earth
    26/28 Underwood Street
    London N1 7JQ
    01-490 1555

Gas Consumers Council
    Abford House
    6th Floor
    15 Wilton Road
    London SW1V 1LT
    01-931 9155
General Consumer Council for
Northern Ireland
    Elizabeth House
    116 Hollywood Road
    Belfast BT4 1NY
    0232 672488

General Dental Council
    37 Wimpole Street
    London W1M 8DQ
    01-486 2171
General Medical Council
    44 Hallam Street
    London W1N 6AE
    01-580 7642
General Optical Council
    41 Harley Street
    London W1N 2DJ
    01-580 3898
Glass and Glazing Federation
    44–48 Borough High Street
    London SE1 1XB
    01-403 7177

Health Service Commissioner for
England
    Church House
    Great Smith Street
    London SW1P 3BW
    01-276 2035
    WALES
    4th Floor
    Pearl Assurance House
    Greyfriars Road
    Cardiff CF1 3AG
    0222-394 621
    SCOTLAND
    2nd Floor
    11 Melville Crescent
    Edinburgh EH3 7LU
    031-225 7465
Health and Safety Executive
    Baynards House
    1–13 Chepstow Place
    Westbourne Grove
    London W2 4TF
    01-229 3456
Heating and Ventilating
Contractors Association
    Esca House
    34 Palace Court
    Bayswater
    London W2 4JG
    01-229 2488

Housing Corporation
    149 Tottenham Court Road
    London W1P 0BN
    01-387 9466

IBRC (Insurance Brokers'
Registration Council)
    15 St Helens Place
    London EC3A 6DS
    01-588 4387
IMRO (Investment Management
Regulatory Organisation)
    Centre Point
    103 New Oxford Street
    London WC1A 1PT
    01-379 0601
Independent Broadcasting
Authority (IBA)
    70 Brompton Road
    London SW3 1EY
    01-584 7011
Independent Committee for the
Supervision of Standards of
Telephone Information Services
(ICSTIS)
    67–69 Whitfield Street
    London W1P 5RL
    01-636 6577
Independent Schools Information
Service
    56 Buckingham Gate
    London SW1E 6RAG
    01-630 8793
Independent Schools Joint Council
    25 Victoria Street
    London SW1H 0EX
    01-222 4957
Industrial Assurance Commission
    15–17 Gt Marlborough St
    London W1V 2AX
    01-437 9992
Institute of Plumbing
    64 Station Lane
    Hornchurch
    Essex RM12 6NB
    04024 45199

Insurance Ombudsman Bureau
31 Southampton Row
London WC1B 5HJ
01-242 8613

Investors Compensation Scheme
3 Royal Exchange Buildings
London EC3V 3NL
01-283 2474

HM Land Registry
32 Lincoln's Inn Fields
London WC2A 3PH
01-405 3488

SCOTLAND
Registers of Scotland
Meadowbank House
153 London Road
Edinburgh
031-659 6111

NORTHERN IRELAND
Northern Ireland Land '
Registry
River House
48 High Street
Belfast BT1 2PT
0232 233552

Law Centres Federation
18–19 Warren Street
London W1P 5DB
01-387 8133

Law Society
113 Chancery Lane
London WC2A 1PL
01-242 1222

SCOTLAND
26–27 Drumsheugh Gardens
Edinburgh EH3 7YR
031-226 7411

NORTHERN IRELAND
98 Victoria Street
Belfast VT1 3JZ
0232 231614

LIBERTY (NCCL)
21 Tabard Street
London SE1 4DA
01-403 3888

Life Assurance and Unit Trust
Regulatory Organisation
(LAUTRO)
Centre Point
103 New Oxford Street
London WC1A 1QH
01-379 0444

Linked Life Assurance Group
12–16 Watling Street
London EC4M 9BB
01-236 0861

Liquefied Petroleum Gas Industry
Technical Association (LPGITA)
Alma House
Alma Road
Reigate
Surrey RH2 0AZ
0737 224700

Lloyds of London
1 Lime Street
London EC3M 7DQ
01-623 7100

Local Government Ombudsman
21 Queen Anne's Gate
London SW1H 9BU
01-222 5622

SCOTLAND
Princes House
5 Shandwick Place
Edinburgh EH2 4RG
031-229 4472

London Regional Passengers
Committee
8 Duncannon Street
London WC2N 4JF
01-839 1898

London Regional Transport
Golden Cross House
8 Duncannon Street
London WC2N 4JF
01-839 1898

Mail Order Traders Association
25 Castle Street
Liverpool L2 4TD
051-236 7581

Mencap
123 Golden Lane
London EC1Y 0RT
01-253 9433
MIND (National Association for Mental Health)
22 Harley Street
London W1N 2ED
01-637 0741
Ministry of Defence
Whitehall
London SW1A 2HB
01-218 9000
Motor Agents Association
201 Great Portland Street
London W1N 6AB
01-580 9122

National Association of Estate Agents
Arbon House
21 Jury Street
Warwick CV34 4EH
0926 496800
National Association of Funeral Directors
6/8 Warwick Road
Solihull
West Midlands B91 1AA
021-711 1343
National Consumer Council
20 Grosvenor Gardens
London SW1N 0DH
01-730 3469
National House Building Council
58 Portland Place
London W1N 4BU
01-637 1248
National Rivers Authority
30–34 Albert Embankment
London SE1 7TL
01-820 0101
National Union of Students
461 Holloway Road
London N7
01-272 8900

Nature Conservancy Council
Northminster House
Peterborough PE1 1UA
0733 40345
Noise Abatement Society
PO Box No. 8
Bromley
Kent BR2 0UH
01-460 3146
Northern Ireland Office
Stormont Castle
Belfast BT4 3ST
0232 63255
Northern Ireland Railways
Central Station
East Bridge Street
Belfast BT1 3PB
0232 235282
NSPCC (National Society for the Prevention of Cruelty to Children)
67 Saffron Hill
London EC1N 8RS
01-242 1626

Occupational Pensions Advisory Service
8A Bloomsbury Square
London WC1A 2LP
01-831 5511
OFFER
2nd Floor
Hagley House
Hagley Road
Birmingham B16 8QG
021-456 2100
Office of Arts and Libraries
1 Great George Street
London SW1
01-270 5866
Office of Fair Trading
Chancery House
53 Chancery Lane
London WC2A 1SP
01-242 2858

OFGAS
Southside
105 Victoria Street
London SW1E 6QT
01-828 0898

OFTEL
Atlantic House
Holborn Viaduct
London EC1N 2HQ
01-353 4020

OFWAT
13th–15th Floor
Centre City Tower
7 Hill Street
Birmingham B5 4UA
01-793 0115

Parliamentary Commissioner for
Administration
Church House
Great Smith Street
London SW1P 3BW
01-276 3000

Patients Association
18 Victoria Park Square
Bethnal Green
London E2 9PF
01-981 5676

Personal Insurance Arbitration
Scheme
725 Cannon Street
London EC4N 5BM
01-236 8761

Pharmaceutical Society of Great
Britain
1 Lambeth High Street
London SE1 7JN
01-735 9141

Police Complaints Authority
10 Great George Street
London SW1P 3AE
01-273 6450

POUNC (Post Office Users'
National Council)
Waterloo Bridge House
Waterloo Road
London SE1 8UA
01-928 9458

Press Council
1 Salisbury Square
London EC4Y 8AE
01-353 1248

Public Carriage Office
15 Penton Street
London N1
01-278 1744

Registered Nursing Homes
Association
Calthorpe House
Hagnay Road
Birmingham B16 8QY
021-454 2511

RIBA (Royal Institute of British
Architects)
66 Portland Place
London W1N 4AD
01-580 5533

SCOTLAND
3 Labell Place
Glasgow G3 7OH
041-332 7227

NORTHERN IRELAND
37 Malone Road
Belfast BT9 6RX
0232 381732

Royal College of Veterinary
Surgeons
32 Belgrave Square
London SW1X 8QP
01-235 4971

Royal Institution of Chartered
Surveyors
12 Great George Street
Parliament Square
London SW1P 3AD
01-222 7000

RSPCA (Royal Society for the
Prevention of Cruelty to Animals)
Causeway, Horsham
W. Sussex RH12 1HG
0403 64181

Scottish Child Law Centre
Melrose Street
Glasgow G4 9BJ
041-333 9305

Scottish Consumer Council
    314 St Vincent Street
    Glasgow G3 8XW
    041-226 5261
Scottish Office
    New St Andrew's House
    Edinburgh EH1 3TD
    031-556 8400
Securities and Investment Board
    3 Royal Exchange Buildings
    London EC3V 3NL
    01-283 2474
Sky Television
    6 Centaurs Business Park
    Grant Way
    Isleworth
    Middlesex PW7 5QD
    01-782 3000
Society of Motor Manufacturers
and Traders
    Forbes House
    Halkin Street
    London SW1X 7DS
    235 7000
Solicitors Complaints Bureau
    Portland House
    Stag Place
    London SW1 E5BL
    01-834 2288

Timeshare Developers Association
    23 Buckingham Gate
    London SW1E 6LB
    01-821 8845
Transport Users Consultative
Committee (Central Office)
    Golden Cross House
    Duncannon Street
    London WC2N 4JF
    01-839 7338
    SCOTLAND
    249 West George Street
    Glasgow G2 4QE
    041-221 7760

WALES
    St David's House
    East Wing
    Wood Street
    Cardiff CF1 1EF
    0222 227247
TSA
    Suite 1
    26 East Tenter Street
    London E1 8DN
    01-480 5428
TV-AM
    Hawley Crescent
    London NW1 8EF
    01-267 4300

Unit Trust Ombudsman
    31 Southampton Row
    London WC1B 5HJ
    01-242 8613

Welsh Office
    Crown Buildings
    Cathays Park
    Cardiff CF1 3NQ
    0222 825111

INDEX

C eleste's gloved hand traced a line down Emily's plump upper arm, coming dangerously close to the swell of her breast beneath her arm. "You must not be afraid, Emily. The Ecole will become like a good mother—strict, caring, loving. You're embarking on a journey—an odyssey you were meant to take. You must trust me....

"At the Ecole, we have a saying. 'A young woman's beauty can only be fully understood by another woman.'" Emily blushed furiously at her thoughts as Celeste continued. "We believe the love between two women is a perfectly woven fabric; seamless, warm, and wonderful to wear."

The
Transformation
of Emily

NIGEL McPARR

MASQUERADE BOOKS, INC.
801 SECOND AVENUE
NEW YORK, N.Y. 10017

First Masquerade Edition 1997
First Printing April 1997

ISBN 1-56333-519-0

First Top Shelf Edition 1997
ISBN 1-56333-898-X

Manufactured in the United States of America
Published by Masquerade Books, Inc.
801 Second Avenue
New York, N.Y. 10017

BOOK I
Lilac Row

CHAPTER 1

Driving rain sheeted off the dormer roof and windowsill, sending damp, cool air through the bedroom. It was a plain room, and small, with bare flooring, and curling Maxwell Parrish prints taped to the sloping walls. An ancient chest of drawers and a brass double bed took up most of the room. The first light of a gray, wet morning was coloring the humped bedclothes when Mrs. Bertram's wake-up call trumpeted up the back stairs.

"Five-thirty, girls!"

Emily Johnson stretched, and curled herself back into the warm hollow of her bed partner. Her partner's arm was wrapped tightly around her waist. All night that hand had teased her breasts until her nipples were

7

engorged and ached with latent arousal. She twisted her head. Susan was still asleep. Her long red hair flowed from her face onto her pillow like a bright splash of scarlet. Her breathing didn't change as Emily unwound her slender arm and sat up in bed.

"Kissable lips."

The phrase wouldn't go away, kept running through her head. Susan had said it the previous night before kissing her. Remembering made her want to blush. How much longer could she hold Susan away?

It was naughty and wrong, but…

She stared out the window into the pale, wet dawn. Six months ago no boy or girl had touched her. And now, Susan kissed her and played with her breasts. But she hadn't opened her thighs. Last night Susan's hands had wandered like trailing cobwebs over her upper arms and breasts. She could still savor the warm electricity of Susan's lips brushing hers. Feeling herself weaken, wanting Susan, she threw back the covers and slid out of bed. The worn pine flooring felt cool on her bare feet. Far below, sparrows and buntings chirped and fluttered for space at the feeders. A wet breeze lifted the curtains. The draft was like a wraith, wrapping the thin flannel of her nightgown around her calves.

She shook Susan. "Mrs. B. called. Get up."

"Mmm hmm." The slender shape beneath the covers didn't move.

"Okay, Susan. Don't say I didn't try to wake you."

She undid her long single braid and pulled a hairbrush through it in long vigorous strokes. The twisted light brown strands glistened in the early morning light, crackling in protest. She brushed her hair until the braid was transformed into a wavy, flowing sheen. Bending at the waist, she caught her hair in her hands and twisted it into a single strand as thick as her wrist, before coiling and pinning it on top of her head. She rummaged through her drawer for panties, nylons, and garters.

"Susan, please get out of bed."

"In a minute."

Looking, she saw Susan was deep in fantasy. Her knees were drawn up, her hands between her thighs.

Emily sighed. Susan wouldn't listen. She was going to get it again. The notion of Susan being belted sent an odd thrill through Emily. She put Susan's misfortune out of her mind and turned to the mirror. The pearl gray light played softly over her bare arms and breasts, painting her skin a translucent alabaster hue. Frank green-blue eyes stared back at her beneath brows she thought too thin. Her mouth was agreeably shaped. Her nose was slim and slightly turned up. At eighteen, her breasts were already too large. Unsupported, they were deep and full, smooth fleshed and tipped with dark elongated nipples. Her tiny waist made them seem even larger. Susan said they were perfect, but Emily thought she was beginning to look like Mrs. B., with a bosom that rose like a balloon from her lap when she sat. Her hips and bottom were fleshy and wide set, tapering into a slender waist and full thighs. Her sex lay half hidden beneath her panties and a wisp of reddish gold hair.

Emily looked at Susan.

"Susan! Please! Mrs. B...." Susan stirred and moaned, half opened her eyes. Emily pulled away the quilt.

Susan's eyes opened slowly. "Oh, go away!" Her arm flung out.

"I warned you."

"Mmm." Susan pulled the sheet over her head and drew up her knees again.

Emily put on a bra and the gray uniform prescribed by Madame Christiansen and Mrs. Bertram. Since coming to Christiansen House, Mrs. B. had fed her too well, adding inches to her bust and hips. The housekeeper had refused to alter her uniforms, saying it was an unneeded household expense. In the last month it had become a struggle to close her uniforms. The smooth, rounded outlines of her breasts and nipples showed clearly as she buttoned the gray cotton over them. In a few years, without the benefit of a sturdy bra, she would look like Mrs. Bertram, with great swollen breasts that compressed and settled comfortably into a grand monobosom at her waist.

She glanced at Susan. Susan's eyes were open, watching her. "You're fortunate," Susan said.

"Why? Because you're going to get it, and I'm not?"

"No, silly. Mrs. B. is on your side. She really likes you."

Emily blushed. "Susan, that's nonsense. Why—"

"I'll tell you why. When she retires, you will be the next housekeeper." Susan giggled. "Will *you* spank me when I'm a bad girl?"

"Susan, stop that! Please get out of bed. You're making me uncomfortable."

"I don't understand you. You kiss and pet, but you keep those damn legs locked. Come to Mama." Susan held out her arms.

Emily could have cried. "I can't. I must leave or risk the belt myself."

Susan lowered her arms. "Go downstairs," she said.

Knowing Susan was about to get the belt left Emily feeling sad and a tiny bit aroused. As she hurried down the back stairway to the kitchen, she could hear Mrs. Bertram coming up. The housekeeper was a big woman, thick-waisted and tall with thinning steely hair, fleshy arms, and an enormous bosom that completely filled her wash dresses and overflowed the waists of the aprons she wore. A stout leather belt, less its buckle, and stained dark by countless applications, hung from her waist. She wore a starched white apron, sensible brown oxfords, and thick-seamed support hose.

"Good morning, Emily. I'm pleased you had the sense to get out of bed."

"Mrs. B., S-Susan will be down in a moment."

"Yes, and cows fly." Mrs. Bertram smiled. "It's wash day. I've fixed you a good breakfast. You eat every bit of it."

"Mrs. B., I love your breakfasts, but—"

"I said eat everything, girl. You need to grow, flesh out. Become as big as me." She looked over Emily's shoulder. "So where is Susan?" The housekeeper's voice echoed loudly in the narrow confines of the hallway.

Emily shrugged nervously. They both heard Susan's

feet hit the floor. Mrs. Bertram looked up the stairwell. "She's up now, but it's too late. Darling Susan's going to get my belt." Mrs. Bertram lifted the long, thick strap of leather at her hip. With her other hand she squeezed Emily's upper arm. The back of her hand pressed hard into the bulging arc at the side of Emily's breast. "A lengthy belting and a day in the cellar stocks will teach her to get up."

Emily turned pale. "Do you really have to belt her? Isn't there anything else?"

"So we care about Susan. Do you play lovers up there like randy little bitches?"

"Mrs. Bertram," Emily whispered.

She had no idea the housekeeper might know what they were up to. The back of Mrs. Bertram's hand pressed hard into her breast. Mrs. Bertram's small mouth shaped itself into a lopsided smile. "Susan will get what she deserves. She's had this coming for weeks. Besides, she won't have to wash clothes today. That will be your gift to her. Go on down to the kitchen while I see to Susan."

"Yes, Ma'am."

"Dear girl," Mrs. Bertram whispered. She planted a wet kiss on Emily's forehead before hurrying up the stairs. Her belt was off her waist now, doubled and dangling loosely from her hand.

Flattered and puzzled by Mrs. Bertram's kiss, Emily continued down the stairs. As she stepped into the kitchen, she heard the first chilling smacks of Mrs. Bertram's belt and the cries of Susan's protests. The air was heavy with spices and the faint odor of Hilex bleach Mrs. B. used to clean her worktables until they shone bone white. Wooden racks held stacked copper kettles, utensils, spoons, and paddles. An ancient black stove stood along one wall. Its radiant heat warmed her back when she sat down at the table.

Mrs. B. had fixed a bowl of steaming hot oatmeal, most of it hidden beneath a glistening layer of brown sugar. Raisins dotted the rich mahogany surface. There were slabs of toast streaming with butter, a pitcher of whole cream, a pot of raspberry jam, and a mug of hot coffee arranged around the bowl. Emily's heart beat faster as she sat.

She tried to ignore Susan's cries and the rhythmic slap of the housekeeper's belt floating down the back staircase. It reminded her she'd better finish and start the laundry.

The phone rang as Emily finished her coffee. She wasn't supposed to answer the phone, but Madame Christiansen wasn't up yet, and Mrs. B. was still busy with Susan. She got up from her chair.

"Christiansen residence."

"And who might this be?" a voice asked softly.

Emily hesitated. "I'm not supposed to... Th-This is E-Emily Johnson, Ma'am. Madame Christiansen's maid. Mrs. B....I mean Mrs. Bertram is upstairs."

"And cannot come to the phone because she is leathering Susan with that belt of hers."

Emily let out her breath. "Ma'am, I cannot interrupt—"

"Emily, you tell Mrs. Bertram that Leah Talons is holding."

"Y-Yes, Ma'am," Emily stuttered, driven by the compelling tone of the woman's voice to lay down the phone and hurry up the back stairs. To her surprise, Mrs. Bertram stopped the punishment to take the call. She could hear the housekeeper clearly on the floor above.

"…Yes, Miss Talons,…I understand,… No. Of course not…wouldn't think of… Yes, Miss Talons."

Emily couldn't help listening to Mrs. Bertram. She was speaking loudly and sounded different. The mysterious female caller seemed to hold all the cards. It was a brief conversation. Susan's belting resumed with more intensity than before. Emily could only assume the caller must have upset Mrs. Bertram.

Moments later, Mrs. Bertram came down. Her belt, refastened to her waist, swished softly as she entered the kitchen. Susan was behind her, completely naked, her slender bottom and thighs crisscrossed with angry welts. She did not look at Emily.

Mrs. Bertram pointed to the wringer washer set in a corner of the kitchen. She spoke to Emily in rapid-fire fashion, her voice strained. "Strip the beds and start the wash. Your bed partner is going to the basement. Madame Christiansen is visiting friends. I'll see you in my bedroom at three." Before a stunned Emily could respond, Mrs. Bertram had taken Susan down the basement stairs.

CHAPTER 2

Emily could think of nothing but Susan—what she was about to go through—as she hurried up the stairs to strip beds. She vividly remembered right after coming here Mrs. Bertram taking her to the basement and proudly showing her what she called the perfect implement for correcting disobedient domestics. The gleaming, padded-leather horse with its ankle and wrist restraints had shocked and frightened Emily. She'd never been put over it, but once when stubborn Susan was to be punished, Mrs. Bertram had made Emily watch. She'd laid Susan head down over the horse and fastened her wrists and ankles to the corners of the stout wooden frame. It was a surreal scene—stark black and white. An overhead bulb cast stark shadows over Susan's snow white body. A long, slender paddle hung on the wall. Susan's bottom was poised and high, as if she were begging to be whipped like an animal. Emily was struck by the fact that Susan could do nothing except scream when Mrs. Bertram took down the paddle, lifted her arm, and began to dispense her maternal wrath.

Now as Emily carried an armload of sheets down the stairs to the laundry, she heard Susan's wails and knew the stern housekeeper was soundly spanking her only friend's flanks with the paddle she kept in the cellar. Susan would spend the day on the horse, alone with her pain and shame. Perhaps tonight she could make it up to Susan, maybe even spread her legs.

The workday passed too quickly. Laundry. Ironing. A quick, almost wordless lunch with Mrs. Bertram. Then more ironing until a quarter to three, she folded the last of the ironed sheets, carried them up to the second floor and Mrs. Bertram's bedroom.

The housekeeper's quarters were as plain as its occupant. A stout wooden bed, a dresser, a couple of chairs. A faded hooked rug covered a portion of the polished, planked floor. Unbleached muslin curtains hung at the windows. A framed photo of a bewhiskered black-suited minister hung on the wall. Emily had no idea who it was. He looked even more stern than Mrs. Bertram. Was it her father? As she went in, she heard Susan getting another belting. The leather smacks and shrieks floated faintly up the back staircase. Time weighed heavily. Finally, a little after three, the house-keeper came down the hallway, red-faced and breathing heavily. Her belt flopped over her hip as she came into the room. Emily could see the fresh wet stains on the leather. Mrs. Bertram's expression softened when she saw Emily.

"That one won't be disobedient again."

Emily stood up. "I-I'm sorry. I should have gotten her up."

"You're not her nurse." Mrs. Bertram looked intently at Emily. "That one's won you over."

Emily blushed. "M-Mrs. B-Bertram..." Tears filled her eyes.

"She's a contriving little bitch. I'll give her that." Mrs. Bertram sat down on the bed. "Come here." She slipped her arm around Emily, pulled her close. Her vast bosom overflowed her dress onto Emily's arm. Her voice was an unlikely whisper. "You're such a sweet girl, Emily. A delectable morsel. What a shame. I had wonderful plans for you. First, properly fatten you, and then when I retired, turn this house over to you."

Emily turned to stare at Mrs. Bertram. "I-I never thought—"

"No, I don't suppose you did. But it's all changed now." Mrs. Bertram looked away. "I must send you away. God knows I wouldn't, but I have no choice." She kissed Emily's forehead. Her voice became a soft moan. "Emily, I don't want to lose you. You are so unlike Susan and the others." Her arm tightened around Emily's waist.

Emily squirmed, tried to extricate herself. "Mrs. B-Bertram, p-please..."

"This is our last time together. I've been so good to you—fed you as if you were my own. Even spared you my belt and paddle." She wet-kissed Emily on her cheek.

Emily's voice was like a scared little child's. "You're frightening me. I-I don't understand…."

"Emily, don't be frightened." Mrs. Bertram's voice was as soft as smoke, liquid in her throat. Relax. Let your mama make you feel good." Her hand slipped over Emily's breast, cupping it gently.

Emily could not stop the shudder that ran through her. "I-I'm sorry, Mrs.—"

Mrs. Bertram's voice hardened. "I know what you and Susan do—kissing and playing in bed like a couple of sorority girls. My paddle got to the truth." She withdrew her arm. "Stand up."

"Mrs. B-Bertram—"

"Stop whining."

Emily was shaking as she got to her feet. Mrs. Bertram's hands rose to the front of her uniform. Emily bit her lip, stared at the wall behind Mrs. Bertram as Mrs. Bertram's fingers flew down the front of her uniform. "You have adorable titties, Emily. So large and full. Nearly as big as mine. Susan loves them. Did you know she plays with my titties? Can't get enough. She's a greedy little girl when I open my blouse."

Emily was shocked. How could Susan have betrayed her? She began to cry. Her tears dampened the front of her uniform and splashed softly on Mrs. Bertram's hands, which had reached her waist. Her uniform was open now from neck to waist. The taut white fabric of her bra pushed through the gap. Mrs. Bertram's mouth was slack and wet, her eyes hooded and filmy. Her thick lips curled into a half smile. Emily felt like fresh fruit in the older woman's hands. She drew in her breath. "I-I c-can't. I-I simply cannot—"

"Emily!"

Emily's body shook at the housekeeper's voice.

"You want this. You want this as much as me. I can see it in your eyes." Mrs. Bertram's voice was languorous and throaty again. She put her hands on Emily's waist. "It's your last chance, Emily. Don't refuse me."

Emily shuddered again but remained silent as the housekeeper pulled the cotton uniform down and over Emily's hips to expose her panties, garters, and black-seamed nylons. Emily was desperate to cover her bare thighs. She turned scarlet when Mrs. Bertram ran her hand over the straining fabric of her sturdy bra. The housekeeper teased her engorged nipples until they stung with pain and popped through the coarse fabric of her bra.

"Emily, take off your bra."

Emily felt herself slipping into a trance. She closed her eyes, and reached behind and unhooked her bra. The straps slid easily from the reddened grooves in her shoulders. In spite of her shame, it felt wonderful to free her swollen breasts. Her nipples responded in kind, hardening beneath Mrs. Bertram's gaze. And then Mrs. Bertram's fingers were pressing into her thighs, freeing her nylons from their garter clasps. Emily did not look down as her stockings were rolled down her legs. When the rolls reached her ankles, she stepped out of them without being told. She shivered and uttered a little sigh as Mrs. Bertram inserted her thumbs inside the waistband of her cotton panties and unceremoniously drew them down to her ankles. She stepped out of them as she had her stockings. She was completely naked now, standing before the housekeeper, ashamed and afraid, trembling with latent passion. Her hands were small white knots at her sides.

Mrs. Bertram gently lifted her breasts. No one but Susan had ever touched them before. "You shouldn't be ashamed of these. Leah—any woman—would treasure these. Along with the rest of you."

Emily's voice was a tremulous whisper. "Oh, Lord, please. I'm so embarrassed—"

"You mustn't be. Look at my titties. They turn men into drooling little boys. Women appreciate them. Actually, where you're ultimately going…well, never mind."

"I-I don't know what you mean." Emily convulsed into sobs.

"Poor baby." Mrs. Bertram wrapped her arms around Emily's hips, drawing Emily's thighs close to her face. Emily was mortified. She could feel Mrs. Bertram's breath painting her thighs. Not even Susan had ever been that close to her.

"Spread your legs," Mrs. Bertram whispered. "I want to have a better look at you."

The housekeeper's hands were gentle, unintrusive. Emily expected invasive, aggressive thrusts, but Mrs.

Bertram had become as soft as her breath. Emily shivered and weakened as Mrs. Bertram slipped a tentative finger between the velvety petals of her outer sex. Part of her wanted to resist, but Mrs. Bertram's aura was too powerful. She could only look down as the housekeeper slipped another finger into her and began to tease her clit erect. Her lips made little moaning sounds. Her legs nearly buckled beneath her as she thrust her hips into Mrs. Bertram. "Why you naughty, naughty girl."

"O-o-g-h, Mrs. B., please...don't...s-stop...." Emily's hips had turned to jelly. They moved sinuously, riding the housekeeper's squishy fingers.

Mrs. Bertram opened her dress. Her stark white breasts and dark slash of cleavage settled slowly, like a basket of fruit, into her lap. Her nipples were the size of baby fingers, as dark as molasses. They rose from chocolate-colored aureoles the size of tea saucers.

Emily was both stunned and aroused. A tiny part of her still fought against the maternal aura of Mrs. Bertram. Her conscience reminded her the woman was old enough to be her mother. But the housekeeper's fingers, her aura, her fleshy warmth were too persuasive. Mrs. Bertram was different now. She seemed sensitive and caring, instilling an insouciance in Emily she'd never known.

Without taking her eyes off Emily, the housekeeper stood up and unhooked the thick leather belt from her hip. She laid it out on the dresser next to an ebony hairbrush. When she turned back to Emily, she was unbuttoning the rest of her dress. Her elongated breasts turned to swaying water-filled balloons as she bent to remove the dress. She wore a plain garter belt and white panties. Emily could see the shadowy texture of her sex. Mrs. Bertram took Emily's hands in hers.

Fear, hot and jagged, stabbed through Emily. "M-Mrs. Bertram, I-I...don't know if—"

Mrs. Bertram pressed a finger to Emily's lips. "You mustn't be afraid. It's the way things were ordained. No young man will ever touch you." Emily tried to nod, but she was shaking so, her head simply bobbed. "Now turn yourself around. I want to have a look at your backside."

Emily moaned softly, "Oh, God, no. She's going to spank me." She turned her back and waited, stood perfectly still, while the housekeeper's hands squeezed and fondled her succulent bottomcheeks and inner arcs of her thighs.

"I've never seen a bottom as large and fleshy as yours. Yet so firm and plump. You also have an uncommon ability to absorb punishment. When did I last take my belt to you?"

Emily stared at the floor. "Monday last."

"Yes, I remember. You and Susan had not gotten in the last of the laundry before the rain started. I laid the two of you side by side over the hood of Henrietta's Rolls and gave you both a lesson in domestic deportment. Your backside is completely clear. Susan was marked and tender for days." Mrs. Bertram's hands spread Emily's fat bottomcheeks. "Bend over," she said. "Take hold of your ankles."

Emily looked into Mrs. Bertram's eyes. "P-Please," she whispered, "don't punish me."

"Don't be ridiculous. Now bend over."

As Emily leaned forward, the housekeeper's fingers slipped deep into the narrow valley between her buttocks. She couldn't see Mrs. Bertram, but she knew the housekeeper was also leaning forward. She could feel her moist breath on her bottom and thighs and was grateful she'd bathed that morning. Mrs. Bertram slowly spread her bottomcheeks until they hurt. The older woman suddenly dropped to her knees. She thrust her face hard between Emily's cheeks. A silent scream rose in Emily's throat. Her pulse quickened. She fought off the urge to flee as the housekeeper's lips pressed themselves to her glistening sex. She had never been so frightened—or aroused.

Susan had never kissed her there. Susan would have, but she'd never allowed her. Wasn't this different? She wasn't doing what *she* wanted to do. She was being forced to follow Mrs. Bertram's instructions. How could she be responsible for what might happen? She had to obey the housekeeper or be punished. A series of shivers ran though her as Mrs. Bertram's tongue flicked out to taste her. Her sense of helplessness ebbed and flowed, confounding her, leaving her weak and unsure.

"Emily, bring me my hairbrush."

For a second Emily couldn't move. She turned, looked over her shoulder at the housekeeper. Her eyes were dark and wide, imploring Mrs. Bertram not to spank her. What could she have possibly done to deserve the hairbrush? Tears splashed onto her bare breasts. Mrs. Bertram heaved a sigh as she rose to her feet. She put her arms around Emily, drew her head down onto her shoulder, and kissed her on the cheek. "I'm not going to spank you. I'm going to brush out that pretty chestnut hair." Emily looked up with an awkward expression and saw what looked like a tiny smile on Mrs. Bertram's lips.

Emily went to the dresser. The leather belt was close enough for her to touch. The hairbrush looked very old. It was made of ebony with yellowing bristles. Its polished back was large enough to cover half her seat. Seeing it brought to memory all the shrieks she'd heard as Mrs. Bertram smacked her maids over and over. Susan had been here numerous times. So had the others. She suddenly understood why she'd only gotten it once. Susan always said it was because Mrs. Bertram wanted to bed her. Emily never believed that until now.

She gave the hairbrush to Mrs. Bertram, who was watching her with such bright eyes and soft expression, Emily knew the older woman had nothing to hide. Her huge breasts were a trembling shelf of flesh, rolling and slapping as she moved. Seeing the housekeeper nearly naked diminished Emily's fright. Fear slunk off as she handed over the hairbrush.

"Sit."

Mrs. Bertram pointed to a tall-backed cane chair. The extended acorn tips of her breasts grazed Emily's shoulders and neck as she unbraided Emily's hair. The light brown strands untwisted themselves easily, spinning free in Mrs. Bertram's hands. Emily's hair turned to gold, streamed like molten metal over her shoulders, fell in shimmering waves to her thighs.

24

"Rapunzel, Rapunzel, let down your sweet hair," the housekeeper murmured as she picked up the ebony brush and began to draw it through Emily's hair. The strands crackled and curled, flowed like caramel through the stiff bristles. Emily's head went back with each stroke.

"Did your mother brush your hair when you were a girl?" Mrs. Bertram's voice was insinuating.

"Every day, Ma'am. Before I went to school."

"Did she spank you with her hairbrush when you were naughty?" Emily shook her head. Mama rarely spanked her. "What a pity. A mother who spoiled her daughter. I wouldn't have spoiled you." Emily remained silent, her head bobbing with the brush strokes. "You can't make up your mind. You don't know if you should give in to me. Perhaps you'd rather be with a young man. But you're becoming one of us. You cannot stop that." Mrs. Bertram's lips brushed the edge of Emily's neck, sending rippling shivers down her spine. "You are so luscious. I could eat you for dinner."

Emily stiffened and let out a sigh as the housekeeper's hands slipped to her waist. The hairbrush clattered on the floor. Mrs. Bertram was singing softly to herself. She lifted Emily's breasts, kissed her bare shoulders, the strands of her hair, the velvety hollow of her neck. Emily's nipples hardened and throbbed with pleasure. The room spun. She was helpless now as Mrs. Bertram lifted her from the chair and took her in her arms, crushing her to the pillowy warmth of her breasts and her open thighs. Emily barely felt Mrs. Bertram's lips covering her face and neck with wet kisses. As if in a dream, she was being drawn down onto the bed.

Mrs. Bertram is going to have her way.... And I don't care.... I want this to happen.

Imprisoned by the housekeeper's warmth, Emily leaped without thinking into a spinning dark void, an abyss of pleasure that was so attractive and frightening, she wondered if she would ever return. She was vaguely aware that Mrs. Bertram had removed her own panties and was settling herself on top of Emily, spreading Emily's thighs until they hurt. Mrs. Bertram's heavy thighs and breasts had pinned her to the bed. When Emily lifted her head, the housekeeper pushed her back onto the pillow.

"Lie still, Emily. Accept what I am about to do."

Mrs. Bertram rose on her arms. Her thighs and sex were still covering Emily. The housekeeper began to rotate her hips, grinding her sex into Emily's now-wet mound. The woman's great breasts swayed and clapped, molding themselves to one another. Pinned beneath the housekeeper, the warmth and pressure of the woman's body overwhelmed Emily. She knew she was safe and secure. Susan had never been like this. Shivers of naughty pleasure cascaded through her thighs. Suddenly, with no warning, the tiny voice within broke free. Her conscience began to scream and rail.

Emily, what are you doing?

Her eyes opened. A hard slap. And then she was buried in Mrs. Bertram's bosom.

She struggled to free herself. But Mrs. Bertram was

too much for her. The big woman's breasts covered her face. She could barely breathe. Mrs. Bertram was quick. Lifting herself, she pinned Emily's arms to her sides. In that instant Emily saw the real Mrs. Bertram; leering, determined, unyielding. Her head sank back onto the pillow. There was no escape—except a long punishment on the horse. Madame Christiansen was gone, and wouldn't have come to her aid if she were there. She was alone with this woman. In desperation, she clamped her eyes shut. "Emily." Mrs. Bertram's voice was silky with passion.

Emily slowly opened her eyes. Mrs. Bertram's breasts swayed inches from her face. Their skin was stretched so thin Emily could see the delicate tracery of blue-green beneath. Walnut nipples as erect and hard as stumps. Emily could see the pinpoint opening at the tip of each nipple.

Where Mrs. Bertram nursed her babies. Mama's flowing milk. Oh, Mama, help me….

The silent scream faded and died. Emily drifted, she no longer cared that her arms were trapped at her sides. Before her eyes blinked shut, Mrs. Bertram's vanilla breasts and chocolate nipples descended, parting Emily's reluctant lips. As she stared into the darkness, her mouth was stretched wide, eagerly filling, sucking at the sturdy nipple. She sucked as naturally, exuberantly, and unashamedly as a baby at Mrs. Bertram's breast. It was an exquisite, nurturing moment for Emily, the weight of Mrs. Bertram's breasts pushing her deep into the pillow.

"Poor baby," the housekeeper sighed. "How long

have you been wanting this? Mama's not a moment too soon."

Emily's cheeks were slick with saliva. She gurgled and moaned, lifted her hips into the soft fleshy warmth of the older woman's body. Mrs. Bertram's rhythmic breathing, the pounding pulse in her elongated nipple, merged with Emily's itching, screaming sex, reducing Emily to a clamoring, self-centered child.

What are you doing, Emily?

Not that damn voice again! She tried to smother it. Thrust its carcass deep into the darkest corner of her mind. Her hips thrust hard into Mrs. Bertram. Both of her hands could not surround one of the housekeeper's massive breasts. How could anyone so deliciously warm and this arousing be bad? Trapped beneath the mountain, a virtual prisoner of flesh, Emily's body went slack.

"I've been a bad girl," she said to herself, her mouth full of Mrs. Bertram's breast. "I should be put to bed. And in the morning, Mistress, you must spank me with that awful belt. And I promise I won't cry when you tie me to my bed." Her words sang, vibrated through her senses, arousing her even more. Pleasure radiated from her sex in great shimmering waves. Her whole body shook with submissive desire. Mrs. Bertram could devour her if she liked. And the tiny shrill voice of her conscience persisted.

Susan will know what you were doing while she was in the cellar.

Susan's slender face appeared behind her closed eyes. The vision of her friend shattered her reverie. She loved Susan. Susan was like a sister, tender and sweet. Could she do this to her? She envisioned poor Susan in the cellar. Saw her as clearly as if Susan were in the bedroom watching her. It was a cold dash of water. She sagged beneath the housekeeper's weight. The delicious moment was gone in an instant. It was over and would not return. Mrs. Bertram was deadweight now, an oppressive, smothering presence from which she had to be freed. She pushed up with her arms.

Mrs. Bertram opened her eyes. She looked down at Emily, saw the fear and anger in her eyes. "So," she hissed, as her eyes shaped themselves into narrow slits. "Is this is what it comes down to? I'll bet you wouldn't refuse Susan."

"S-Susan? No—" Emily blanched at the house-keeper's insight.

"Don't lie to me. I know all about you and Susan. She told me everything. Did you honestly think she wouldn't? I own that girl, body and soul. You prefer her to me, don't you?"

"Mrs. Bertram! I-I—"

The housekeeper's slap caught Emily off guard, spun her head sideways into the pillow. The speed at which Mrs. Bertram moved shocked Emily. The house-keeper was alongside the bed, closing her dress.

"Get out of that bed, Miss Emily Johnson. I'm going to teach you a lesson in submission to your superiors!"

Emily moaned as she slid off the bed, aware and ashamed now of her nakedness. Mrs. Bertram grabbed her arm and hurried her to the foot of the bed. She shoved Emily over the footboard, burying her head in the rumpled bedclothes.

"Spread those legs to the corners, and be quick."

Too frightened to refuse, Emily did as she was told. Mrs. Bertram quickly lashed her ankles to the bedposts. Tied to the bed, unable to move her lower body, Emily knew she must present a tantalizing picture to the housekeeper. Her sex had to be in full view. She blubbered softly into the sheets while Mrs. Bertram took her belt from the dresser and doubled its ends in her hand.

The first slap of the leather shocked Emily more than it hurt her. Mrs. Bertram had belted her before, but never with such intensity. She tried to think of Susan, alone in the cellar surrounded by bugs and mice. Nothing could be more horrible than that. But the stiff leather belt burned. She forgot about Susan. Her entire being focused on her backside. The belt sung, smacked loudly as it ridged and welted her bottomcheeks. She twisted, jerked, bucked her hips as the leather ate into her.

"O-o-g-h, p-please! A-a-g-h! N-o-o-o!"

"Will you stop that shrieking! And hold still. You deserve every lick." Mrs. Bertram's voice had the furious tone of a woman scorned. "I'll leather your fat bottom until my arm drops off." Had it not been for the soft knock on the door, Emily thought it might have come to that....

Mrs. Bertram ignoring the knock, kept on punishing Emily. The slapping leather sounds and Emily's screams bounced off the walls. Another series of knocks, louder this time. The belting stopped. An obviously irritated Mrs. Bertram growled, "You may come in, but it had better be important or you'll be next."

The door opened slowly. Emily heard her mistress step into the room. "It's only me, Florence. Please, don't let me stop you."

"I've already stopped, Henrietta. What is it you want?"

Henrietta Christiansen gently closed the door behind her. Emily couldn't see her mistress, but she could imagine the old woman in the same ill-fitting black dress, her plump cheeks hiding most of her small mouth while she fanned herself.

Madame's voice was strained. "I don't mean to interfere, Florence. You know I would never overstep your authority. May I come in?"

"If you must."

With no warning, Mrs. Bertram swung the wet belt again, smoothly, laying a swath across Emily's bottom. "F-Florence,…wh-why are you punishing Emily so severely?" Henrietta moved to the side of the bed. She smoothed the damp strands from Emily's face. The old woman looked like an angel of mercy. Emily tried to smile as the belt struck her seat again, never varying in its rhythm.

"Wh-Where is Susan?"

"In the cellar."

"Well, you know best, Florence." Henrietta stepped away from the bed.

31

Emily let out a long anguished shriek. Her mistress looked down at her with a pained expression, silently asking her why she had to start crying when *she* came into the room. Emily knew her mistress wouldn't stop the punishment. She closed her eyes, tried to ignore the searing pain in her bottom. It was the worst day of her life. Everyone had abandoned her.

"F-Florence,..."

Mrs. Bertram did not look up. "I'm busy, Henrietta."

"C-Can you tell me what she did?" Mrs. Bertram swung the belt, cracking a wide swath across Emily's thighs. "F-Florence, please...I-I must talk to you."

Mrs. Bertram continued, unyielding, not looking at Henrietta.

"Florence...Mrs. Bertram!" Henrietta's voice was a shriek.

Mrs. Bertram paused.

"Don't you think she's had enough?"

"She's earned it, Henrietta. And I do not like your interfering. She has to go."

"Why? She's been—"

"Henrietta, she cannot stay here."

"Wh-Where will I send her?"

"Call Harriet Godwin," Mrs. Bertram snapped as she knelt to unstrap Emily's ankles.

"I don't understand. You've always liked Emily."

"Henrietta, just call Harriet. The issue is closed." Mrs. Bertram left the bedroom.

"Oh, dear," Henrietta said as she helped Emily off

the bed. "I had no idea she was so upset. Can you tell me why?"

Emily straightened up and dressed quickly. She could not bring herself to tell Madame what had happened before the belting. "I-I don't know. P-Perhaps it has to do with S-Susan...."

Madame looked at her strangely, then smiled to herself. "I understand perfectly," she said, and caressed Emily's cheek. "Susan is a pretty young woman and not to be denied." Emily wanted to cry out of sheer embarrassment.

"Leave your panties off, dear, and come with me." Emily followed the plump old woman down the hall to her suite. She winced as her mistress gently applied a soothing balm to her bruised seat. "This must hurt. I'm amazed how well your backside has stood up to Mrs. Bertram's belt. She'd told me you could take a severe strapping. I had no idea." She turned Emily around to face her. Her watery blue eyes looked into Emily's. "Can you tell me?..."

Emily started to cry. "Madame, that woman is... she's mean...and spiteful. Susan is...my only friend."

"Do you love Susan more than...say...a sister?"

Emily blushed to her breasts.

Henrietta sighed. "Dear me. I feel badly for you. Mrs. Bertram can be difficult. And she's not going to change. There is nothing I can do now but call Madame Godwin. Perhaps she has a position open.

"I-It's...just not fair, Madame!"

Henrietta crossed Emily's lips with her finger. "Shush,

child. Don't say something you'll be sorry for." She planted a mushy kiss on Emily's forehead. "You go on up to your room and lie down while I call Harriet Godwin. Lord, I hope she has something for you...."

CHAPTER 3

Harriet Godwin was going over the week's menus with Mrs. Henley when the phone rang. The housekeeper took the call, handed the phone to Harriet.

"It's Henrietta."

"I'm not surprised," Harriet said as she took the phone.

"Harriet, is that you?"

"Of course, Henrietta. Who else do you think it would be?"

"I apologize for such short notice, but I have to see you…tomorrow. Would that be all right?"

Harriet glanced across the kitchen at Mrs. Henley. "Tomorrow morning. Eleven would be fine."

"Thank you so much. I'll see you then." Harriet could hear the old woman's relief filtering through the phone line.

Mrs. Henley lifted an eyebrow. "Another new girl?"

"Yes. Leah has put out a call. Can't say as I blame her for choosing this one."

Mrs. Henley watched Harriet hang up the phone. "Who is the girl?"

"Emily Johnson."

"You already knew, didn't you?"

"Leah called."

Mrs. Henley smiled, and began to peel potatoes for dinner....

When Harriet came down for dinner that evening, her husband Charles was waiting for her in the library. He whistled softly when she entered the room. She was a tall woman, full busted and trim through the waist. Her widening hips were the only sign she was approaching fifty. Her thick auburn hair was swept off her neck into a loosely layered pompadour. She wore quaint plump-heeled oxfords, seamed nylons, and a lavender silk blouse with a pleated front that did nothing to hide the generous motions of her unsupported breasts. The heavy fabric of her midcalf khaki skirt made rustling sounds as she crossed the carpet to kiss her husband.

"Wolf whistles will get you nowhere."

"I finished another ten pages. Pour you a drink?"

"I'd love one."

With his back to her, he said, "How do you manage

to look so pin neat and lovely at the same time? I can't decide if you're a Frederick's model or a country school-marm."

"Probably both," she said. "Depends on my mood."

He gave her a scotch, and lifted his glass. "To my lovely wife. May she continue to minister the fates of young women."

"To Leah Talons. She made everything possible."

"Always the realist. But she couldn't have done it without you."

"Flatterer."

"What have you heard from Leah?"

"She called to say she wants one of Henrietta Christiansen's girls. Henrietta's coming out tomorrow—to see if I'll take her off her hands. Would you mind staying in the cottage while she's here?"

Charles sipped his scotch. "No, Ma'am. Do I know this one?"

"You might have seen her in town. Name is Emily Johnson. Very pretty, makes Jane Russell look like a boy. Who's that stripper with the unbelievably huge bust-line?"

"Evelyn—Treasure Chest—West?"

Harriet nodded. "Emily is that big."

Charles whistled softly. "How does she get along with Florence Bertram?"

"You can imagine. Henrietta, herself, cannot contain Florence. Henrietta's such a twit. She has more money than God. Florence runs her home and orders Henrietta about as if she were a domestic. Henrietta didn't mention Emily, but it's why she called. I wish I'd been there when Leah called Florence. It must have really upset her."

"You've got that sad look in your eyes. Can you handle training and losing another girl to Leah?"

Harriet took a long sip of her scotch. "I'm not sure. Leah's a dear friend, and she pays well, but I know a few things about Emily. It will not be easy."

Charles kissed her lightly on her mouth. "You're too kind, too compassionate with those girls. You ought to turn into an ogre like Florence B."

"Dear Charles, always there for me. In spite of your predilection for young men, which I've learned to overlook, you are the only man I've ever loved. The perfect partner for our unique lifestyle."

He smiled broadly at her. "Why thank you, Mrs. Godwin. You are exactly what I need; a loving wife who puts me in my place. You should have been my mother."

"Sometimes, I think I am," she said softly.

He rose on his toes and smartly clicked the heels of his polished loafers. "Touché. Madame."

Were she not so caught up in Henrietta and Emily, she might have skipped dinner and taken Charles upstairs to her suite. He was tall, desperately slender. Weight lifting and obsessive daily workouts kept him trim and flat bellied—stronger than most men half his age. He had dark hair, combed straight back like a World War One aviator's. His eyes were an impersonal blue. Women were attracted to his stark white hands, long slender digits that tapered into perfectly groomed nails. He looked forty. In fact, he was over fifty. Years before, women would have called him a dandy.

Mrs. Henley stuck her head into the library. "Dinner is ready." Charles extended the crook of his arm, and led his wife into the adjoining dining room.

That night, for the first time in months, Harriet took Charles into her bed. They made love most of the night. Perhaps it was Charles's genuine concern or the spring storm that blew through that night, thrumming and cascading off the porch roof. Or perhaps it was knowing that Emily would be coming to Lilac Row. Whatever it was, Harriet was never more passionate and alive than she was that night. She drew Charles the boy from deep within himself, caning him so severely and long, she woke Mrs. Henley. Brimming with Harriet's maternal ardor, a chastised Charles slipped out of her bed at dawn and returned to his cottage.

Harriet ate a late breakfast alone in her suite. She did not come down until nearly eleven. Mrs. Henley was waiting when she came down the stairs. "Harriet, I've never seen you looking more invigorated." A smile flitted across her face.

"Let's leave it at that, Mrs. Henley. I'm going out to fetch the mail."

The storm had moved east, trailing a bright, rain-washed sky. Sprays of lavender and white lilac blooms edged the dark-plowed fields. The air was quiet, saturated with the smell of lilac, apple blossoms, and damp earth. It was Harriet's favorite time of the year. A time to foster, to plant in the soft, dark loam. Time, also, to prepare another young woman for the Ecole. The thought of preparing Emily and then losing her wrenched at her stomach.

She had seen Emily in town with Florence Bertram. Florence hovered over her like a mother hen, prodding and fussing, smacking the poor girl's backside right there in the market when Emily had stopped to look at something. Emily had been so frightened and afraid of making a mistake in front of the housekeeper, she'd not noticed Harriet watching her. Harriet was impressed by Emily's reticence, her willingness to obey her domestic mistress no matter how unfair the order might be. And mistress was the correct word. Even though Florence was only the housekeeper, it was she, not Henrietta Christiansen, who ran the Christiansen household.

Emily had a sweet expression, full lips, and dark hair that Florence kept in a single long braid. As she'd said to Charles, her most notable feature was her bustline. It was much too large for the rest of her. Even in those sturdy no-nonsense bras Florence made her wear, Emily still bounced and jiggled beneath her gray cotton uniforms. Heads turned as Florence hurried her young charge through the shopping crowds. She imagined dressing Emily in one of her maids' uniforms. The effect would be stunning. Emily would be ashamed, which would only enhance the uniform's effect. For the first time, she felt a trace of anger toward her old friend, Leah. It wasn't fair. She did the work, and Leah reaped the ultimate benefit.

The bright sunlight warmed her back as she opened

the mailbox and took out a thick bundle of mail. She heard the hum of an approaching car. Looking into the sun, she saw a rapidly approaching vehicle, a dark green Rolls Royce. Its brightly polished wheels glinted in the sunlight as it bounced and swayed over the rutted road. Henrietta Christiansen had arrived. The old woman drove with a vengeance, madly, completely out of control. The long shining car squeaked to a stop at the mailbox.

"Yoo-hoo! H-a-r-r-i-e-t."

Henrietta's seamed face emerged at the driver's window. A plump hand clutching a linen handkerchief mopped at her glistening brow. "How nice to see you again...I'm sorry to trouble you. I really should see you more often. I would, but it's so far from the city, and after that rain the roads are awful. Get in. I'll drive you to the house."

Harriet tried to look pleasant. "Henrietta, you look wonderfully healthy. It's been ages since I've seen you."

Henrietta's damp face gleamed wetly. Harriet could see the stress lines etched across the old woman's forehead. Florence Bertram's tirades would do that to any woman. "I need to talk, Harriet. About one of my girls, but I'll wait until we get to the house. I'm so parched, I can hardly speak."

Harriet slid into the car. It smelled of old leather, perspiration, dust, and Henrietta's cloying Tigress perfume. She gripped the open windowsill as the car rocketed the half mile to the house. Henrietta's black-gloved hands were laced around the wheel, nervously guiding the car. Neither woman spoke. Harriet concentrated on the cedar-lined curves of the approach to her home, hoping Henrietta wouldn't hit one of the old trees.

She helped Henrietta out of the car, guided her up the steps to the shaded portico. Henrietta was shorter than Harriet, heavyset with steel-gray hair cleanly parted and pulled back severely into a small bun at the back of her head. Her rouged and jowly cheeks nearly hid her small pursed mouth. In her too-tight black silk dress, pillbox hat, and netting over her face, she looked like she'd stepped out of a Dickens novel.

A maid in a cotton-ticking uniform was waiting for them in the soaring foyer. Her slender wrists were folded primly over her swollen belly. The white arcs of her milk-swollen breasts rose dramatically above the low round neckline of her uniform. Henrietta glanced at the girl and frowned indignantly. She unpinned her hat and handed it to the maid. The maid returned Henrietta's gaze with one of her own.

Henrietta looked at Harriet. "The last time…your maids weren't… When did you start dressing them… like that?"

Harriet smiled. "You haven't been here in some time. She turned to the maid. "Sarah, bring a pitcher of lemonade to the back porch. Mrs. Henley has fresh-squeezed in the icebox." Sarah nodded and left the foyer. "Don't you like my uniforms? I think they are appealing."

Henrietta gave Harriet a look that silently conveyed she didn't get it.

"We'll go out to the porch. It's cooler there."

Harriet led Henrietta through the house to a screened porch that ran across the back of the house. She sat Henrietta in one of the wicker chairs, then sat down opposite her. Henrietta began to fan herself vigorously. She reminded Harriet of a fat old bumblebee.

"You have a lovely place, Harriet."

"Charles brought me here as a bride. I will never leave Lilac Row."

"Is he still writing?"

"Every day. He's hard at work on a new detective story."

"I admire him. I could never write anything."

"How is Florence?"

"Florence is Florence. Been my housekeeper for thirty-five years. Sometimes, I wish... Oh, you know what I mean."

Harriet smiled, sympathetically. "Yes."

Henrietta leaned forward. "That maid's uniform; does Penny sew them?" Harriet nodded. "I thought so. She sews for me too—though nothing like that." Harriet waited patiently for Henrietta to get to Emily. "How did Sarah, umm...get...pregnant?"

Harriet stiffened at the question. "God only knows. She's a randy bitch. She won't be here much longer. I'm sending her away."

"I-I don't mean to pry, but what does Charles think?"

Harriet studied her old friend. "If you mean what does my husband think of Sarah's being pregnant, it's

43

none of your business. I will tell you he did not seduce her. Sarah may have tried to seduce him."

Henrietta blushed like a schoolgirl. "I'm sorry, Harriet. I-I only meant what does Charles think of your maids' new uniforms?"

"He enjoys décolleté as much as me."

"I-I s-suppose," Henrietta said weakly.

Harriet pitied Henrietta. The old woman was clearly uncomfortable. She had no idea that Harriet was willing to take Emily. Not being in Leah's inner circle, she did not understand Mrs. Bertram's tenuous connection with Leah. Henrietta would never know why Emily was being taken from her. Were she to find out, she might have a heart attack.

Henrietta glanced behind her. "H-Harriet..." She sucked in her breath. Her fingers fidgeted in her lap. "This is very difficult."

Harriet took Henrietta's hand. "Relax. Breathe slowly. Now tell me."

Henrietta's brows furrowed with determination. "You've always come straight to the point. I'll...I'll try to do the same." She paused to sip her lemonade. "Florence —Florence Bertram—my housekeeper...she runs my home for me, and very strictly. Better than I could do. She's not easy to live with."

"I understand she's handy with a belt."

Henrietta grimaced. "Other implements too."

Harriet spoke patiently. "What does this have to do with me?"

Henrietta wiped her brow. "Harriet I'm so ashamed

to beg. But I have no alternative. I must find another live-in position for Emily Johnson. Florence has developed an intense dislike for her. She says Emily must go. Emily's not a bad girl, rather docile, actually, and mild tempered." Henrietta looked hopefully at Harriet.

Harriet felt her heart begin to pound. "How old is she?"

"Eighteen. Harriet, I hate to impose...." She began to cry.

Harriet gave her a fresh handkerchief. "It's not the end of the world." Keeping her voice level, she said, "And it's not your fault."

Henrietta took a deep breath. "I just don't understand...what might have come between them...."

While Henrietta prattled on, Harriet's mind wandered to Leah Talons. Henrietta did not know of the eccentric heiress, nor the years Harriet had spent with Leah at Concord College. Leah was two years older than Harriet, vibrantly attractive and the most controlling person Harriet had ever met. She could still recall every word of that conversation they'd had the first time Leah had bedded her.

"What will you do after college?" Leah wanted to know.

"Marry Charles. Move to his place in the country."

"Does he love you?"

"Well enough."

"There might be complications," Leah warned.

"I know, but it's worth the risk. He knows about us." Harriet stiffened as Leah gently entered her. Leah's fingers were like smoke drifting deep inside her. "And what will you do?"

"I'm going to find a place, remote and beautiful, where I shall transform the finest compliant young women into jewels, lush objets d'art that women like you and I can appreciate."

"And the not-so-fine *jeune filles*, Mademoiselle?"

Leah kissed the slender tip of Harriet's nose. "Always the practical one. I shall turn them into domestic pieces, useful things to be scattered about one's home."

"And how on earth will you do this?"

Leah whispered in her ear.

Harriet shivered at the flagrant brilliance of Leah's plan. She shivered as Leah's fingers entered her and began to squish noisily. Moonlight poured through their window. "Sounds like a daunting task," she whispered, and turned herself over to Leah.

"With my money, dear Harriet, I think I can do it. Will you help me?"

Harriet bit her lip and nodded, as the first orgasm cascaded through her belly and thighs. Just thinking of Leah's plan sent the second wave of pleasure stabbing through her sex.

"I shall call it the Ecole...."

Leah had made good on her word. After graduation, she'd created her Ecole. Harriet had married Charles and moved to Lilac Row. Leah visited Harriet, bringing with her the first of her efforts. Harriet had been stunned at Leah's accomplishment. She was even stronger, and more beautiful, than Harriet had remembered. And then Leah had said, "Harriet, you said you wanted to help me. I'd like you to train the next young woman for the Ecole. A sort of undergrad course before they enter the rarefied atmosphere of The Ecole...."

Harriet had lost count of the young women she'd prepared and sent on to Leah. She'd become very attached to some of them. Would Emily be her last?...

Henrietta droned on in her high thin voice, "...grown so busty, she can barely close her uniforms. Florence makes her wear them. Says they aren't bad enough to cut up for rags. I wouldn't let Emily out of the house looking like that. She jiggles horribly. You can even see her nipples." Henrietta paused to catch her breath. Harriet couldn't help smiling at her discomfort.

Sarah came onto the porch with a pitcher of lemonade. When the maid bent to set her tray on the table, her heavy breasts plumped forward against the edge of her low neckline. Henrietta turned away, shocked, while Harriet studied her maid with more than casual interest. She derived a great deal of enjoyment from Sarah's soft contours, the way her breasts nearly fell out of her uniform.

Henrietta wiped her brow. She waited until Sarah left the porch. "She must be due any day—"

"You were talking about Emily."

"Well, as I said, Emily is a good girl. She can clean a house, do wash, whatever you ask. Until recently, Florence rarely took her belt to Emily."

Harriet nodded as if she knew none of this.

"You must know Florence has never been shy about

using her belt on her maids. After Farley passed away, God rest his soul, Florence assumed the role of domestic disciplinarian. Lord knows it had to be done. Florence can be very difficult. Nevertheless, my home would be a shambles without her." Henrietta's lower lip was trembling. "I'm so embarrassed," she whispered. "Asking for your help. I've made an awful mess of things."

Harriet lifted Henrietta's hand. The old woman's flesh was damp and cool. "So Florence has introduced Emily to her belt."

Henrietta nodded. "I could hardly believe my ears when she said Emily had to go. Just like that. No reason." She leaned back into her chair, her bosom rising and falling like a sea of black in her lap.

"Did it ever occur to you that Emily might need discipline? Perhaps Mrs. Bertram should have turned her over her knee and spanked her months ago."

"Oh no! She's too well behaved."

"I don't believe it."

"Am I being naive?"

"Dear Henrietta, at times you try a woman's soul. My girls frequently receive lengthy spankings. Mrs. Henley handles most of the discipline. I step in as needed. I am their sole mistress, their surrogate mother. I am responsible for their welfare and training. I train them to take their places as housekeepers and mistresses of their own homes. Mrs. Henley's paddle does not gather dust. And she keeps a fresh bar of soap in the kitchen for a sullen maid's mouth. Emily's training will start immediately. I assure you it will be rigorous."

"Oh dear." Henrietta dabbed at her eyes. "You're so strong."

"Emily will find that I'm a demanding mistress. I make no exceptions. If she violates my rules, she will be punished. I will feed and clothe her, care for her if she gets sick."

Harriet watched Henrietta fidget. "Then, you'll see her?"

Harriet nodded. "Send her out at four tomorrow."

Henrietta's face crinkled into a round smile. "Harriet, thank you so much. You are a saint."

And you're a fool, Harriet thought, as she kissed Henrietta's cheek.

She helped Harriet through the foyer and out to the portico. In twenty-four hours, Emily Johnson would be under her roof, safely away from that despot, Florence Bertram. She considered it a favorable sign that Emily had refused the woman's boorish advances. Another maid might have given in to avoid the housekeeper's belt. Emily would find a new life at Lilac Row—at least for the summer. When she was ready, she'd be sent to Leah. Already, Harriet realized, she was preparing herself to lose Emily. "How many more times must I do this?" She pushed the question into the back of her mind as she threw a wave to Henrietta and went into the kitchen to find Mrs. Henley.

CHAPTER 4

Charles Godwin sat in his dining room at Lilac Row, sipping Colombian coffee, engrossed in a copy of *Writers' Review*. Morning sunlight streamed into the elegant dining room, transforming the crystal chandelier above the table into an explosive array of shimmering colors. He had risen at dawn but would not eat breakfast until Harriet came down.

Mrs. Henley came into the dining room with a fresh pot of coffee. Charles glanced up at her sturdy face. "You're looking wonderful, Mrs. Henley. If I were thirty years younger, I swear I'd divorce Harriet and marry you."

Mrs. Henley blushed as she poured his coffee. "Get on with you," she said in a thick Belfast accent. "I've heard that blarney before. If you'll pardon my saying so,

I've read it too—in those books of yours. Still, I don't mind your saying it. Are you waiting for the missus?"

"Yes." He glanced at his watch. "Soon, I hope. I've things to do in the cottage."

Mrs. Henley gave him a dark look. "Ring me when you and the missus are ready," she said, and pushed through the swinging door that led to her kitchen.

Charles returned to his magazine. A few moments later, Harriet came down. She pecked her husband's cheek, poured herself a cup of coffee, and sat down across from him. She was dressed in fitted indigo denim jeans, a sleeveless cotton top beneath which she was not wearing a bra, and glossy, slender-heeled boots. The boots had been a gift from Leah Talons. Genuine Ecole boots, and hard to come by. Her hair was still sleep tousled. She'd given it a perfunctory brushing after her shower.

"Good morning, Charles. Sorry I'm so late. What a glorious morning. Did you sleep well?"

No response.

"Charles? You there, behind the magazine."

"Mmm hmm."

"Charles, please put down that magazine. I have something to tell you."

Charles sighed, and lowered the magazine. "Harriet Godwin, you look ravishing, and I love you dearly, but sometimes you do try a man's patience. I'm right in the middle of a great article. Can it wait until I finish?"

"No." She said, simply. "I want you to listen to me. If you don't, I'll spank you right here in the dining room. It would make Mrs. Henley's day."

Charles laid down his magazine. "Henrietta must have been here yesterday."

Harriet nodded smugly. "I thought you might like to know Emily Johnson is coming today for what she thinks will be an interview."

Charles looked evenly at her. "I'll be damned. Florence is going to give her up."

"Florence Bertram had no choice. She knows which side her bread is buttered on. She does what Leah tells her to do."

"When will Emily be here?"

"Henrietta's dropping her off at four. Where will you be when she arrives?"

"Not to worry. I have Alex in the cottage. I expect he'll remain there for the night."

Harriet gave him a droll smile. "I would certainly think so—and perhaps tomorrow night too."

Charles feigned offense. "Madame, you offend me." He smiled wickedly. "By the way, what was that dreadful ruckus last night? I should have slept out in the cottage. I swear I didn't sleep a wink—and I was at the other end of the house."

"Oh, Charles, I am sorry about that. I assumed you were in the cottage. Mrs. Henley and I were disciplining Annie. She's a spiteful little thing. Absolutely incorrigible. Needs her bottom tanned at least once a week. I want to send her to my sister, but Mrs. Henley insists the girl can be trained. She was thoroughly taken to task last night."

"So I heard. Would Frances take her?"

"In a minute. She's perpetually desperate to find

live-in laundry maids. I don't want to put Annie through that, but I may have to."

"I cannot imagine any girl wanting to live and work under her. And those bitchy daughters of hers." He lifted his eyebrows in mock fright.

"Charles, please. This is important to me. When I get a maid as stubborn as Annie Trivett, I won't have you joking about it. I ought to bundle you up and send you off to Leah. She'd shape you up."

"I'd be lucky to matriculate alive from The Ecole."

Harriet got up and kissed Charles's forehead and poured him another cup of coffee. "I told you I was sorry. We didn't mean to disturb you. You ought to let me or Mrs. Henley know when you're sleeping in the house."

Charles leaned across the table. "I will," he whispered, "except I don't want Mrs. Henley listening—"

"Charles!"

He laughed softly. "I couldn't resist a jab at our straitlaced Mrs. Henley." So Emily's really coming here." His eyes shone at the prospect.

"You don't have to look that pleased." Harriet paused to sip her coffee. "Henrietta Christiansen is an even bigger fool than I thought. She has no idea Leah is behind this. Florence Bertram will eat that woman alive."

"Well then, Madame, Henrietta's loss is our gain. To coin another cliché, we shall have to make hay while the sun shines."

"And so we shall," Harriet said, and poured a dollop of cream into a fresh cup of coffee.

Later that morning Harriet left the house for the

cottage. She didn't usually bother Charles during the day—especially when Alex was there. But there were estate papers he had to sign before she could put them in the mail. She'd forgotten to give them to him at breakfast. In any case, it was a lovely walk.

The path to the cottage stretched nearly a mile. It was covered with a cushiony layer of rotting leaves and evergreen needles. First-growth ash, maple, and pines wove a thick canopy over the path, blocking out most of the sun. On rainy days, the dense canopy kept the pathway reasonably dry. Alone with her thoughts, it was anything but quiet. She heard the random startled movements of nearly invisible animals scuttering through the underbrush. Does paused to stare with dark soft eyes before leaping away in bounding white-tailed flight. Overhead, the air was filled with the raucous clatter of birds and the wing-flapping-pumping sounds of geese as they struggled to become airborne. Harriet relished these solitary walks through the dappled, leaf green space. She loved the path, its smells, sounds, and sights. A devout pantheist, these solitary walks were a contemplative time where she was able to reestablish her sense of the omniscient female presence. Sun-drenched mornings, towering gray-green storm clouds, sullen rainy nights; all of these things were manifestations of the goddess she'd worshipped since college. The goddess controlled her life and compelled her to do what she and Leah did.

The cottage was nestled in a thick stand of towering cedars. Behind it was a small lake thick with bass and crappies. Mallards and Canadian geese populated its surface. The lake was Charles's retreat, where he went to fish and reinvigorate himself. The cottage was over a hundred years old, had been the original farmstead. Its walls were made of mortared fieldstone with tiny shuttered windows. The roof was slate, overgrown with a thick layer of green moss. There were two rooms inside. The living space contained a fireplace, desk, and other furniture. Charles slept in the other room. There was no electricity and no heat. A huge stone fireplace warmed the interior and was often lit during the summer months. Oil lamps provided a minimal measure of light, and an ambiance which Charles and Harriet liked.

The upper half of the Dutch door was open as Harriet approached the cottage. Her boots left deep heel imprints but made no noise on the soft path. She paused outside the door to peer into the semidark interior. She could see Charles. He was sitting at his desk, seemingly engrossed. His hands were uncharacteristically flat on the desk on either side of his typewriter. He was staring unmoving into the unlit fireplace. On a chair next to the desk a pair of wash-worn jeans, white cotton briefs, and a T-shirt were neatly folded. She could see a pair of slender feet and ankles protruding from beneath the desk opposite Charles.

Alex!

She'd forgotten Alex.

He was a brilliant young writer. A year ago, he'd sought out Charles and asked him to be his mentor. Charles had read some of his stuff and thought it had great potential. He enjoyed lecturing and teaching his craft. He also needed a new lover. "My God, I'll never see you," Harriet had said when Charles asked her if she objected to his taking in the young man. She wasn't surprised when Charles began to spend more and more time with Alex. It was not the first time he'd become infatuated with one of his young students. Still, she didn't mind. Charles loved her deeply, in his own way. Occasionally, he'd come to her, at her insistence, and prove he was not by any means completely gay.

Alex would not have been Harriet's choice for her husband. The young man was too smart-alecky and self-confident. He'd gone so far as to criticize Charles's writing. Charles hadn't the stomach or the heart to put the boy in his place. Probably for fear of losing him. Harriet felt nothing of the kind toward Alex. She would have liked nothing better than to give that tight ass of his a damn good leathering with the leather-covered paddle she kept in her armoire. That he would not forget.

From where she stood in the open doorway, she could almost hear Alex, literally sucking up to her husband. She could imagine his slender face, contorted now, his pretty lips wrapped tightly around Charles's erect cock, slurping, swallowing, controlling his mentor, sucking the very life from Charles. The act itself didn't bother her. She understood Charles's need to relieve his sexual stress in a way she could not. Another man could do that much better than she. Charles needed Alex to keep his creative juices sizzling. The young man added a certain something that women adored in Charles's books. The fact that Charles was predominantly gay meant little to Harriet. She herself had been a mostly nonpracticing lesbian since her college days.

She returned her attention to Charles. His head had begun to bob. She watched his lips part, heard him exhale sharply as he began to pump the first jets of his sperm into Alex's eager mouth. His chair squeaked in protest as he worked his hips forward in it, thrusting aggressively into Alex. For no reason, he looked up then with drooping eyes. She wondered if he could sense her presence, her maternal silhouette looming over him from the doorway. He threw her a boyish smile. Where did he get the stamina to come as long as he did? She waited a long time before he finally stopped shuddering. When he looked up again he wore a sheepish grin.

"I wasn't expecting you."

"Obviously." She unlatched the lower half of the door. It was cooler inside the cottage. The smell of damp stone pervaded her senses. She wrinkled her nose. "You really ought to light the fire, Charles. I don't know how you can work in here. It's so damp and moldy."

She threw a sheaf of papers onto his desk. "Sign these. I have to mail them today."

"Christ, Harriet. Now?"

She stood her ground. "Yes."

While he scribbled his name, she moved around the room, arranged his books and magazines, straightened a cocked lampshade, knocked down a spiderweb. While her back was turned, Alex extricated himself from beneath the desk and hurried into the bedroom. She caught a glimpse of his boyish white buttocks and pale thighs before he shut the bedroom door. Charles did not stand up. He would not reveal his sagging cock to his wife. They both knew his tryst with Alex would continue as soon as she left. He would wait a half hour, then bend Alex's slender body over his desk and bugger the boy silly. That vision pleased her. The young man deserved it, along with her paddle. She moved behind Charles and began to massage the rock-hard muscles of his shoulders and neck.

"Migod, you're tight this morning. Is this what Alex does to you? You really ought to—"

"Harriet, please don't start on Alex. He's too good. I won't let him go."

"He's taking advantage of you, love, milking you dry."

"He thinks he is. He's a smart-ass. The stuff of youth. Bullshit and nonsense. Keeps asking me if his stuff reads like Hemingway."

"Let me have him for a night. One night. I'll take my black leather paddle to his skinny butt. I'll show him the stuff of correction."

"I couldn't do that. Maybe later when I can't stand his brashness. But not now. And I doubt he'd go up to the house."

She pulled away. "Why?"

"You're not going to believe this, but he's afraid of you."

"He should be." She resumed massaging his neck. "How is the book doing?"

"I'm stuck. I need a reason for the killer to leave London. It can't be obvious or contrived."

"Lovers' quarrel?"

"Doesn't fit."

"Urgent business? A summons from his sick mother? You'll think of something. That's why you're the writer, and I'm the…housemother and domestic disciplinarian."

"And damn good on both counts, my love." He turned to look up at her. "If Alex weren't here and I didn't have to get this damn book done…

She rumpled his hair. "You'd what? Take me to bed? Ravish me? Not on your life, Mister. I take you to bed or not at all."

"Did you bring the mail?"

"Of course." Harriet dumped a packet on his desk. She bent to kiss his cheek.

"My baby's tired. He didn't sleep well last night." She bent to nuzzle the beginnings of a bald spot. "Charles, you're sweet, and a good husband." Her voice dropped to a whisper. "Now why don't you get rid of Alex? I'll find you a nice young man. You deserve someone better than him. I'll find a boy, train him myself to be properly submissive and obedient." She kissed the top of his head. "How does that sound?"

"You don't mean a word of that."

"No, but I know you like to hear it."

He reached up and took her arms in his hands, stroking their warmth. His touch was as gentle as a woman's. She pressed the plump contours of her breasts onto his shoulders and began to nibble at his ear.

"Harriet, will you and Mrs. Henley promise to be more civilized and whip your domestics during the day instead of at all hours of the night?"

She stroked his cheeks with the tips of her fingers, teasing his shaved cheeks into tiny ridges of sandpapery flesh. "Charles, Charles, you know as well as I there is something special about nighttime punishment. Sometimes a punishment simply can't wait. Annie threw another tantrum after dinner. I won't bore you with what she said, but suffice it to say she's not going anywhere for a few days."

"You're a mean, hard-hearted woman, Harriet. Are we closer to sending her to Frances?"

"Much. Not yet, but she is closer. I'm afraid she wouldn't last a minute the way she behaves now."

"Can you imagine what those girls would do to—?"

"Yes, and my sister as well." Harriet shook her head. "She'd better shape up…."

"Where did you leave her last night after you paddled her?"

"In the armoire. She won't move for another twenty-four hours."

"Then she didn't spend the night with you?"

She slapped his face lightly. "You silly, naughty boy! No, she didn't sleep with me. She spent the night sitting up straight."

Charles laughed softly. "Do you think it will do any good?"

"Of course," she said indignantly. "I wouldn't punish my girls if it didn't work."

"You are delightfully bristly when you get your dander up." He held the palm of her hand to his lips. His nibbling lips set her on edge, made her think of

Emily. "I am working too hard," he said. "I'm getting too old to be kept up by squalling young women."

Harriet shivered and pulled her hand away. "Be careful, my beloved boy. You're not too big to go over my knee. And I just might let Alex watch before I spank him too. You're both too full of yourselves, and you both need good spankings. Don't you tell me when I should correct my domestics."

"Can we talk about something else? This damn book—"

Harriet laughed. "Changing the subject won't make the book or Alex go away."

"I'm sorry. We need to get away. Just you and me."

"It won't be soon. I'm expecting Emily this afternoon at four."

"And I've got to get this book finished." He kissed her hand again. "Alex and I are going into town for a late dinner." He handed her the signed papers. "See you at breakfast tomorrow?"

"It's a date, and do bring Alex," she said petulantly. "I'll bring my leather paddle." She bent to kiss his cheek. "We'll get away soon. I promise. As soon as Emily is on her way."

As soon as she'd left, Alex appeared naked and erect in the bedroom doorway. "Come on in," he said with a smile. "I've a great new idea for a book."

CHAPTER 5

"You're going to enjoy Lilac Row. Madame Godwin is a wonderful woman. And ... wealthy, too. We've been friends, intimate friends, for years. You must be a good girl there. Don't embarrass me. Her housekeeper, Mrs. Henley, can be quite strict."

Emily wondered, but didn't ask, if Mrs. Henley wore a belt like Mrs. Bertram. "Will Madame provide uniforms?" she asked weakly.

"Yes, if you can call them that."

Henrietta didn't say much after that. Emily was quiet for the rest of the drive. Her falling from grace with Mrs. Bertram had happened so quickly. She had no idea what lay in store for her at Lilac Row.

The first glimpse of Harriet Godwin's estate nudged Emily up in her seat. The mansion sat on the crest of a hill, surrounded by meadows and fields that reminded her of groomed gardens. Beyond these, woodlands stretched to the horizon. Lilac bushes as big as trees were covered with lavender and cream blossoms. Their scent floated into the Rolls.

The house was much larger than Madame Christiansen's. It was made of rough-cut fieldstone and stood three stories high. Rows of white-framed windows gleamed in the slanting sunlight. Four-paned dormers punctuated the mansard roof. Emily hoped her room would look through one of the dormers. The view would be spectacular.

"Mind your manners, Emily," Henrietta whispered.

She took Emily's arm, clung to her, as they ascended the broad steps to the portico. An obviously pregnant young woman answered the bell. Emily couldn't help staring at the maid's deep cleavage and swollen belly. The maid returned Emily's look with one of clear disdain for Emily's dress.

The maid smiled broadly at Madame Christiansen. Emily wondered if there was something between them. The girl led them into the spacious, sun-filled parlor, then disappeared. Emily was so nervous she barely noticed the domestic's rebuke. She wanted to ask Madame Christiansen about the maid's uniform, but the old woman was too agitated. Henrietta touched her arm. She spoke in a whisper.

"I really should be going. It would be better if you

met Harriet—Madame Godwin—alone." She stood up, clutching her purse.

Emily went pale. "Madame, please. Don't leave me here. How do you know Madame Godwin will take me?"

Henrietta kissed Emily's cheek. "You needn't worry about that," she said, and left the parlor. At the front door she turned. "Good-bye. Make me proud, Emily." She opened the front door and disappeared into the bright rectangle of sunlight.

Emily heard the big Rolls rumble into life, the sounds of her first mistress inexorably slipping out of her life. She stared out the window as if she could will Madame Christiansen to return. Madame had said she wouldn't be abandoned, but she'd never felt more alone. She sat down on a posh, overstuffed black leather couch. The leather was pliant and warm, yielding comfortably. She folded her hands and glanced around the room. It was handsomely furnished with plump couches, chairs, and ottomans, all covered in rich shades of gleaming leather. The woodwork was glossy white, the walls pale green. Heavy drapes and Persian carpeting soaked up the sunlight pouring through the tall mullioned windows. The room had an air of intimacy and comfort that made Emily feel comfortable. Above the fireplace was a portrait of a woman in a white satin ball gown, arm-length gloves, and tiara. Madame Godwin? Slanting rays of sunlight struck the portrait, highlighting the woman's diamond tiara and the pearls encrusting her gown. Emily was transfixed. At first she did not notice the long, slender rod in the woman's hand, half hidden in the folds of her gown. Seeing the cane sent a chill through her. A small brass plate was fastened to the frame. She went to the painting.

LEAH TALONS—1949

Leah Talons must be a dear friend—and by the look of her, a wealthy woman—to have given Madame Godwin such a sumptuous gift. Emily looked away from the painting. A young woman stood in the foyer, smiling at her. Her uniform was the same as Sarah's—sturdy cotton ticking, long skirt, and daring neckline. The thought of wearing that uniform made Emily blush. The girl held a stack of folded sheets in her arms.

"You must be Emily Johnson. Did Sarah tell you Madame Godwin was busy upstairs?" Emily shook her head. "I suspect Madame won't be down for a bit."

Before Emily could think of a question, the maid was hurrying up the stairs. She tugged her gloves off, folded them neatly in her lap. Her dress was so tight she could hardly breathe. Moments passed. Then, a faint report floated into the parlor.

The sound drew Emily to the parlor doors where she heard several more sharp smacks as smooth and abrupt as a metered cadence. A thin, sweet voice shrieked in protest. Emily tried not to listen. The sounds made her edgy and afraid. Spankings were painful enough in the privacy of a bedroom without having to share a punishment with the entire household.

She returned to the sofa and shut her eyes. Her mind filled with Susan, their last night together....

A warm voice interrupted her vision, sweeping Susan's presence from her mind. "I'm downstairs, Sarah. You may bring in the tea."

Harriet Godwin came down the stairs and into the parlor, filling the room with her presence. Her clothing was as plain as the uniform of her maids'—pumps, seamed nylons, calf-length khaki skirt, and a navy sweater with a soft white blouse beneath. She was not wearing a bra. The plump outlines of her unsupported breasts rose and fell as she crossed the room. Her open expression, her carriage, overwhelmed Emily. She didn't know what to say to this captivating woman.

"Good afternoon, Emily. I'm Harriet Godwin. I've been expecting you. Has Madame Christiansen left?" Emily nodded slowly while Harriet stood over her. Harriet was holding a bristled brush in her hand. The way she held it reminded Emily of the woman in the painting. "Emily, you must learn to stand when I come into the room." Emily nervously uncrossed her ankles and glanced down at her bosom before getting to her feet. Harriet's frank gaze terrified her. She wanted desperately to say she hadn't picked this horrible-fitting dress.

Harriet glanced at her brush. "I'm frightening you, aren't I?" She smiled warmly. "On the other hand, had you not turned pale, I might have sent you away. You may put the brush on the table in the foyer. I'm sure you know what it's for."

Emily turned scarlet. "I can guess, Madame Godwin," she responded as she laid the brush on the table.

Harriet gestured to a pair of chairs flanking the fireplace. "Please, come and sit down with me." Harriet took the chair opposite Emily. She leaned across the space between them and smoothed Emily's hair. "That stray lock has been bothering me. You're frightened. You're quite safe here. No more Mrs. Bertram."

Emily worked up a small smile. "Thank you, Ma'am."

Sarah entered the room with a tray of tea and petit fours. Emily rose from her chair to help Sarah. "Sit down," Harriet ordered. "Sarah will serve." Emily couldn't help staring at Sarah's blatant display of breast as she lowered the tray. "Sarah, I want you to look in on Annie. Mrs. Henley will be up later."

Sarah nodded to her mistress. Emily caught the flash of defiance in Sarah's eyes and the petulant set of her mouth. Harriet dismissed the girl with a wave. "Emily, pour my tea. Two lumps and a dollop of cream." Harriet crossed her nyloned legs and folded her hands in her lap. "The last time I saw you, Mrs. Bertram had your hair in a long braid. Who did it today?"

"Madame Christiansen. She thought a French roll would be appropriate."

"You needn't blush, Emily. You're a very pretty girl. Madame Christiansen says you're sweet and unassuming. I look for those virtues in my maids."

"Madame, I-I—"

Harriet held up her hand. "There'll be no more

young men, strutting like banty roosters, breeding anything in skirts. You saw what they did to Sarah. It won't happen again on this premises. Thank heavens, Mrs. Bertram kept you on a short leash. And I will do the same. You belong to us, Emily." Harriet paused. She took Emily's hand in hers, ignored Emily's hot blush. "All that lovely hair. It should be twisted into a soft chignon. A touch of brow accent and eyeliner will set off the luminosity of those eyes. Lipstick, too, for that sweet mouth. Did you know your dimples deepen when you smile."

"Madame, p-please..."

"I know all about Mrs. Bertram's doings. She promised you her position, treated you to rich meals. It was her way of controlling and ultimately seducing you. Your unwillingness drove you away. And a good thing, too. Had you stayed, she would have won. Florence Bertram is a very determined woman."

"I-I just could not give in to that awful woman. Sh-She whipped me with her belt...."

"You may be leathered here. It depends on you. Madame Christiansen says Mrs. Bertram added inches to your bustline. In some circles, such a deep bosom might be considered gauche. Here—"

"Madame," Emily protested, "I'm only eighteen. Already my bosom has begun to descend. Bras don't fit."

Harriet glanced at the clothes brush in the foyer. "Another outburst like that, young lady, and I'll take you upstairs. Your shape is fine. If I didn't think so, you wouldn't be here."

Emily's eyes dropped to the taut bodice of her dress.

The dress had a modest neckline, but when she sat, the tight silk bodice squeezed the sumptuous arcs of her breasts, forcing them to rise above the neckline. The outlines of her nipples popped like acorns through her bra and thin silk dress. To alleviate the problem, Madame Christiansen had wrapped a scarf around Emily's neck, stuffing its ends deep into her cleavage. Harriet ignored Emily's discomfort, did nothing to reassure her.

Emily could feel Madame's gaze focusing on her bosom. Harriet gestured with her teacup. "I'm going to remove that silly scarf. Henrietta's idea, I'm sure. It doesn't hide a thing, and it doesn't become you. A bosom like yours shouldn't be hidden under a scarf."

Emily lifted her hands, then dropped them back in her lap. "M-Madame…" Her voice faded.

"Henrietta Christiansen hasn't an ounce of style or fashion in her entire body."

Harriet rose from her chair. She moved behind Emily. Her long fingers were suddenly in Emily's hair, primping, smoothing, tucking strands into place. Her touch was light and sure. Emily was helpless to stop her new mistress. She let out a tiny gasp, but otherwise sat quietly as Harriet slipped the scarf from her neck.

Emily didn't dare look down at herself while Harriet returned to her chair. She tried to make herself smaller, but the loose neckline was open now to Harriet's gaze, effectively pinning Emily to her seat.

"Pour me another tea, Emily. Two lumps, one dollop, and stir it."

As Emily leaned forward to pick up the heavy teapot she knew she was trapped. Her exposed breasts sagged forward against her dress to offer her new mistress a tantalizing view of her breasts. And there was nothing she could do but pour the tea and fix the cup per Harriet's instructions. Her hand shook as she tonged two lumps of sugar into Harriet's steaming cup.

"Leah's going to love you," Harriet murmured. "I do envy her."

Emily glanced up. "Madame?" She spoke in a half whisper. "I want you to know I didn't…Madame Christiansen made me wear this. I-I would have worn one of my old uniforms—"

Harriet raised her hand. "You have the most stunning décolleté. I think I shall go one step further. I have a wonderful seamstress. What would she do with that bosom?"

"M-Madame Godwin, I-I don't feel good…."

"Look straight at me, Emily."

Emily reluctantly lifted her eyes.

"There is nothing wrong with you. You're frightened and ashamed. I want you to tell me how it felt when that woman touched you…there."

"M-Madame!"

"Tell me honestly, or I'll take you straight over my knee." Harriet glanced at the clothes brush in the foyer. Emily followed her glance and turned bright crimson. She dropped her eyes to the tips of her shoes.

"Do you mean Mrs. Bertram?" Her voice was so low Harriet had to lean forward to hear her.

"Of course. Have you done it with other others as well?"

Emily's fingers twisted into a white mass of flesh. She did not answer the question.

"I see. Your silence speaks volumes. You liked it, didn't you? For one moment you let yourself let go. Reveled in another woman's touch, her lips, her hands in your hair and on your breasts." Emily buried her face in her hands. "I thought so."

Emily sobbed into her hands. Her body shook as she tried to breathe.

"Emily! Must I use my brush? Cross your hands in your lap. I won't remind you again."

Emily reluctantly lowered her hands. Her cheeks were rosy now, her eyes red and tearstained. "I can see it in your face. You've done it with other girls."

Emily spoke in quick gasps as her awful hidden weakness overcame her, spilled out of her in a torrent. "Y-Y-Yes, M-Madame. S-Susan, Mrs....Mrs. Bertram... made me f-feel...I-I don't know wh-what."

Harriet's voice was low now, soft and motherly. "Did Mrs. Bertram take you to bed?"

"Y-Yes," Emily whispered. She couldn't stop the shaking in her hands. "Sh-She k-kissed me and laid on me. Finally, I-I just couldn't..."

"Couldn't what?"

"I-I couldn't l-let her make love to me."

"Were you afraid of her?"

"Y-Yes."

"That I can understand. I've seen her leather belt. I

won't deny she's a formidable woman. What did she do to you when you refused her?"

"Sh-She t-tied me to her bed…a-and strapped m-me. Sh-She told me she'd h-have Madame Christiansen send me away." Emily paused to catch her breath. "Madame Christiansen said I-I'd have to come h-here."

"Is that what you want?"

Emily nodded. "I-I'd much rather be here." Her eyes were soft and wet, wide with shame, her mouth a pouty slash.

"Madame Christiansen says you can serve at table, make a proper bed, and not disturb my husband in the process."

"Madame. I'm not well educated, but I can serve and make a bed. I'll work very hard." Her voice fell. "I'm sorry about the trouble with…Mrs. Bertram."

"Did Madame Christiansen tell you of my own proclivity for domestic discipline?"

"Pro…Pro…clivity?"

Harriet smiled. "My penchant to punish lazy and disobedient maids. You probably overheard me upstairs with Annie?" Emily nodded. "My husband is a writer, spends most of his time in a cottage away from the house. You are not to go there unless I'm with you. You are not to speak to him."

Emily tried to smile. "Madame. I will do my best…. Must I wear a uniform like the others?"

"You'll get used to it."

Emily stared down at her lap as she spoke. "I would like to live and work here, Ma'am."

"I thought as much. Come with me."

Emily followed Harriet through the foyer and up the wide staircase to a gleaming hallway that ran from the front to the back of the house. Closed doors lined the long hallway. Harriet opened one of the doors and led Emily inside. She shut the door behind them.

Late afternoon sunlight filtered through the cedars and maples outside the bedroom windows, painting the walls with trembling patterns of pale leafy light. A crystal lamp beside the bed blazed with iridescent shimmerings. The walls were covered with a textured raspberry wallpaper that rose to a cove off-white ceiling. A Persian carpet covered much of the polished maple flooring. A canopied bed, cherry bureau, and writing desk were arranged against the walls. A tall handpainted armoire stood next to the bed. On the nightstand was a black-and-white photo of a younger Madame Godwin and another woman who Emily thought must be the one in the painting downstairs. They were in shorts, on the beach, holding hands, smiling intently at each other. Emily thought it a wonderfully intimate photo of two girls who were either very good friends or in love.

A breeze played through the open windows, shaping the curtains, bringing lilac scent and announcing imminent rain. Emily shivered, hugged her bare arms. The room was warm and intimate. She spoke softly. "I'm glad now Mrs. Bertram sent me here. I've never seen such a lovely home."

"I'm glad you like it. This is where I come to get away; to read and think." She smiled ruefully. "And sometimes it is where I bring my naughty maids to correct them in private. You are never to enter this room without my permission. Do so, and you will pay dearly for your indiscretion."

"Yes, Ma'am," Emily whispered, and wondered if the sounds she'd heard had come from this room.

Harriet sat down on an upholstered black leather chair. She snapped her fingers, impatiently. "Come here. Lift your skirt."

Confused, Emily stared at her new mistress. She'd never seen an upholstered chair so plump and over-stuffed. It was positively huge. "M-Madame! Lift my skirt—why?"

"I want to have a look at your bottom. Madame Christiansen tells me Mrs. Bertram rarely took her belt to your backside. Considering Florence Bertram's penchant for strapping her girls, I find that most unusual."

Emily blushed. "M-Madame, p-please…I-I…"

"Come here and lift your dress. Or I'll do it for you!"

"Please, Madame Godwin, I-I c-can't," she sighed as she moved closer.

"Of course you can. Turn around. Face the window."

Emily reluctantly turned, lifting her silk skirt, bunching it at her waist. Unable to move, stiff with fear, she chewed on her lip and stared out the window. Harriet's fingers were at her garters. The dark-seamed nylons whispered over her thighs as Harriet freed the stockings and slid them down her legs. The older woman's fingertips were like electric probes, sending tiny shocks through her as the polished tips of her nails pressed deep into Emily's flesh. After Emily stepped out of her stockings, Madame removed her garter belt. Desire shimmered deep in her sex. Would Madame take down her panties too? As if in answer, Harriet returned to her waist to slither the taut band of her panties down and over her hips. Emily shook with fright and shame. What was Madame going to do with her?

"Don't lower that skirt, Miss."

Emily stiffened, crushed the dark green silk fabric in her hands. Tears of shame flooded her eyes. The breeze chilled and teased her bare thighs and bottom, raising and stiffening the silky patch hiding her sex. She felt like a little girl being examined by her mother. Harriet's closeness frightened and titillated her. The woman's hands, her scent, her warm breath on Emily's thighs aroused her. Harriet's ministrations, the way she touched her, made Emily want to respond. Her eyes drifted closed as she slipped away.

She imagined Susan next to her. Susan's hands between her thighs, teasing her clit erect until she silently screamed. Suddenly, the air was filled with Mrs. Bertram. Her thick belt lay in a smooth arc over her hip. The housekeeper's huge bosom rolled and slapped as she unhooked her belt and doubled it over. Susan screamed as the great belt hissed and flew. And Emily realized she wanted to be punished—smothered between those great white breasts, imprisoned forever in Mrs. Bertram's flesh. The realization made her weak with guilt and anger.

How could she ever want that? It wasn't so!

Harriet's voice broke into the swirling conflict. Her hands were on Emily's seat now, squeezing and pinching. "You have a delightful bottom. Mrs. Henley might not agree. She thinks too much fat protects a girl when she needs to be punished. I disagree. I love the shape of a full bottom. The reversal of line from thigh to waist. A well-fleshed derrière can be punished with longer and more severe whippings, and heavier implements. My housekeeper and I do agree on the need for frequent discipline to keep a young woman's mind clear and her bottom toned and firm. Had you not come here, I suspect you would have grown soft and flabby in both body and spirit."

Emily looked down into her mistress's eyes. Harriet's gaze was frank and honest. The woman was not joking. "Oh, M-Madame," she sobbed, horrified at the prospect of being punished. At the Christiansen home, months had gone by without getting Mrs. Bertram's belt or paddle. "I-I don't think I-I could."

"Nonsense! It's the best thing for you, and you'll learn deportment." Harriet pinched her bottom, sending a ripple of pain into her thigh. "Your backside still has the faint marks of Mrs. Bertram's belt. She's done a thorough job." Emily shivered as Harriet's finger traced a hard ridge into the deep cleft between her cheeks. "Covered you from waist to upper thighs. There isn't a single mark that won't be gone in another day or two."

Emily couldn't tell if Madame was praising or criti-cizing Mrs. Bertram's punishment skills. Her voice was expressionless. She swung Emily around by her hips to face her. "You'll be spanked before bed tonight. After-wards, Mrs. Henley will give you a soothing hygienic enema."

Emily's eyes widened. "Wh-Why? I-I haven't done—"

Harriet's expression hardened. "It's how I start all my new girls. Not a word from you. I know better than you when you need to be disciplined."

Emily looked down at her new mistress. Harriet's look assured her there would be no arguing the point of her punishment. The color rose hotly in her face. A damp breeze freshened and chilled her thighs and still-sore seat.

"I'm sorry, Madame. I'll do as you say."

"That's better."

"B-But, I-I can't—"

"Never mind." Emily shivered as Harriet's hand slipped between the plump walls of her thighs.

Emily lifted her eyes to the darkening window frame, watched the curtains flap tautly in the stiff breeze. Peals of thunder growled across the fields. A silvery shaft of lightening exploded, splitting the amber-blue horizon. Her fear dissipated with the steady breeze blowing through the room. Madame Godwin's hand lay on her sex, not enticing, but warm and oddly maternal. She was growing weak. Could no longer think. A lump swelled in her throat. She looked down at her new mistress.

"Was I wrong to refuse Mrs. B-Bertram?"

"Only you can answer that, Emily." Harriet rose from her chair. "Stay right where you are," she said softly. She went to the armoire. Its doors creaked as she swung them open. Emily's body jerked when she saw the armoire's contents.

CHAPTER 6

The pungent smell of old cedar from the armoire gently anointed Emily's nostrils. Inside the armoire, nearly hidden among Harriet's dresses and skirts, a young woman dressed only in panties sat on a low wooden stool. Her legs were folded in front of her. Her arms were crossed and bound behind her. A wide leather belt was fastened over her mouth and around her head. The gag was tightly buckled, forcing her mouth open. A bit of saliva had run from her mouth, staining the curling leather. She looked up at Emily with such a startled expression, it took Emily a moment to realize the girl's expression was frozen on her face by the belt between her lips. She was a pretty little thing with bright blue eyes and white-blond hair in a pair of pigtails pleated so tightly they stuck out from the sides of her head. Her breasts were small and round, standing defiantly upright and away from her ribs. She reminded Emily of a carnival Kewpie doll.

Emily forgot she was still holding up her dress. She watched spellbound as Harriet assisted the slender young woman off her stool and onto her feet. As the girl stepped out of the armoire, Emily saw her arms were pinned high on her back and bound tightly with a nylon stocking. Her pantied seat and exposed thighs were swollen and marked. She'd been well spanked. Emily wondered if Harriet had used her clothes brush. A slender cane, razor strop and belt, leather-covered paddle, and short black whip with dangling knotted thongs were arrayed on the inside walls of the armoire doors. While Emily stared, Harriet acted as if it were perfectly natural to have such an array of punishment implements mounted on her closet doors. Harriet led the girl into the middle of the room where she ran her hand over the blushing girl's swollen bottomcheeks. Harriet looked straight at Emily, who was so shocked she couldn't speak. Mrs. Bertram had never tied, much less confined her girls in a closet.

"Emily, this is Annie Trivett. I want you to see for yourself what happens when you disobey me or Mrs. Henley. Annie was disrespectful to me. Did Henrietta tell you what I do with sassy mouths?"

Emily shook her head. She watched Annie's eyes widen with fright.

"I wash them out with Ivory soap. Put your panties

back on, Emily. Go down to the kitchen. Ask Mrs. Henley for a fresh cake of Ivory." She paused. "And while you're there, ask her to pick out a nice green switch." Emily looked uncertain. "You needn't worry. She's expecting you."

The kitchen door squeaked as Emily nervously pushed her way into Mrs. Henley's kitchen. It was a large room, brightly lit with gleaming white walls. The air was heavy with the rich aromas of baking pies. Hank Snow's twangy voice sang from a scratchy radio high on a shelf. At first she didn't see Mrs. Henley. The house-keeper was at the butcher block behind a suspended line of kettles and long-handled implements. Her hands were buried in a mound of bread dough, her arms white to the elbows. She summoned Emily in a thick brogue.

"Come here, lass. Let me have a look at you."

Emily moved slowly along the line of kettles, suddenly afraid. Would Mrs. Henley be any different than Mrs. Bertram? She felt terribly silly in Henrietta's cast-off silk dress, but Mrs. Henley didn't seem to notice. She studied Emily with liquid brown eyes that registered no emotion, or any trace of surprise at the way she was dressed. Her dark hair was thinning and turning gray. She wore it knotted in a small bun beneath a blue bandanna. A full white apron was tied around her waist. After what seemed an eternity, she returned her attention to the mass of springy dough.

"So, you're Emily Johnson, come to us all the way from the city—and Florence Bertram."

"Yes, Ma'am."

"I wouldn't deny you're a buxom thing. Florence has fed you well. The missus—Madame Godwin—and I, we know of Mrs. Bertram's doings. It wasn't your fault. You needn't worry about such nonsense here." Emily looked down at the taut arc of her breasts. She could feel Mrs. Henley's gaze sweeping over her. "Your bosom—and bottom too—are much too big for the rest of you. There's no excuse for growing so big. You ought to be ashamed. You must have eaten everything Mrs. Bertram put in front of you."

Emily flushed. Mrs. Bertram had wanted her plump. She'd made her eat everything on her plate. Hoping to change the subject from her to Annie, she said, "Madame Godwin sent me down for a cake of Ivory soap,…a-and a switch."

Mrs. Henley sunk her hands into the bread. "I suspected as much. You'll have to wait until I set this dough to rising."

Emily glanced around the kitchen. A row of pies was cooling near an open window. She wondered how Mrs. Henley could bake pies, make bread, and fix meals in a kitchen that looked like it was never used. The long maple tabletops were scrubbed white and smelled faintly of bleach. Gleaming copper pots bubbled on a black iron range. The range's nickel trim shone in the overhead lights. Freshly pressed curtains hung at each window. Mrs. Bertram's kitchen had *never* been this clean. She watched the housekeeper expertly drop the mass of dough into a greased pan, cover it with a towel, and set it on the end of the stove to rise.

Mrs. Henley wiped her hands on her apron. "I'll show you my pantry," she said with a smile.

Emily followed the older woman into a small room off the kitchen. Deep tilt-out flour and sugar bins were built into the lower walls. Rows of cans, spices, and dry goods lined the shelves above. A stone crock in the corner held a sheaf of pale green willow limbs. The limbs were stripped of their shoots. All were cut to the same three-foot length. Willow switches. Mrs. Henley drew one from the crock. It gleamed wetly in her hand. She took an unopened bar of Ivory soap from a stack on the shelf.

"You take these up to the missus. Use the back stairs. I'll be up shortly with the other things."

Emily had no idea what the housekeeper meant by "the other things." She heard the first flurry of raindrops pelting the kitchen windows as she hurried up the unpainted back staircase. The stairs were unlit and airless, smelled of furniture polish and cleaning rags. She felt better when she reached the second floor and Madame Godwin's bedroom.

Handing over the switch and soap cake to Madame Godwin was a terribly awkward moment. She felt as if she herself were sentencing Annie to a punishment. Harriet laid the switch on the table and unwrapped the soap.

"Emily, you may remove Annie's gag."

Embarrassed at being made an active party to Annie's punishment, Emily gently unbuckled the leather belt over Annie's mouth. Annie gave her an imploring look that said they both knew Annie was about to get her mouth thoroughly soaped. Rain tapped at the windowpanes. Annie's bare arms and breasts were covered with goose bumps. Her doll-like nipples were stiff and erect. Harriet turned to her victim.

"I warned you, didn't I? The next time you threw a tantrum, I said you'd spend the night here."

Annie bowed her head. "Yes, Madame, you warned me. And I promised to obey."

Emily caught the faint trace of resentment in Annie's voice.

"Where you're going, broken promises won't be necessary. You're one step closer to being sent to my sister. She has a special place reserved for you in that laundry of hers. Her daughters would just love to put you to work."

Annie looked terrified. She squealed like an animal as Harriet spun her around. A cry caught in her throat as Harriet planted her oxblood pump on a small stool and slung Annie head down over her extended khaki-skirted thigh. She began to spank Annie, briskly, right on her panties with her cupped palm. She covered Annie's small bottomcheeks with angry red splotches that showed through the thin cotton.

Mrs. Henley came into the room. She watched with a broad smile. "So, Annie's getting her seat warmed. Not that she deserves it!" She waited while Harriet finished the spanking. "She's earned a good mouth washing." She picked up the cake of soap. "With your permission, Madame, I'll just get on with it."

Harriet nodded her assent.

The housekeeper stood a head taller than Annie. Her mouth pursed in concentration as she took Annie's slender neck in the crook of her arm and drew her head into the side of her breast, locking the young woman securely in her grip. Half of Annie's face disappeared into the bulging side of Mrs. Henley's bosom. Annie's tears flowed, dripping onto the bar of soap inches from her lips.

Rain laced the windowpanes. Annie moaned expectantly. "Open up, Miss!" Mrs. Henley's command cut through the rainy silence.

Emily watched Annie clamp her mouth shut. She herself would never have done that, especially if someone as formidable as Mrs. Henley had her in her grip. The housekeeper touched the rectangular soap cake to Annie's lips. Annie gulped, but did not open her mouth.

"Open wide, you stubborn girl!" Mrs. Henley's voice was as hard as brass.

Harriet took her cane from the armoire. She caught the waistband of Annie's panties and tore them away. With her other hand she laid a whistling cane stroke across Annie's bare seat. Annie gasped. As her mouth flew open, Mrs. Henley thrust the soap cake into her yawning mouth. Annie bit down hard, arresting the soap's progress.

"Open wider!"

Harriet caned Annie twice in rapid succession. Annie screamed, allowing Mrs. Henley to shove most of the long white bar into her mouth. Annie's lips were stretched taut now, clamped tightly around the soap.

"We'll wait now for the soap to soften." Mrs. Henley looked up at Emily. "Better she than you, you're thinkin'."

Emily didn't answer. Mrs. Henley was right. Annie was completely still now. Mrs. Henley waited until milk white flecks had begun to dribble from the corners of Annie's mouth. She tightened her grip and began to work the softened cake of soap in and out; twisting and thrusting until shining bubbles and lather seeped from Annie's mouth. Annie tried to bury her face in Mrs. Henley's breast, but Mrs. Henley had seen this tactic before. She repositioned Annie's head, gripping her tighter than before. The housekeeper's expression didn't change as she pumped and spun the soap cake between Annie's glistening lips.

"You'll be happy to know, Annie girl, this won't be necessary where you're going."

Annie gasped out something.

"You won't sass Madame's sister! No, you won't be talking at all. You'll be up to your waist in wet wash." Mrs. Henley looked at Harriet. "How much longer?"

"I'm waiting for card club," Harriet said. "I'm going to surprise Frances."

"God help Frances Cartwright with this one," Mrs. Henley said, and worked the soap deeper, nearly gagging Annie.

Harriet smiled. "I doubt my sister needs God's help. She and those five daughters of hers are quite capable. I think she's had enough, Mrs. Henley."

Mrs. Henley took Annie into the adjoining bathroom.

Emily could see Annie bent over the sink, desperately spitting and rinsing the soap from her mouth. Mrs. Henley stood over Annie, holding her forehead and wiping her mouth clean with her apron. The staccato sounds of the rain drummed on the metal porch roof. Wet gray twilight had settled over the estate. Emily glanced at the unused switch on the table.

Harriet picked up the switch. "Now it's your turn, Emily."

Emily was stunned. She began to cry. "M-Madame, I-I don't understand—"

Mrs. Henley's voice drifted down the hall. "Did you hear that, Annie? Emily thought you were going to be switched."

"B-But why?"

"I don't have to explain, Emily. I don't even need a reason to punish you. Now, take down your panties." Frightened by the abrupt change in Harriet's demeanor, Emily slid her panties down just as Mrs. Henley returned Annie to the bedroom. After the housekeeper had seated Annie and closed the armoire doors, Harriet pointed to the bed.

"Lift your dress and lie crosswise on the bed."

Panties around her knees, Emily shuffled awkwardly across the room. Before she had reached the bed, Harriet struck, whipping her across her breasts, nearly cutting through the thin silk. A thin red line grew across her cleavage. The second stroke lashed her nipples, stinging her breasts. She shrieked, tried to cover herself. Her panties fell to the floor.

"How dare you drop your panties on the floor? I did not tell you to do that!"

The switch sung, adding several new scarlet trails across her breasts and the backs of her hands.

"M-Madame,…please, wh-what have I d-done?"

Punctuating each word with a stroke of the switch, Harriet said "In…this…house…I…expect…absolute…unconditional…obedience—nothing…less!" Harriet pointed her switch at the bed. "Now, lift your skirt and get on that bed!" Harriet's face was stretched tight with anger.

Emily gathered up her skirt and stretched her upper body over the bed. Her feet remained on the floor. Cool, damp air flowed across her bare seat. Her breasts hurt terribly, but at least they were safe now, beneath her. Why was this happening? It wasn't fair! Madame Godwin was treating her like an unruly child.

"Extend your arms," Harriet ordered. Mrs. Henley took hold of her hands, drew her arms out and alongside her head. "Don't move, Emily. Do not move a muscle."

"Yes, Ma'am," Emily whispered, and turned her face into the bedclothes.

She heard the switch sigh, whistling softly, as it cut a swath through the air. She barely had time to catch her breath before the supple willow branch tore into her seat, striping her bottom. She jumped in pain, but Mrs. Henley held her tightly. After that first stroke, she concentrated on the sound of the rain peppering the windowsills. The switch burned. It was so exquisitely intense, at first she did not feel its full import. She winced and received a stern warning.

"Hold still," the housekeeper ordered. "Madame will double your punishment."

The switch stung her upper thighs. Each fresh stroke felt like nettles pressing into her flesh. She shrieked in pain. She did not realize her pitiful cries fueled Harriet's need to punish, arousing her and driving her to whip Emily even harder. Harriet continued to apply the switch until Emily's cheeks were bright and swollen and her hair had come completely undone. Golden brown, glimmering in the pale glow of the bed lamp, the last strands of Emily's hair loosened and fanned themselves onto the bed and Mrs. Henley's strong hands.

Emily was quiet now, weeping softly into the coverlet. Her hair lay in a shimmering maple-hued pool. Her bottomcheeks hurt so much she'd lost most of the sensation of pain. She no longer heard the rain. She'd withdrawn deep into herself, where she did not hear or feel anything but Mrs. Henley's hands and her own measured breathing. When Harriet finally dropped the shredded switch to the floor, Emily realized how much her arms ached from being held so tightly by Mrs. Henley.

Harriet leaned over the bed and smoothed the hair away from her wet cheeks. She helped Emily to her feet. "Let me show you something," she said, and led Emily to a full-length mirror. She lifted Emily's skirt and turned her back to the mirror. Emily gasped at the sight of her striped and swollen seat, crisscrossed with dark pink ridges and welts.

"Your transformation has just begun," Harriet whispered in her ear. "Now, pull up your panties. We're going up to your room."

Emily hurriedly obliged, being careful with the waistband over her flaming seat. The armoire was silent, but Emily knew Annie had heard everything and was probably gloating over her punishment. She followed Harriet up to the third floor and down a dark hallway to a row of rooms at the back of the house. Mrs. Henley had not come with them. Harriet opened one of the doors.

"This is your bedroom."

It was a tiny room with sloping papered walls. There was just enough room for a single bed, a chest of drawers, and a table next to the bed. A single small window set into a steeply pitched dormer opened up to the back of the house. Rain pattered on the open sill and slate roofing. Harriet lit the hurricane lamp on the nightstand. Its fanned wick threw a pale cone of flickering amber light over the quilt covering the bed. Harriet went to the bed and turned the covers down. The soft light made her look completely different. She was soft and lovely. Her eyes danced with excitement. Emily felt safe here. The room was small but clean and comfortable. She hoped she wouldn't share it with another maid. In spite of the pain in her seat and thighs, a thin shiver of expectation ran down her spine.

Harriet took the pillow from the bed. "Remove your dress. Get into bed," she said. "Lay facedown, legs spread to the corners. And no tears. You're a big girl. I'm sure you've had enemas before."

Emily looked at her new mistress as she stepped out of her dress. "I-I don't understand, M-Madame. Why?..."

Harriet's voice was so soft it blended with the falling rain. "Must I whip you again?"

Emily shook her head and got into bed. Harriet spread her legs wide to the corners of the bed. Emily knew about enemas. She'd had them before. They were never pleasant.

"The first thing we're doing tomorrow is buying you new panties. These have been washed so many times they're practically transparent. Your bottom shows right through."

Harriet ran the tip of her nail along the inside of Emily's thigh, leaving a thin pink ridge. Emily shivered and moaned, but did not move. When Harriet dropped her whole hand between Emily's damp thighs, Emily mewed in response. She couldn't help the motions of her hips, lifting automatically to the press of Harriet's fingers. It was a magic moment for both women. A current flowed between them, cementing the bond between dominant and submissive.

Mrs. Henley's footsteps in the hallway shattered the rainy silence. Emily's blissful mood disappeared. Harriet was working Emily's panties down when Mrs. Henley came into the room with the folded rubber sheet and bulging enema bag. The bag was wet and glistening. Its contents filled the room with a medicinal odor that reminded Emily of her mother.

She lay waiting while the two women moved into

position on either side of the bed. Mrs. Henley handed the rubber sheet to Harriet. Harriet shook out its folds with an efficient snap. "Lift your hips, Emily." She spread the sheet, smoothing it beneath Emily's hips. Mrs. Henley held the enema bag while Harriet bent over Emily, her face an expressionless mask. Her nursing technique was familiar and sure. She deftly spread Emily's reddened cheeks, causing Emily to cry with pain. Her hands fluttered at her sides.

"Fold your arms beneath your head and keep them there," Harriet ordered.

Emily could sense her mistress's attention was completely focused on her bottom. Her tiny treasure lay hidden between her bottomcheeks, small and puckered like a pink rosebud. Harriet took the black lubricated tip from Mrs. Henley. In one easy motion, she inserted the semihard tip into Emily's bottom. Emily's hips jumped as the bulbous tip entered her. Harriet released Emily's cheeks then, to let Emily's quivering bottom trap the soft tubing, squeeze it firmly in place. Harriet straightened up. She laid her hand on Emily's hip.

"Relax, Emily."

Emily's voice rose from the bed in a muted sob. "M-Madame,…I-I d-don't like th-this—"

Harriet sounded like an exasperated mother. "Be still, or I'll take you over my knee and really give you something to cry about." She slapped Emily's bottom. Ripples spread from the slap over Emily's goose-bump-covered skin. "Mrs. Henley, are you ready?"

"Whenever you are."

"Now."

Mrs. Henley lifted the bulging bag to her shoulder and opened the tiny valve. Both women watched Emily shudder, moan, clench her buttocks. The rubber tube jerked to life, quivering like a snake as the warm soapy solution surged from the bag and flowed into her. Harriet kept her open palm on Emily's seat. For Emily it was a measure of restraint and maternal reassurance. Her hips undulated as the bag slowly emptied. The exquisite pressure lifted her hips off the bed. She could feel Harriet pressing her musculature, rigid and taut, back onto the bed.

"M-Madame,…I-It's too m-much. I-I can't hold it!"

Harriet's voice was soothing and warm. "Nonsense. You're talking like a little girl who's never had an enema. You're halfway through."

Emily moaned loudly, terrified she would have an accident before she could get to the bathroom.

"You may cross your legs."

Emily noisily sucked in her breath and drew her legs together. Every fiber of her being was concentrated on not losing control. The rubber sheet had warmed to her body and was moist against her bare thighs. A thick fold of the rubber worked its way between the lips of her sex. Every time she moved, the soft rubber teased her, made her forget where she was. She began to think if there wasn't so much pressure in her backside, she might learn to enjoy the pleasant surge in her thighs and belly. In a final attempt to block out the relentless pressure that continued to build inside her, she squeezed her eyes shut. She was about to scream for release when Harriet withdrew the nozzle and helped her off the bed. She scuttled to the bathroom down the hall, managing to get there without an accident. When she returned, Mrs. Henley was gone. Harriet was sitting on the bed.

"You've done well. Now take a hot bath and go straight to bed. I'll send Sarah up with a dinner tray. Tomorrow, my seamstress, Miss Devreux, will be here to fit you for new uniforms."

"Yes, Madame," Emily whispered.

Inexplicably, she had no idea why, she shut her eyes. Like a little girl, she delicately kissed her mistress. Her lips formed a small O to plant a kiss on Harriet's cheek. As she drew away, she opened her eyes and looked directly at Harriet.

"I'm sorry. I shouldn't have done that."

Harriet squeezed her hand. "It was very sweet."

Harriet left her, closing the door, leaving Emily alone with her thoughts. The rain dancing softly on the sills soothed her mind, erased the pain of the switching and the awful memory of the enema. Only Harriet's deft touch, the feel of her hand between Emily's thighs remained. As she stepped out of her panties, she thought she might be happy here. She felt ready for tomorrow—whatever it might bring. As she padded down the hall for a long hot soak, she never once thought of poor Annie on the floor below.

CHAPTER 7

I t was still raining the next afternoon when Penny Devreux's little Austin Healey crunched to a halt on the curving stone driveway in front of Harriet's home. Harriet stood in the doorway, peering out into the rain. Gathering Penny beneath a huge umbrella, she shepherded Penny and her wicker sewing basket into the foyer.

"What a horrid day to come to Lilac Row," Harriet said as she kissed Penny's wet cheek. "Let me help you out of that wet raincoat. I'll have Sarah bring you something warm."

Penny nodded, and glanced through the archway into the living room where Emily stood on a low stool in one of Mrs. Bertram's plain gray cotton uniforms. Penny looked pleased.

"She's outgrown that uniform."

"Yes, hasn't she."

Penny followed Harriet into the living room, briskly rubbing her hands. She extended them to the crackling fire in the living-room fireplace. Her dark eyes glowed like cat's in the soft light. She was older than Emily—and from where Emily stood, she looked like a woman to be reckoned with. There was a vibrancy and decisiveness about her, and something else too. Cruelty? Emily could see latent passion smoldering beneath the flush of her cheeks and the set of her mouth. She was a strikingly beautiful woman; transparent complected, coal black hair, and full crimson lips. Her pleated plaid skirt and dark sweater fit her slender shape perfectly. She kept her back to Emily, her palms to the warmth of the fire while Harriet poured two cups of tea.

"Harriet, this fire is wonderful. That damn Austin Healey heater is worthless in this weather. I'm chilled to the bone."

Harriet handed her a cup of tea. "Have a seat by the fire. Warm yourself before you get started."

Penny sat down in one of the wingback chairs flanking the fireplace. Harriet sat down opposite her in a ribbed turtleneck and khaki skirt. The skirt was long enough to cover most of her laced stiletto-heeled boots. Emily wondered why both women wore such expensive boots, as if they were uniform badges of their female authority. She didn't know they'd come from Leah Talons.

"Is Charles well?" Penny asked.

"He's working on a new book. I wish I could keep Alex away from him. He slows Charles."

"That boy is s-o-o cute. It's a shame he's gay. I'd love to take him home with me."

"I wish you would. Charles could get on with his book."

"Is Alex here now?"

"In the cottage."

"With Charles?"

"Of course."

Penny pointed to the bolt of water-spotted ticking emerging from her covered wicker basket. "I presume you want ticking for daily wear."

Harriet nodded. "The skirt must be full."

"So Mama can quickly lift and spank."

"Don't be naughty, Penny. It hasn't been that many years since I lifted your skirts." Harriet eyed her young friend. "You may be too big now for a nanna, but you'll still fit over my lap." Harriet paused. "Why, Penelope Jane Devreux, you're blushing like a schoolgirl."

"You have that effect on me."

Harriet set down her cup. "Penny, I want you to create something new for Emily—in black, I think."

"Sounds exciting. What did you have in mind?"

"I'll show you, later." Harriet turned to Emily. "Emily, say hello to Miss Devreux."

Emily weakened as she looked at Penny. "Good afternoon, M-Miss Devreux."

Penny's glossy lips curved into a thin smile. "Your magic is already transforming her. Her mouth, her shoulders, that plump bustline—they visibly sag in your presence. She's completely under your spell. Leah is going to be pleased. What a shame she has to go—," Penny murmured.

"Penny!" Harriet's voice was sharp.

Penny's cup rattled in its saucer. "I'm sorry, Harriet. I wasn't thinking." She turned to look at Emily. "I can't get over how she's filled out through her hips and bust."

"I've asked Mrs. Henley to prepare a special diet. That and regular doses of Mrs. Henley's paddle ought to trim inches off that big seat."

"Speaking of which, have you spanked her yet?"

Harriet smiled. "Last night before bed, I introduced her to one of Mrs. Henley's switches. If she keeps that lower lip out, she's going to get another lesson this afternoon."

Emily stood motionless, her arms crossed behind her back, bravely listening to the two women. Mrs. Henley had pleated her long honey brown hair into a fat braid that swept across her bottom each time she moved. She stood quietly enough, but she couldn't stop her lower lip from trembling. Dressed in a wash-worn uniform that was faded nearly white and far too tight, she was on the verge of tears. That morning, Mrs. Henley had taken away her bras. She had no idea why unless it had to do with Madame Godwin. Emily was supremely self-conscious without a bra to support her bosom, the shrunken uniform was stretched taut over the plump contours of her breasts and hips. And Harriet had ordered her to stand with her arms crossed behind her. A pose that lifted her breasts, thrust out her nipples, and left her helpless to the seamstress's dark eyes.

"The new dress. Are you going to keep me in suspense?" Penny asked.

"You'll agree that Emily is buxom, pretty in a rustic sort of way. I want to transform her into something stunning. You're the best seamstress in the county. Create something special that says, 'This is Harriet Godwin.'"

"With your taste for discipline, and your appreciation of the classical form and the female shape, it's going be a challenge. With a body like hers, it would be easy to overstate."

"I want understated elegance."

"If I can please you, Leah Talons will know—and Leah might ask *me* to train the next girl for the Ecole."

"Exactly."

"Any fabrics in mind?"

"The material is up to you. You know much more about that than I do. As for color—black, I should think. Basic black."

Penny nodded eagerly. "Black would be perfect. Will you help?…"

"After all these years, and you my heir apparent? I will also need three everyday uniforms."

"Mmm hmm. Long full skirt, tailored bodice, low neckline showing lots of cleavage."

"Décolleté."

"*Mais oui*. Will Madame want ze fitted front-closing bodice?"

"Of course."

"Then I'd better get started," Penny said.

"Yes, I think you should."

Emily smelt an aura of perfume and rain-damp in Penny's hair as she approached. Standing on the footstool, Emily's quivering melon-shaped breasts were suspended inches from Penny's lips. She nearly fainted when Penny matter-of-factly began to unbutton her uniform. She'd guessed this would happen and dreaded the moment. In spite of what Mama had said before Emily had left home, she'd grown ashamed of her bustline, which had always been heavier than the other girls'. Mama understood. She'd had the same shape when she was eighteen.

Penny's hands were at Emily's nipple line, opening the uniform into a deep V to expose generous cleavage and blue-white breast. Miss Devreux's fingertips were pressed firmly into her breasts as she undid each button. Responding to the seamstress's touch, her nipples rose like a pair of pudgy baby fingers through the faded gray cotton.

"Oh, God. Please…no," Emily whispered to herself. Her eyes were hooded, wet-brushed with fear.

"Place your arms at your sides, Emily." Penny sounded like her mother.

Emily whimpered as she uncrossed and lowered her arms. She knew as she dropped her arms that her breasts would descend like jiggling, water-filled balloons almost to her waist, reshaping themselves into a deep, swollen monobosom that would barely fit between her upper arms. As her arms met her sides, her breasts settled comfortably into the waist of the uniform, compressing and rising like inflated twin hemispheres from the deep, arcing V.

"Madame, you wanted décolleté," Penny said softly.

"Yes," Harriet said, staring at Emily.

Unable to face Harriet's frank gaze, Emily studied the deep rise and fall of her bared breasts. Rain danced and spattered on the sills. A wet breeze flapped the sluggish drapes. Time stopped while Harriet crossed the room to a sprawling black leather couch. When she sat down, Emily thought she heard a sigh. Perhaps she imagined it. Everything was so different here. Harriet ran her hand over the gleaming leather.

"The underpinning in this couch need to be tightened," she said.

Penny did not look up. Her attention was on the remaining buttons of Emily's uniform, and the deep valley between Emily's settled breasts.

"Do you suppose Leah will send someone out?"

"Miss Buxton, I should think. I'm going to light the oil lamp, see how she'll look in Leah's light."

Emily shivered as Penny slid the open uniform off her shoulders. The smoky light turned her milk-fleshed breasts and nyloned legs to pale gold. Her nipples popped from her breasts like swollen nuts. Looking down, she cringed with shame and cupped her shoulders in a vain attempt to reduce the impact of her small waist and huge breasts. She was scarlet from hairline to the tips of her breasts. Harriet watched from the couch, tacitly allowing

Penny to close in on her prey. Emily could have died when the seamstress lifted her breasts, testing their fleshy resilience, patting and plumping them into each other.

"What do you think?" Harriet asked.

"I'll bet she has trouble finding tops that fit."

Emily hardly heard Penny. The air flowing through the parlor was damp and cool. She was freezing. When Penny turned to Harriet, Emily lifted a hand to her breasts. Her fingers bumped Penny's wrist, spinning Penny's head around. Harriet came off the couch, moved behind Emily with her clothes brush. The flat of the long slender brush struck Emily's pantied bottom twice in quick succession with so much force Emily was nearly spanked off the stool. The splats echoed loudly in the quietness.

Emily squealed as much in shock as pain. "M-Madame, what did I do?"

"Who told you to lift your arms?" Harriet spanked her again. Her voice was hard-edged, furious.

"I-I'm sorry, Madame." She returned her arms to her sides.

"Don't do that again, Miss!" Harriet emphasized her warning with two more firm smacks of the brush.

Emily tried not to cry out as the brush sent hot shafts of pain resonating into her thighs. Her hands balled against her hips. *I am trying to obey.* She looked outside. A wall of gray was slowly blanketing the glistening green-streaked landscape. She wished she were snug and safe in her bed. Would this day ever end? *Someone, anyone, help me*, she prayed as Penny took her breast in both hands.

"Harriet. It's too big to span."

Harriet nodded like a lioness watching her young cub struggle to devour a prey that was still too much for her.

"You don't see eighteen year olds with bosoms this deep and nipple lines this low, and perfectly shaped breasts. With her shape, I'm sure I can create something original, Harriet."

Penny's frank and almost complimentary assessment stunned Emily. Mrs. Bertram had never said anything like that. Nor had Mama. No one had ever said she was pretty or had a nice bust. She'd never thought of herself as being pretty.

Harriet returned the leather couch. "Penny Devreux, I can see right through you. You've got that look in your eye."

"Harriet, I wouldn't—"

Harriet lifted her hand. "Emily, you'll find out soon enough that our Miss Devreux can teach you something about discipline and correction. You'd better listen to her when I send you home with her. Mind her well. As well as you would Florence Bertram. Miss Devreux enjoys administering lengthy and painful punishments in her punishment room. She has everything she needs there: whips and thick leather straps to hold you down. Disobey her, and she'll have no mercy."

"Why thank you, Harriet. What a nice thing to say. I promise to take good care of her."

Harriet smiled. "I thought it might be easier to do the final fittings at your home."

"You're absolutely right."

Emily was devastated by this young woman with the

black flashing eyes and brisk self-assuredness. She could feel Penny's passion probing like radar, sensing her fear; and see the flush of excitement spreading over Penny's cheeks. She wondered what it might be like to be in bed with Penny, her heavy breasts swaying like bulbous suspended fruit above Penny's open mouth. Penny would kiss and nibble at her hardened nipples. Her fear of being punished evaporated as she felt Penny's lips closing around her breast, ripping, tearing. Darker thoughts lay beneath, fought to get out, but she ignored the truth.

Penny stood back, hands on hips, studying her. "Don't move," she said in a low voice. "I'm working through some ideas."

Emily wondered if she'd ever be warm again. She stared into the fire and thought about what Madame had just said. Would her home be as rich and beautiful as Lilac Row? And what of the punishment room? She'd never heard of anything like that, though she supposed there were wicked women who kept such rooms. She'd never actually been whipped; at least not with those short little black thong things like the movie pirates used on Paulette Goddard and Lana Turner. Deep in thought, she jumped when Penny slipped her fingers inside the waistband of her panties and pulled them down. She heard Penny catch her breath at the sight of her bare crown cheeks. She nearly fell of the stool as Penny's hands spread her cheeks.

"Emily, I'm warning you," Penny hissed as she felt for the nubby outline of Emily's anus.

"What did Miss Devreux just say?" Harriet lifted her brush.

"I-I'm s-sorry," Emily whispered.

"Did you bring it?" Harriet asked.

"I never go anywhere without it."

Emily swallowed hard when she saw the gleaming, coated thing Penny slid from a plastic bag in her sewing basket. Holding it in her hand, Penny moved behind Emily to insert the thick, blunt tip into her backside. It was not going to go in easily. It dilated her beyond what she could endure, and Emily looked plaintively at Harriet, her lips parted, pleading silently with her mistress. Harriet ignored her pleas. "Bend over," Penny ordered. As Emily complied, Penny got the big dildo started. Emily thought she was going to burst. She opened her mouth.

"Not a peep or I'll gag you," Harriet warned.

Emily swallowed hard as the dildo slid deeper. *What does this horrid punishment have to do with my uniforms?* Miss Devreux stopped pushing when the thing was completely inside her. It filled her bottom with a dull throbbing pressure that slowly radiated outward to her thighs and sex. Beneath the pressure-pain she felt the first electric currents of something other than pain. The thing's cord dangled from her seat, trailed against her thigh.

Penny straightened up. "She's a tight one, Harriet. But it will keep her still."

"I think you should put her panties back on. She's freezing."

"Yes. I'm going to measure her now. Emily, put your arms behind you."

Penny dropped to her knees in front of Emily. She placed one end of her cloth measuring tape between Emily's thighs. Emily was certain the seamstress could feel the damp heat through her panties. Already, the pain of the thing inside her had begun to subside and was evolving into a vague sensation that was more a promise of pleasure than hurt and humiliation. She bit her lip and groaned softly, hoped she could maintain her composure while Miss Devreux pressed the metal tape end to her sex, and ran the tape down the inside of her leg. Madame Godwin's look reminded her to remain perfectly still or risk a punishment. Penny's fingertips nudged her sex. Oddly aroused, caught up in the heat of the big dildo in her backside, Emily dared to drop her arm.

Penny rocked back on her heels. She looked up at Emily, then at Harriet. "I cannot make measurements if she won't be still."

"I know a way to keep those arms up."

Harriet picked up one of Emily's nylons. She wound it around Emily's crossed arms, drawing Emily's arms together, forcing her arms higher on her back. The restraint didn't hurt her, but lifted her bustline until her breasts stood off her ribs. A dark shadowy hurt crept into her eyes. Harriet and Penny could see she was ashamed and uncomfortable, and didn't seem to care.

Harriet touched Emily's cheek. Her voice was soft and motherly. "You're not accustomed to restraints.

Florence had no idea of the power behind restraints. Before you leave Lilac Row you'll feel naked without them."

"M-Madame...," Emily's lips trembled. Her eyes filled with tears which spilled down her cheeks.

Harriet wiped away Emily's tears, smoothed the odd strands of hair from Emily's face. "Not a word, young lady, or I'll gag you with the other stocking and give you an old-fashioned spanking like the ones I'm sure you used to get from your mother."

Emily looked away. Madame was treating her like a naughty little girl, and the big thing inside her was swelling now, actually seemed to be growing larger. With an expression bordering on a sulk, she watched Penny unroll a bolt of heavy pillow ticking. Why did she have use that for uniforms? It wasn't at all flattering. Penny rummaged through her sewing kit for several swatches of black fabric. She spread them and the ticking material over the carpet.

"I have more black fabrics at home. Do you like any of these?" Harriet fondled each swatch, pressing them to her lips. She gave one to Penny. "This one. She'll be stunning. How long to make the dress?"

"Penny shrugged. A few days."

"With you working all night. A week?"

"Harriet, I want to do this. I'll just finish up the measuring."

Penny ran her tape beneath Emily's trussed arms and drew the ends together over Emily's uplifted breasts. Penny acted as if Madame Godwin were not there, as if it were just the two of them in front of the fire. Emily stared out at the rain-streaked window while the seamstress squeezed the tape ends together over her nugget-hard nipples. "Nice long nipples," Penny whispered. "Your mistress and I like that in a young woman." She glanced at Harriet. "Every bit of this girl is in her bust, backside, and hips."

"It's good she left Christiansen's," Harriet said. "Had she stayed, she'd be as big as Florence."

"How low do you want the neckline for her workaday uniforms?"

"I'll show you."

The tip of Harriet's manicured forefinger scribed a thin red line that dipped from Emily's right shoulder down and across her breasts, then up again to Emily's left shoulder. Emily looked down at the fresh welt Harriet had just scribed above her nipples. She'd never stay inside her uniform!

Harriet ignored the stricken expression on Emily's face. "Can you cut it that low? Will she fall out when she bends to serve?"

"It will be a challenge, but yes, I think it can be done."

"It's lower than the others, but we must make the most of Emily while we have her."

Penny smiled wickedly. "But of course, Madame."

As Emily opened her mouth to protest the low neckline, she remembered Harriet's warning. Terror caught in her throat, cutting off her speech. Her skin still burned as hotly as if Madame Godwin had drawn the tip of a glowing poker across her breasts. Why didn't Miss Devreux say something? The neckline would never hold her in. Her eyes filled with scalding tears. She wanted to scream. Madame Godwin's words rang in her mind.

"While we have her…special punishment room…"

Penny stripped several yards of the striped denim from the bolt. Lining a row of straight pins between her lips, she began to arrange the stiff cotton fabric around Emily's hips, draping, pinning, shearing panels of material for Emily's skirt. Harriet watched from the couch.

"You're a genius," Harriet said. "You don't need patterns. Your uniforms fit perfectly. How do you do it?"

With several pins still in her mouth, Penny spoke in a mutter. "I've always sewed this way."

"Amazing."

"Darling, will you tell that to Leah?"

"I already have."

Penny paused to look at her mentor. "Really?"

"It won't be long."

"Harriet. Are you serious?"

"Never more so."

"How can I thank you?"

"Design something smashing."

"You can bank on it," Penny said.

Emily listened with no understanding as the women chatted on. She shifted her weight to the opposite leg. A difficult move with her arms pinioned behind her. She nearly lost her balance. Penny glanced up from her kneeling position in front of Emily where she was basting the hem of the skirt. Her voice had an annoyed edge to it.

"Emily, hold still while I pin this hem!"

Emily looked down at the seamstress, nodded silently. The denim skirt covered her ankles. It was much more elegant than Mrs. Bertram's uniforms. The material was stiff and heavy at her waist, but at least it covered her bare legs. Washings would soften the cotton fabric. The rain continued to slant down, spattering noisily on the lilac and honeysuckle alongside the house. The green landscape had turned slate gray. The logs in the fireplace snapped and burned but did little to ward off her damp chill. *Why doesn't Madame throw a shawl over my shoulders?* Warmly dressed in their boots, skirts, and sweaters, the two women seemed not to notice how cold she was.

"Are you staying for dinner?" Harriet asked.

"Am I invited?"

"Of course. I'll tell Mrs. Henley you're staying."

As Harriet got off the couch and left the room, Emily noticed Penny had taken a straight pin from her mouth and buried it in the cotton material. Emily knew what was coming and was helpless to stop it. The seamstress casually straightened the basted skirt over her hips and suddenly jabbed Emily in the seat as she unpinned the stiff denim from her waist. Emily let out a startled yelp, swayed awkwardly, and stepped off the stool.

Penny threw up her hands, stopping Harriet in the foyer. "Harriet, I know a disobedient girl who needs her seat reddened."

"I-I'm s-sorry," Emily muttered

Harriet returned to the sofa to pick up her clothes

brush. She led Emily to the leather couch. "I warned you, didn't I? You've earned yourself a spanking"

"I-I don't understand," Emily whispered.

"You will when I finish with you." The moment was awkward and tender. Penny sat down by the fire to watch.

"M-Madame—"

"Not one word, Miss!"

Harriet's eyes narrowed to cat slits. Her mouth hardened into a thin line. Emily stood by the couch, caught in Harriet's iron grasp. She was unable to take her eyes off the long-handled brush in Harriet's hand. Her fright and shame drove her to put on a pouty look that was more silly than indignant. With her arms caught behind her, her milky bosom high and jiggling, she said, "I-I won't…I-I cannot wear th-that uniform. It's…It's indecent! M-Mama would kill me. And M-Miss…Miss D-Devreux…"

"Every word earns you a longer punishment."

"I-I don't care! Sh-She stuck me with a pin. It's…It's not fair…wasn't my fault. Why should I be spanked?" Her voice became a soft plea. "M-Madame, please…."

Harriet held onto her young charge, silently, while Penny watched and Emily poured out her frustration. It took a moment for Emily to realize she'd gone too far. Harriet released her, pushing back the hair from her face.

"You've been a very naughty girl. It's time I spanked some sense into you."

As Harriet took Emily's panties down, Emily's lush,

113

tangy scent hung like a pall in the room. Emily wondered if Madame Godwin had caught the smell of her. The older woman said nothing as she drew her down, causing the thick thing inside her to flex and swell as she went headlong over Harriet's lap. She'd expected the sofa's leather upholstery to be cold and sticky to her bare flesh. Instead, the leather was as supple and warm as Harriet's thighs.

Madame didn't seem in any hurry. Before lifting her clothes brush, she thoroughly examined Emily's buttocks. Emily had examined herself many times in Mrs. Bertram's full-length mirror. Her bottom was too wide, fleshy, and full; silky smooth with a thick, fatty layer of flesh covering the musculature beneath. Her crown cheeks tapered smoothly into heavy rounded thighs. Caught in Harriet's web, she felt herself slipping back in time. Her lips moved, made tiny supplicant sounds.

She remembered home, Mama's spankings. While Mama marched her upstairs, she would tell Emily how reddened and sore her bottom was going to be when she came up after supper. It was a poignant mother-daughter tableau made even more enticing by Mama's unflinching conviction and concern. Emily treasured those moments. In those few seconds before Mama's correction began, she knew instinctively that Mama loved her and was spanking her for her own good. She held her breath as Harriet laid one hand on her waist and raised her brush high.

She became a little girl again. Alone with Mama.

Mama sat on the bed in her nightgown, her hair down. Her soft round face and brown eyes expressionless. Her coiled belt lay in her lap. The belt gleamed like a shining sword as Mama uncoiled it and doubled it over in her hand. Emily would cry out as Mama took her over her lap and pulled up the back of her nightgown to expose the small twin rounds of her bottom. As Mama lifted her arm, her breasts pressed into Emily. There was nothing she could do as the doubled belt descended. Even before the leather had made its first mark, her eyes were shut tight. Her mouth stretched into a silent scream.

Harriet's clothes brush landed, snapping her back to the present.

"A-a-e-e-g-h!"

Another smack.

"M-M-a-m-a-a!"

The big brush landed again. This time with more authority.

"How does that feel, Emily? Will you disobey me again?"

"N-N-o-o-o, M-Madame! N-o-o-o!"

"I don't believe that for one second."

Emily's voice crescendoed into a long wailing sob. Madame Godwin reminded her so much of Mama. Mama, who loved each of her daughters, but thoroughly enjoyed the role of maternal disciplinarian, and applying her hand, and later her belt, to her misbehaving daughters' backsides. She spanked her girls until their bottoms were shiny and red before letting them off her lap. Her maternal lessons in deportment kept her girls submissive and respectful, right up until the time they each left home.

Mrs. Henley came into the living room, wiping her hands on her apron. She looked dispassionately at Emily's reddened seat, then asked, "Will Miss Devreux be staying for dinner?"

"Yes," Harriet answered. "And Emily's going to serve. I have a new outfit for her to wear." Harriet continued to apply the brush while Mrs. Henley looked on.

"Not her uniform, then?"

"No, Mrs. Henley. It's something quite different."

"I see," Mrs. Henley said dryly. "I'll just get on with dinner."

Harriet delivered a solid smack to Emily's swollen cheek. The intense pain in her made her shriek, which earned her a warning and several additional smacks from Harriet before Harriet paused to smooth the hair from her face.

"That's enough crying. I've barely begun."

Emily lay unmoving over Harriet's lap, her head on the supple leather of the couch, her legs stretched out behind her. She blubbered softly, no longer caring that Miss Devreux sat watching across the room. Her bottomcheeks were on fire. When it came to spankings, Madame Godwin was every bit as competent as her mother and Mrs. Bertram. The room had fallen eerily quiet. It was almost dark now. The rain was still coming down. The clatter of pans could be heard in Mrs. Henley's kitchen. A log in the fireplace exploded in a fiery shower of sparks before crumpling into a glowing mass of coals.

Harriet spoke softly. "There's more to come. Be still while I correct you. Or I'll have Miss Devreux hold down your legs."

Emily's head shook frantically as she blubbered out a response.

"It's time," Harriet said.

She raised her arm and brought the brush down with a swoosh, catching Emily on the twin plateaus of her bottom, bridging the steep valley between, leaving another bright blushing mark. She stepped up the pace and force of the spanking until she was exhaling hard each time she delivered the brush to Emily's seat. Emily's legs stiffened. Her crossed and bound arms made her roll drunkenly with each spank. Harriet was leaning over her, holding tightly onto her waist. Emily could feel her plump, hard-tipped breasts as they swung from side to side beneath her sweater. Madame spanked her in a smooth, steady rhythm. Each spank blurred into the next so that Emily felt a continuous burning in her seat. Strands of her hair fell over her cheek and onto the leather while Madame delivered several more brush strokes in quick succession. The spanks echoed like rifle shots in the foyer.

"Are you learning from this, Emily?"

"Y-Yes-s-s, M-Madame."

The clothes brush flew in a heart-stopping series of splats. Each one sank deep into her haunches before bouncing off her cheeks. The polished flat of the brush was a powerful stimulus, making her shriek uncontrollably. Emily felt every nuance of the older woman's body as she delivered her brush to Emily's seat. She was very much like Mama, and yet not like her at all. She could imagine each application of the brush leaving another spreading stain of scarlet on her jiggling derrière. She was shrieking uncontrollably now, had the temerity to kick up a leg. That earned her another pair of hard smacks. Emily knew she'd never been spanked this hard and long—not even by Mrs. Bertram. And Madame Godwin was not finished.

"Stop! You're wriggling like a worm. A bottom larded with this much fat can take more. What a shame Mrs. Bertram didn't spank you."

"M-Madame!... O-o-g-h,...M-M-a-m-m-a-a-h!" Emily shook as the brush fell, smacking her hard across her swollen crimson thighs. "I-I...a-a-m sorry! P-Please s-stop."

Harriet had reduced Emily to a sobbing, shivering lump of damp streaming hair and tears. She sobbed, squirmed, and squalled like a child in a tantrum. She thought of how Mama had spanked her. The excitement she'd felt when the spanking finally ended. Madame Godwin was dispensing her discipline as easily as a well-oiled machine. The living room and foyer rang out with the smacks and cracks of the big brush on Emily's welted flesh. She pleaded to no avail with her new mistress.

"Of course it hurts! When I spank, I guarantee you it's going to hurt. Stop your thrashing!"

By the time the spanking ended, twilight had begun to settle over the house. Beyond the warmth of the fireplace and pale cone of kerosene lamplight, the living room was dark, echoing with the slapping sounds of Harriet's brush.

"Harriet, it's getting dark. Should I turn on another lamp?"

Harriet's rhythm did not change as she responded. "No…I prefer the light…from the oil lamp."

In the flickering semidarkness, Emily could imagine the state of her punished bottom: puffy, crisscrossed with ridges and welts. Her sobs floated out the open windows and into the wet, dark countryside. Harriet no longer seemed to hear her as she delivered the final set of smacks to Emily's upper thighs and the deep valley between her buttocks.

Harriet leaned down to Emily's ear. She spoke in a soft, maternal tone. "How does that seat of yours feel now, Miss Emily? If I send you home with Miss Devreux, will you obey her?"

Emily pumped her head up and down furiously. "O-O-g-h, y-yes, Madame,…I-I will!…A-a-g-h!"

"Harriet!" Penny exclaimed. "You are going to send Emily with me. I really wasn't sure. I'm so pleased."

She crossed the room to Harriet, watched the matron deliver a final flurry of smacks, each one reverberating throughout the living room. Emily's cries were momentarily lost in the racket of brush smacking flesh. When Emily was finally and awkwardly allowed to get to her feet with her arms still tightly bound behind her, Harriet looked at her with an expression of relief and satisfaction.

"Penny, please pull up her panties."

Emily noted that Penny took her time pulling up the thin panties over her reddened bottom.

"And please untie her arms as well. She's going upstairs for a hot bath. With the exception of her bottom, I suspect she's frozen." She turned to Emily. "Your serving outfit for tonight is laid out on your bed. I'll send Mrs. Henley to fix your hair. Hurry upstairs. Take your bath. You don't want to keep Mrs. Henley waiting."

Emily whispered her assent and left the room, relieved to be out of sight of her mistress. Harriet's final words made her pause in the foyer. "Emily, you're going to serve Miss Devreux and me tonight at dinner. I hope for your sake Mrs. Bertram has trained you to serve at table." With a sweep of her hand she sent Emily awkwardly up the stairs, clutching her dress and stockings over her bare breasts.

Harriet splashed brandy from a Waterford decanter into twin snifters. Drinks in hand, the two women sat across from each other in front of the fire, comfortable, content to be silent and listen to the rain. Harriet laid another log on the fire and refilled their glasses. Over the next hour, they talked of Leah Talons and The Ecole.

Mrs. Henley came down the stairs and into the parlor with Emily trailing behind in a ghostly swirl of black silk. "Dinner is ready when you are," Mrs. Henley said. She turned to leave. "I'm sure you'll want Emily with you. She's of no use to me in the kitchen in that outfit." With a lift of her chin she disappeared into the kitchen, leaving a barefoot Emily framed in the living-room arch.

The housekeeper had washed Emily's hair and brushed it until it flowed in lush streaming rivulets from her shoulders to her waist. Her costume hid none of her. Backlit by the foyer chandelier, her plump shape stood out in stark relief beneath flowing black silk harem pants and a loose-fitting high-necked silk top with bell-shaped sleeves buttoned tightly at her wrists. Emily wore nothing beneath.

"O-o-o-lah-lah," Penny whispered. "You didn't buy that outfit around here."

"Frederick's catalog. Emily, come here by the fire."

Emily complied, keeping her eyes directed to the floor in front of her. Her face was sweet and soft and tinged scarlet in the firelight. The lush rounds of her breasts swayed gently, touching and separating as she walked. Her nipples had been teased erect by Mrs. Henley. They nudged and tented the diaphanous silk. Mrs. Henley had applied a too-thick layer of red gloss to her lips, and darkened and highlighted her eyes. Her eyelids were shaded bright blue, accented with mascara and liner. Her cheeks were rouged a deep pink. Clunky gold earrings dangled from her earlobes. An African fertility amulet hung suspended between her breasts. Harriet smiled proudly at Emily, who stood nervously between the two women, her hands together beneath her breasts.

"Harriet, she's scrumptious. Can I take her home

tonight? This will give me more time to fit her cotton uniforms, and create something brilliant in black silk."

"Penny Devreux, you're as transparent as water. Yes, you can take her home, but it won't be this evening. We have to wait until her backside has recovered."

"Harriet, I wouldn't dream of—"

"Oh, yes, you would. Remember me? The teenager who changed your diapers. I know you too well."

Penny looked disappointedly into the fire.

"Don't be so impatient." Harriet laughed. "You look like a petulant little girl. I ought to give you a good spanking. Now put away that sulk."

"Yes, Mother," Penny said with a glum voice.

Harriet smiled at her young friend's frustration. "Emily, go into the kitchen. Tell Mrs. Henley we're ready to dine."

Mrs. Henley's dinner that night was delicious. It was made even more exquisite by Emily's waiting on the two women. Emily was drawn into the dining ritual; unwillingly at first, consensually as the dinner wore on. She felt drawn to Penny. She was barely aware of her subservient role. She had never mixed serving with such a sensuous atmosphere. When she bent to serve, she allowed the full weight of her breasts to brush Penny's cheek. Mrs. Henley had put a lilac scent on her breasts and neck that wrapped her in its delicate air. She hoped it would have the same effect on Miss Devreux. She wanted to bury her face in Miss Devreux's silky hair, and slip her hands between her slender thighs. Her hands shook as she served the seamstress. By the time she served dessert, both Harriet and Penny knew that she'd forgotten her spanking and was beginning to enjoy the singular attention they were showering on her.

She had no idea everything was about to change. That it was just a matter of time.

CHAPTER 8

"Out of bed, girl! Last night's evening in silks won't be repeated in my house."

Mrs. Henley swept back Emily's coverlet and spanked her hard on her still-sore bottom. While Emily struggled to open her eyes, Mrs. Henley went to the closet and took out one of Mrs. Bertram's gray cotton too-tight uniforms.

"I'm keeping you in these until Miss Devreux makes up your uniforms. I won't deny I don't like them. Frankly, I have no time for housemaids who parade about my house in long skirts and their bosoms hanging out. They certainly aren't designed for housework. I don't understand why Madame does it, but she's the boss." Emily lay on the edge of the bed, watching the housekeeper rummage through her underwear drawer.

"I'm putting you to work in the laundry under Molly. She's a good girl, plain, no false illusions about her role here. She'll show you what I expect of my girls." Mrs. Henley turned around to face her.

Half asleep, Emily found herself being pulled to her feet. Mrs. Henley yanking her long nightie over her head. "Get a move on, girl. The day's half over!"

For the next several days from dawn to dusk, Emily stripped beds, washed, hung out, and ironed mountains of laundry under Molly's and Mrs. Henley's watchful eyes. Mrs. Bertram had never worked her this hard.

It was her third—or was it her fourth?—morning at Lilac Row. She and Molly were on the second floor, making beds. She watched Molly crisply snap a clean-smelling sheet onto a bed. The sheet floated perfectly to the corners of the mattress.

"Molly, you make that look so easy. I'll never learn."

"Where you're going, it probably won't matter."

"Do you mean Leah Talons's?" Molly nodded. "Is that her portrait in the parlor?" Molly nodded again as she smoothed the sheet over the bed. "I keep hearing of her. Who is she? She's beautiful."

Molly grinned. "I've never seen her. Can't tell you anything. If I did, I'd lose my position."

"Molly, you're being naughty. Stop teasing me—"

"Tuck the corner of that sheet before I paddle your fat behind."

Molly's uniform matched the striped blue-and-white

ticking of the bare mattress. What Emily would soon be wearing. She liked the idea of an ankle-length skirt. They were much more attractive and less revealing than her short-skirted gray uniforms, which rode up to her thighs when she bent to make beds or stretched to hang wash on the line. As Molly bent to tuck the sheet, her low neckline fell open under the weight of her breasts.

Emily stared at the twin half moons of Molly's bosom. "Doesn't that bother you?"

Molly glanced down at herself. "At my age I pray it will turn Master Charles's eye. He is a handsome devil."

Emily blushed. "I haven't seen Mr. Godwin. "Mrs. Henley says I'm going to Miss Devreux's—"

"Not before your backside's healthy. Miss Devreux will do more to you than just sew uniforms."

"Wh-What do you mean?" Emily asked breathily, already knowing the answer.

"I myself don't know, but others have told me if a girl doesn't cooperate, Miss Devreux strings up the girl up in some sort of truss and whips her for hours. Sometimes, she whips them anyway." She looked slyly at Emily's horrified expression. "I can't wait to see your new outfit. With that bust of yours it should be spectacular."

Emily's mouth dropped. "How did—"

Molly shrugged off the question. "Master Charles likes his boys, but I'll bet he won't kick you out of bed."

"Molly!"

"Too bad he didn't kick out Sarah. Now she's as big as a house."

"Mrs. Henley, sh-she said it was a stable boy."

"Hogwash! It was Master Charles."

Mrs. Henley's profile suddenly filled the bedroom doorway. She looked sharply at Molly. "That's enough gossip, Molly! Filling this girl's ears with nonsense. Emily, lift your skirt." Emily's face turned white. "I'm not going to spank you, child. I want to have a look at your bottom."

While Emily reluctantly lifted the skirt of her uniform, Mrs. Henley lowered her panties. "Saints preserve us," the housekeeper murmured. "There's barely a mark. Amazing. I'm telling Madame to call Miss Devreux." Emily yanked up her underwear. By the time she'd smoothed her skirt over her hips, Mrs. Henley was gone.

At dusk the next evening, Mrs. Henley drove Emily to Penny Devreux's lavish row house in the most fashionable section of the city. Mrs. Henley did not go in. "Miss Devreux is expecting you," she said, and let Emily out of the car. Emily waited until the taillights of the housekeeper's car had disappeared around the corner before she twisted the old-fashioned door chimes. She did not know Harriet and Charles' car was parked behind the house in the narrow alley, already there and waiting. A plump dark-skinned maid in a black uniform opened the door. Penny stood behind the maid.

"Have you eaten dinner?" Penny asked.

Emily silently nodded, completely overcome by Penny's persona. Penny was dressed in tall heels, fitted indigo jeans, and a billowy scarlet satin blouse. Her dark hair was bobbed neatly around the slender oval of her face. There was an intensity to her eyes and expression now that Emily hadn't seen at Lilac Row. Penny was not wearing a bra. Her small mouth curved into a sly smile as she waited for Emily to speak.

"M-Mrs. Henley dropped me...and left." Emily shrugged her shoulders.

"Have you been fed?"

"Y-Yes."

"Good. We'll go straight upstairs." She waved her maid away.

In her gray uniform, Emily felt like a peasant next to Penny. Even the maid's uniform was prettier than hers. Penny's look softened. She slipped her hand inside Emily's.

"You look very nice in those heels. Come with me."

Emily followed Penny's denim-clad hips and bottom up the stairs through a maze of halls and rooms to the third floor. Except for the repetitive click-click of their heels, the house was completely silent. The seamstress paused in a long hallway, facing a pair of doors.

"You'll stay here," Penny said, stroking Emily's cheek. She spoke in a low, soothing voice. "A-a-g-h, my little pigeon, you really are frightened. Has Mrs. Bertram told you of my punishment room? Or perhaps it was Annie. I find your naïveté so refreshing."

She pinched Emily's cheek, unlocked the door, and disappeared into the dark room. A match sputtered into flame. Emily watched Penny ignite an old oil lamp, filling the room with soft amber light. It was a large room with rough-plastered walls. High above Emily, dark-hewn beams slanted up and across the ceiling. Two narrow shuttered windows opened to the night air. A wooden bed with quilted coverlet stood between the dormers. A sturdy cane chair and table were set against the inside wall. Emily drew in a breath when she saw the razor strop, leather-covered paddle, and riding crop arranged on the table. A pair of chest-high laced leather cuffs hung from chains that ran up to a ceiling beam. Another set of cuffs was bolted to the floor beneath the pair of hanging ones.

Harriet and Charles sat in the unlit adjoining room, peering through small openings in the wall that were invisible to Emily in the shadowy lamplight. Charles's cock was already hard, thrusting aggressively against his pants leg. Harriet was calm, her hands in her lap, watching silently.

Emily looked at the suspended chains, then turned slowly to Penny with a look of astonishment. Her mind refused to work. What kind of trap had she fallen into? Chains. A razor strop. This must be the punishment room. It was more like a medieval torture chamber. She glanced at the open door.

Penny moved quickly to shut and lock the door. She slipped the key into her jeans. "Come to Mama," she whispered. "You needn't be frightened. It won't be that severe."

Emily stiffened as Penny took her in her arms. She tried to scream as Penny pressed her mouth tightly to hers, smothering her. She groaned, struggled to push her tormentor away.

This wasn't the same Miss Devreux.

"You're being naughty," Penny hissed in Emily's ear. "Let go. You know you want this." Penny nibbled breathily at her earlobe. Reluctant waves of pleasure tried to engulf Emily. Penny's hands ran over bottom. She stiffened as her thighs and sex met Penny's. Penny's persistent lips slid wetly over her mouth, kissing her brutally, smearing her lipstick over Emily's mouth and cheek. The seamstress's hands were like claws tearing at her buttocks, hurting her. Her mouth was tightly sealed by Penny's lips, forcing her to gasp for breath. Why had she ever thought she could trust Miss Devreux?

The seamstress had amazing strength. Twisting her face away from Penny's thrusting tongue, Emily let out a scream as she gulped for air. Penny released her, nearly dropping her to the floor. The seamstress's hand came from nowhere to slap her hard across her face. Emily's head jerked back. She teetered crazily on her heels, her arms folded over her breasts. A bright crimson blotch spread over her cheek. She did not look at Penny, who was glaring at her, quivering with anger.

"Get out of that uniform, Miss High-and-Mighty. When I'm finished with you, you'll be kissing my feet and pleading for more."

Emily began to cry. "M-Miss D-Devreux, p-please don't—"

Penny's open hand caught Emily's other cheek. The slap rang in the hard-shelled space. "Get out of that ill-fitting uniform before I rip it off you!"

Sobbing softly, Emily unbuttoned her uniform. She

felt like a condemned criminal as Penny went to the table and picked up the razor strop. She waited until Emily was down to heels, bra, panties, and stockings. The seamstress doubled the ends of the strop in her hand and slowly circled Emily, reminding her of a she-wolf.

"You're disobedient. Your seams aren't straight. Look at your hair! You're a mess. Lesson one. Clasp your ankles."

"Omigod," Charles whispered, as Emily moaned and bent over. Her bottom spread dramatically, widening into her hips, tightening her panties over her plump cheeks and shadowy cleft. Charles took his extended cock in his hands, began to play with himself. Harriet didn't notice. Her eyes were locked on Emily. Penny moved in. The leather strop creaked, and landed with a solid-sounding whap across Emily's bottom. She jerked up in surprise, nearly toppling from her heels by the force of the strop. The leather hurt, but at least it wasn't as bad as Madame Godwin's clothes brush.

"One more step and I'll double your punishment."

"M-Miss D-Dev—"

"Who said you could speak?" The strop cracked her again.

"I-I'm...I-I didn't..."

"Not a word, Miss High and Mighty."

The strop sighed, igniting another red slash across the backs of Emily's gartered thighs. Her nearly naked body gleamed with a tawny yellow glow in the soft flicker of the kerosene lamp. Emily twisted her head sideways to look at her tormentor. She lifted her eyes to Penny. The strop landed again, eliciting a soft cry.

Charles groaned and let himself go, spattering softly on the dusty floor. Harriet looked at him, disgusted. "Couldn't you have waited until we got home?" she whispered.

"You take the strap well, Emily. We'll see how you do when really I zebra-stripe your fat bottom."

Penny laughed and delivered another half dozen strokes of her strop in quick succession. Emily moaned, but didn't cry. The wide leather strap had numbed her bottom more than it hurt her. She began to think what was to come wouldn't be as painful as Madame Godwin's clothes brush. Penny stopped. The strop dangled from her hand.

"Stand up. Remove your panties." Penny's voice was as hard as stone. She waited until Emily had stepped out of her panties before she led Emily between the suspended chains. "Extend your arms."

Emily stared at the table and its implements while Miss Devreux laced the leather cuffs around her outstretched wrists. "Spread your legs. I'm not through with you yet." Emily stood in shock while Penny knelt to fasten her ankles to the floor chains. She could hardly believe what was being done to her. When she tried to move, the chains held her securely in their padded grip. She was completely helpless. Had she been wrong to resist Miss Devreux's advances? She began to think she might have earned, even deserved, this punishment. The realization covered her with shame.

"This is your first time, isn't it?"

Emily nodded, unwilling to look at Penny.

"Mrs. Bertram never tied you—not even once?"

Emily blushed. "T-To the bed. Once." She looked at Penny with a such bewildered expression, she drew a sympathetic smile from Penny.

"How often did she spank you?"

Emily shrugged. "Once a month…I don't know," she blubbered.

"You must have been the apple of her eye. She fed you well enough. But tonight, my pretty, you're just another of Miss Devreux's maids." Emily lifted her head. She looked at Penny with eyes swollen with fear. "You're terrified aren't you? I adore that look in a girl." Penny stood back, her hands resting on her slender hips. She took a long, fat dildo from the table drawer. Its black leather skin gleamed wetly with lubricant. When Emily saw the thing she squirmed.

"N-No…p-please…M-Miss D-Devreux—"

Penny gave her a sharp spank.

"Lesson two. The sausage. Some of my girls have actually grown to like their sausage punishment."

Penny spread Emily's heavy bottomcheeks, guided the fat leather cylinder into her with a steady thrusting motion that forced Emily's hips away from the plug. It was bigger than the one Miss Devreux had used on her at Lilac Row. Unable to escape the awful pressure, she stiffened and tried to scream, but the shriek lodged in the dryness of her throat. The awful sausage was all the way in now, inflating her insides. She was so preoccupied, she didn't notice Penny had picked up her shining crop. It whistled softly as Penny whipped it through the air. She turned to Emily, brought the crop around to her bottom.

In that instant, Charles grew hard and stiff again.

Emily had barely begun to accommodate the pressure and thrust of the big leather dildo when the crop bridged the deep cleft between her reddened cheeks. The polished instrument sank into the cushiony resilience of her bottomcheeks. The crack of the crop against her flesh filled the room. She shrieked in unmitigated pain.

"How did that feel? Does it make you wish you'd given in to Mrs. Bertram?" The crop flew again, leaving a thin scarlet ridge across Emily's thighs. Emily shook and rattled her chains in a vain effort to escape the crop.

"No more kid-glove treatment by Madame Christiansen for you, girl!"

The crop struck twice, drawing harsh cries from Emily. "Miss D-Devreux—"

"Be still! You're being punished."

Penny stepped into the next stroke. The crop caught Emily high on her cheeks, sending waves of rippling flesh across her thighs. She'd never been whipped with a crop, had no notion of what it would do to her bottom. Each lash stung like fire. The whistling crop, the constant pressure of the dildo, her shame at being bound and whipped, filled her with remorse. She wanted to tell Miss Devreux she was sorry, but it was too late. The crop arced, molded itself around her hip. She should have let Mrs. Bertram fatten her, have her way. None of this would be happening. She would still be safe with Susan.

The crop lashed out again, made her cringe in pain. She could imagine what her seat would look like tomorrow, all scarlet ridged and crisscrossed over her reddened flesh. The crop stung her right cheek, then her left. It was like sitting on a beehive. She shrieked as Penny changed her whipping stance and applied the last half dozen strokes in rapid-fire fashion. Pain washed over Emily like a fiery flood. Her damp wrists jerked at their leather restraints. Her hips thrust forward to escape the terrible crop strokes. Her shrill screams filled the room until her ears hurt with her cries. The snow-white rounds of her breasts lifted and compressed into each other with each crack of the crop. She nearly fainted at Penny's words.

"Your backside is growing ripe, Emily, but there is still plenty of room for a sound paddling."

"M-Miss Devreux,…"

"I've waited a long time for this." She laid the crop on the table. "Perhaps there is a way for you to escape a paddling."

Penny put her arms around Emily and pulled her into her hips. Emily could feel the soft, wet mound of her sex pressing tightly into Miss Devreux. The plump contours of her breasts flattened themselves against the silk of Penny's blouse. Penny's small, firm breasts merged with hers. The taut denim over her thighs warmed Emily's bare skin. She forgot about the pain in her seat as Penny's body heat soaked into her. Penny began to move her jeaned hips in a circular motion, screwing herself into Emily's nest and thighs. It had been too long. Far too long. Emily's eyes lidded. She gazed into Penny's perfect face, waited for Penny to bring her lips close and kiss her. Penny obliged, crushing her lips to Emily's unresisting mouth.

With every fiber of her being, Emily tried not to respond to Penny's overtures. She knew Penny could sense her reluctance. Penny kissed her again and again, while keeping her thighs pressed to Emily's. Emily moaned, tried to twist away. But Penny was determined to transform her reluctance to desire. Penny's persistent mouth, the press of her body, her hands on her breasts, made Emily feel naughty and unwanted. In that instant, her fear and the hurt in her seat melted away and were replaced by the need to be held in Penny's arms. She came alive then, began to respond with thrusts of her own.

She squealed softly as Penny slipped a finger between her thighs. Penny's hand saddled the dampened mound of her sex while a lone finger wormed its way into her. Emily held her breath, waiting for the first delightful spasm. She moaned softly, pleading. Her lips parted, begging for Penny's tongue to enter. Penny slid another finger into her. Her tongue met Emily's. She languished in her restraints, weak, awash in pleasure. Her cuffs added to her pleasure. Penny's fingers squished deep into her sex. Emily threw back her head as she drifted to the brink with this ebony-haired fox. She was beginning to see stars when Miss Devreux suddenly withdrew her fingers, her lips, and her body. Emily opened her eyes. Miss Devreux was looking at her with a pitiful expression. Her face had turned into a mask. She stepped back and slapped Emily across her cheek.

"You little slut! Did you think you could escape your paddling by closing your eyes and making noises for me?"

Harriet watched intently. Her eyes shone with wetness. "Penny is the perfect tease, Charles. No woman does it better." Charles nodded dully. He was trying to hold himself for the paddling.

"M-Miss D-Devreux, I-I didn't...I-I m-mean...I'm s-sorry—"

"Not sorry enough, my plump raisin. Lesson three. When Aunt Penelope says you're going to get a good paddling, believe it!"

Penny removed her jeans and blouse. Beneath them she wore black high-cut silk panties, garter belt, and fishnet stockings. Her breasts were high on her chest, smallish and rounded, with tiny nutlike nipples. The black underwear set off the pale alabaster luster of her skin. She unhooked her garters with easy catlike motions while her dark eyes held Emily so that Emily could not look away from Penny's slender shape, high firm breasts, thighs barely larger than her upper arms. Her sex, buried in an ebony haze, was girlish and piquant in the pale light. Emily felt an odd sense of excitement. Heat flowed from her thighs into her belly to mingle with the subtle pressure within her backside.

As warm as she was, she couldn't help shivering. The simmering throb in her sex suddenly exploded and geysered upward through her body. Through a filmy sheen of tears, ecstatic with desire to be taken by Penny, she watched the seamstress pick up her paddle. Her buttocks tightened. She waited.

Without a word, Penny approached her, holding the gleaming paddle high for her to see. It came around with a solid whoosh. Charles came in his hand just as the slender blade made its first abrupt contact with Emily's already-swollen welted cheeks. Emily heard the abrupt slap and felt the sting of the paddle, its flex when it landed, before she felt the first red-hot column of pain in her seat.

Harriet watched dispassionately, assessing Penny's technique and Emily's response. She barely heard Emily's screams. She, too, was caught up in Penny's rhythm. The gleaming paddle flew as if it were automated. Emily hung in her cuffs. Each paddle stroke rippled and sank into her larded buttocks. Penny spanked her unmercifully, finally easing off, allowing her paddle to caress rather than punish Emily's flesh. She paddled Emily's thighs, inflaming her desire.

Emily moaned, but it was not in pain. She whispered encouragement to Miss Devreux. The soft flesh of her bottom and thighs slowly darkened from cream to polished copper to scarlet. She lost control of her senses when the paddle clattered on the floor.

"M-Miss Devreux," she cried. Sensing her need, Penny took her warm supplicant body in her arms.

Emily opened her mouth and thrust her thighs as best she could into Miss Devreux's panties. She moaned when her lips met Penny's.

"You little slut," Penny whispered, "pretending you didn't want to be punished. Lesson three went well." Emily nodded vigorously, kept on kissing her. "Next time I won't be so gentle. You might not be so eager—"

"Miss Devreux. I've never been cropped…or p-paddled…never punished like that. I-I had no idea—"

"Be still! You're chattering like a schoolgirl on her way to the principal's office."

"M-Miss Devreux, will you take me to…b-bed?"

Penny smiled and moved away. "Changed your tune, didn't you? No, I'm not going to take you to bed. You're spending the night here, but it won't be with me. She jerked a rope hanging from the ceiling. "I've summoned another girl. A girl who has learned to do exactly as she's told. She'll spend the night with me while you watch and listen how to conduct yourself in my presence. Don't move or make a sound. I'll get my paddle out again."

"I don't understand," Emily pleaded.

"Lesson four, Emily." There was a soft knock on the door. "You may come in, Maria."

The door opened slowly. It was the pretty dark-skinned maid who'd met Emily at the door. She was dressed for bed—barefoot, in a long cotton nightgown. Her hair was pleated into a single thick braid that ran down her back. Her breasts were large and full, jiggling gently beneath her nightgown as she came into the room. She glanced at Emily, then looked tentatively at Penny with wide, soft eyes.

"Into bed, Maria. Draw up your legs and spread your thighs. Place your hands at the head of the bed and keep them there."

Penny blew out the oil lamp and slid into the bed. A full moon flooded the room with silver light. Emily imagined herself pressed into Penny's warmth. She heard Penny laugh. In the pale light she could see Miss Devreux teasing the half-hard tips of Maria's nipples until they grew erect. She heard a floorboard squeak as Harriet and Charles tiptoed out of their room and left the house.

Penny dropped her head. Emily imagined she was kissing Maria. Her head did not come up. Maria must have responded as she would have, with parted lips. Emily swallowed hard with envy as Miss Devreux removed the maid's nightgown. In the moonlight, the young woman's body shown like polished mahogany. Penny's hands lifted and shaped the gleaming hemispheres of Maria's breasts. A shiver ran through Emily as she remembered Miss Devreux's hands on her body. Her all-night lovemaking with Susan, their uncontrolled frenzied orgasms. Unable to watch any longer, Emily drew in her breath and closed her eyes.

The nesting dildo had done its job. Were Miss Devreux to touch it, Emily would have exploded in a fiery blast of passion. Miss Devreux was at Maria's breasts now, head down, sucking hard at the girl. Emily looked down at her own nipples, distended and hard. She imagined Miss Devreux's lips at her breast, her mouth over her nipple and the surrounding ring of dark nubby flesh. The imagined sucking pull of Miss Devreux's tongue and lips was so powerful that the imagined sensation stabbed deep into her breasts and weeping sex. The sucking sounds and Maria's moans triggered spasms of pleasure. She was about to have an orgasm without touching herself. She shut her eyes tight and let the feeling build within her until it finally burst into flame when Miss Devreux brought down her crop in a frenzied swing across Maria's big breasts. Maria's scream brought the second wave.

Propelled dizzily downward now into a bottomless abyss by the smacks of the crop and Maria's pleas, sparkling splinters of bliss flashed in front of her closed eyes.

She vaguely heard Miss Devreux's voice.

"And you thought I'd forgotten your bit of misbehavior this morning. Miss Devreux never forgets a maid's mistake. Let this be a lesson to you." Maria sobbed out her apology as the crop covered her breasts and thighs and belly with thin welts. "Get between my legs, you fat bitch! Show me just how sorry you are."

Stunned by her passion, only half conscious, Emily wondered if Miss Devreux was speaking to her. She reluctantly opened her eyes. Maria's face was tucked between Miss Devreux's thighs. By the looks of Maria's bobbing head and the sounds she was making, she was doing everything possible to prove how sorry she was. Emily's sex throbbed and wept at the sight, ached with a need her imagination couldn't possibly satisfy....

The next morning, Emily was asleep in her chains

when Penny shook her awake. Puzzled and confused, Emily dreamily watched Miss Devreux unlace the supple leather cuffs that had been her bed for the night.

Penny dressed her in her old uniform, then took her downstairs to feed her before they spent the day in Penny's sewing room. Working furiously, by early evening, Penny had cut and nearly finished Emily's special black outfit along with one of her workaday cotton uniforms.

Maria had washed the heavy denim until it was pliant and soft. As Penny dressed Emily in her new uniform, she told Emily she would no longer be wearing Mrs. Bertram's hideous bras beneath her uniforms. Emily's fingers were shaking so badly as she buttoned the bodice over her breasts, Penny had to finish closing the front herself. The bodice fit like a tight-laced Victorian corset. It pinched Emily's waistline, forcing her breasts upward into the open bodice. She could scarcely draw a deep breath. When she did inhale, the upper halves of her breasts ballooned over the low-scooped neckline. Not satisfied with the low neck, Penny worked the neckline lower until it stopped just above her nipple line.

"We don't want to show everything," Penny said with a smile.

Looking at herself in the mirror, Emily was startled by the expanse of breast and deep cleavage. She could see her nipples beneath the soft cotton. "Isn't it...isn't it too low?" she asked.

Penny laughed. "*Vraiment*, Emily. You are too naive for words. Don't you understand it's what your mistress wants? You will wear what she dictates."

Emily blushed at the prospect of making beds in such a low-necked dress. She'd show much more than Molly or Sarah. She turned sideways. She had to admit she liked how the blue-striped cotton dropped over her hips, falling gracefully to the floor. She'd never worn a dress that fit as well as this one. Without a bra, the tailored bodice supported, but allowed her breasts to assume their naturally round contours. She leaned forward slowly, holding her breath.

"You won't fall out, Emily. Very nearly perhaps, but unless it's intentional, you will not fall out. The bodice is designed to permit intimate caresses. There are women who will want to touch you there."

Emily looked at Penny. "D-Do you m-mean—"

Penny smiled. "I mean Madame Godwin or one of her associates might take out a breast."

"Miss Devreux," Emily said weakly.

Penny shook her head. "You are such a prissy thing. Now get into the black silk."

The silk skirt rustled as Penny dropped the new dress over Emily's shoulders, shrugging it down and over Emily's hips. Penny positioned Emily in front of the full-length mirror while she closed the high back of the dress. Emily nearly fainted when she saw herself.

"Your fabulous bosom screamed to be done in the French Empire style. Though Napoleon's Josephine was much smaller through the bust, that slender neck and clear complexion made me think of this style. I think the dress sets off every one of your best features."

The dress was startling. Expertly tailored of heavy

black silk, elegantly simple in design and execution, the neckline, trimmed in tiny white pleats, flowed in a dramatic descending-ascending arc from shoulder to shoulder. It disappeared beneath Emily's bare breasts where it intersected the high waistline. Emily's ivory breasts, dark nipples, and aureoles rested side by side like a basket of fruit in a fluted framework of starched white linen. The skirt fell in a straight line from the Empire waist to the floor. Emily brought her arms up, but she could not bring herself to cover her breasts. The dress had begun to change her. She turned to Penny, hoping this wasn't all a dream.

"Miss Devreux, I-I don't know wh-what to think."

Penny smiled proudly. "It's my finest work. But you do give a designer something to work with. Turn around for me."

As Emily spun, her breasts rippled and spread. Penny pulled up a chair and sat. "Now serve me as if you were holding a tray." Emily bowed slowly, her arms extended. Her breasts plumped heavily between her arms. Penny teased the elongated tips of her breasts.

"I really ought to color them," she murmured. "Make them even more startling. In gold or a bright scarlet I should think."

"Miss Devreux!"

"Hush, you silly girl. You like the idea every bit as much as me."

Emily giggled then. In relief, she laughed out loud like a little girl. She could hardly wait for Madame Godwin to see her.

CHAPTER 9

The next morning, before Penny loaded Emily into her tiny sports car for the long drive back to Lilac Row, Mrs. Henley had rousted Molly and Annie out of bed and sent them to the cellar laundry to start the wash. She was not in a good mood that morning. For no good reason, Madame Godwin hadn't let the housekeeper know she was expecting Miss Viola Baker later in the day, and that her guest would stay for a couple of nights.

"Madame, with all due respect, I do not like being told you're expecting a houseguest in the next few hours. My house is a mess. It's wash day. The girls are washing clothes and bedding. The laundry won't be off the lines for hours. What will Miss Baker think when she arrives and sees wash hanging on the lines? Now, I'll have to change the bed again in the Rose Room. Isn't that where you want her?"

Harriet nodded. "I'm sorry, Mrs. Henley. Viola didn't call until late last night. But since card club is tomorrow night, and Emily is due home this morning, I thought it would be nice if I asked Viola to stay over. She does have a long drive. I don't think she'll mind seeing wash on the line."

"But I mind, Madame. I take a great deal of pride in running this house as it should be. I am a full-charge housekeeper, and I take that responsibility seriously."

"I know you do, Mrs. Henley. As I said, I'm truly sorry. Emily will be back soon. She can change the beds and do what has to be done inside." She glanced at the clock. "I really must go. I have an appointment in town. I'll probably pass Penny and Emily on their way out here."

"As you say," Mrs. Henley said stiffly, and hurried out the door to wake the girls and get them started on the wash.

Annie sighed as she came down the back stairs. She hated wash days, and liked the cellar even less. It was a dreary place to work. As many times as she went down there, she knew she'd would never get used to it. The stairs were narrow and worn, and creaked beneath her feet as she went down them, lugging a heavy basket of wash. She kept one shoulder to the rough limestone wall, her eyes in front of her to spot fresh cobwebs. The smells of laundry soap, dampness, and mold stung her nostrils as she descended. At the bottom of the stairs, she heard a scurry and an abrupt squeal. Thick warm fur as stiff as Madame's hairbrush slipped beneath her skirt and began to rub itself against her leg. She jumped in fright, almost lost her balance and dropped the wicker basket before she looked down to see Bert, Mrs. Henley's huge tomcat. He stared up at her with shining wide-set amber eyes. In his proud jaws he held the remnants of a tiny mouse. Annie's snort of fright made Bert flick his thick tail in disdain and disappear into the gloom while Annie paused to regain her composure.

"God, Molly, will you get down here?" she whispered. "This place gives me the creeps." She hurried through the gloom to the old green Maytag and began to sort the laundry into lights and darks, all the while praying to herself that Molly would be down soon. Her coarse denim skirt, made of the same material as Emily's, outlined a young woman's bottom as she bent to the wash. Her blonde hair was pulled back into a hurriedly brushed ponytail. She was nineteen, but looked more like sixteen.

The morning light did its best to find its way through the small windows set high along the walls. But as dirty as the windows were, the cellar remained mostly dark. Rough-hewn log beams covered with a thick coat of whitewash ran in uneven rows directly above her head. The beams were so low she could hardly stand without brushing her hair against them.

She wiped a tendril of cobweb from her face, stepped carefully on the hard-packed dirt floor. She just knew there was another mouse waiting quietly for her to turn her back. "Here, Bert," she whispered. Along the walls the dirt was soft, providing a natural haven for rodents and spiders. She could hear Bert. He was out of sight now, somewhere nearby, his raspy purr occasionally interrupted as he crunched and gulped his prey. The yellow-white pocked limestone walls seemed to close in, enveloping her with their damp, cold breath. The place was more like a dungeon than a cellar.

She heard Molly hurrying down the stairs. Rock-solid Molly. Nothing bothered her, including Mrs. Bertram, who never seemed to find fault with her work. Molly dumped an armload of sheets on the floor. She smiled brightly at Annie.

"You look like you've seen a ghost."

"I think I did. Bert had it in his mouth."

"Come on, let's fill the washing machine."

While Annie ran a hose to fill the washer and pair of tubs with fresh hot water Molly added bluing, soap, and a load of whites to the surging water.

Annie glanced toward the steps. "We've got a few minutes while that first load is washing. I'm going to the fruit cellar."

"Annie, why don't you do that sort of thing at night?"

"I would have, but I was so tired last night, I fell asleep before—"

"You're crazy! Go away. Get it out of your system. I'll watch for Mrs. Henley." Molly shook her head as she poked the wash paddle into the gurgling wash.

"Thanks loads, Molly."

Annie giggled nervously as she lifted her skirt and hurried into the fruit cellar at the far end of the basement. It was an unbearably dark place, but it was the only place during the day where she could put a stop to the infernal ache and itch in her sex. She'd woken up with it that morning and there was only one way to make it go away. Safe inside the small wood-framed structure, she hoisted her skirt above her waist and slipped a hand inside her panties. Bert wandered in, brushed his coat against her bare leg, but this time she ignored him. Her eyes were closed. Nothing meant anything now, except the two wet fingers between her thighs. Her mind was filled with Jack, the grocery boy, who'd taught her how to pet. She was inching toward an incredible orgasm when she heard Mrs. Henley's heavy steps on the cellar stairs.

"Omigod," she whispered, knowing there was no way she could get back to Molly and the laundry without the housekeeper seeing her. Nor would she be able to explain what she was doing here when she was supposed to be washing clothes. "Oh, God," she sobbed. "I'm going to get it again." Her knees shook as she pushed open the wooden door and stepped back into the basement, knowing she was one step closer to being sent away to live and work in Madame Cartwright's laundry.

Molly was feeding wash through the wringers. She did not look at Annie. Mrs. Henley stood next to her, her hands on her hips, staring at Annie. "Well, well. What have we here? Were you having a good time in there? Come here!"

Annie reluctantly approached, knowing she was going to be severely punished. Mrs. Henley lifted her skirt, thrust her hand between Annie's thighs. Annie's wetness had seeped into her panties, dampening Mrs. Henley's fingers. Mrs. Henley lifted her fingers to her nose.

"I could understand if you'd been foolish enough to wet your pants. With what you've got coming that would make sense. But you didn't wet your pants. You were playing with yourself." Mrs. Henley's open hand flew, striking Annie hard across her cheek. Molly gasped behind her. "How many times have I told you not to do those dirty things to yourself? Get up to the kitchen! I'm having another word with Madame. You're bound to be packed off to Madame Cartwright, and I for one will say good riddance."

Sobbing, Annie hurried up the narrow staircase with the angry housekeeper right behind her.

"When I get through with you, young lady, you'll wish you were under Madame Cartwright's thumb this very minute."

Fifteen minutes later, Penny and Emily arrived in Penny's tiny sports car. They were standing on the portico, waiting while Penny pushed the doorbell a second time. No answer. She pushed it again. "Where is everybody?" she asked impatiently. "Harriet—Madame Godwin—said she'd be in town this morning. But where is Mrs. Henley?"

"I thought I saw Molly bringing up a basket of wash. Perhaps, she—"

Penny didn't wait. She went to the side of the house while Emily tried the front door. The big brass knob turned easily. "It's open," she called to Penny, who was about to disappear around the side of the house.

"Thank heavens," Penny said, and hurried into the house with Emily following behind her.

As soon as they were in the foyer, Emily heard the sharp splats of Mrs. Henley's paddle. Penny's mood returned. "Someone is getting her seat warmed. We'll just go see."

They followed the sounds into the kitchen where they found Mrs. Henley seated on a bench. Annie's slender body was sprawled across her lap. The girl's arms were tightly bound behind her with a length of clothesline. A dish towel was tied around her head, forced between her lips, so that she could only utter moans as the paddle sank into her bottom. Penny led Emily into the brightly lit kitchen. They stood off to one side, watching.

In between strokes of the paddle, the housekeeper managed to say, "I'll be done in a few moments, Miss Devreux. This one was supposed to be washing clothes. She had the temerity to run off...and, well, I'll explain later. She won't do it again—at least for a while."

Penny's voice was silky. "Please, Mrs. Henley, don't hurry the punishment on my account. What a wonderful idea to gag her. I've adopted the same practice at my home."

"It keeps her quiet while I paddle her."

The housekeeper's gleaming paddle mesmerized and

frightened Emily. She'd not seen it before. It was long and thick with a handle large enough for both of the housekeeper's hands. Each stroke flattened Annie's seat, splotching and swelling it. The poor girl wouldn't sit for a week. Seeing Annie in uniform reminded Emily that she was dressed in the same outfit. She couldn't look down at herself. Her breasts lay in a deeply rounded cradle of denim that offered a spectacular display of jiggling breast and cleavage. Penny hadn't seemed concerned as she drove her through town, but then, she didn't have to wear the uniform either.

Mrs. Henley finally stopped the noisy paddling and set Annie back on her feet. Annie looked hopefully at the housekeeper, expecting to be released and her gag removed. "No such luck, naughty girl." Emily watched in horror as Mrs. Henley dragged Annie to the kitchen table and sat her down on a straight-backed chair where she retied her arms to the chair back and tightened the dish towel covering her mouth. Penny looked on with an approving expression.

"It's a pretty sight, Mrs. Henley. I would not want to be one of your domestics."

"It'll do for now, until I finish her later, upstairs." She hung her paddle among the overhead pots.

Penny pinched Emily's arm. "And what do you think of this one in her new uniform?"

The housekeeper leaned her hips against the counter and crossed her long arms over her chest. "Bosom like a cow. They'd pass for tenderloins." She came to Emily, squeezed her breasts until they hurt.

"Firm enough, but far too large. Look at that fat bottom. My paddle could be put to good use there."

"No doubt," Penny smiled.

"Miss Devreux, if you don't mind, I'll be getting myself and Emily here back to work. Emily's going upstairs to vacuum and dust. Miss Baker is coming this afternoon. Will you be joining her and the others at card club tomorrow night?"

Penny nodded. "You go on with your housework. Is Madame Godwin returning soon?"

"I expect her shortly."

"I'll run Emily's new dress up to her room, then wait for Harriet in the living room."

"Very good, Miss Devreux."

Mrs. Henley told Emily to get busy or she'd find herself over the worktable getting her first dose of the housekeeper's paddle. Emily hurried upstairs, grateful to be away from Mrs. Henley's sharp tongue. She was mortified at being made to wear such a revealing uniform, but neither Annie nor Mrs. Henley had made much of a fuss.

That afternoon, Emily was running a vacuum on the second floor when she felt a hand on her shoulder. Spinning around with a startled look, she bumped into Mrs. Henley. The housekeeper handed her a stack of folded sheets. They were Madame's best lavender linens, still warm from the mangle.

"Strip the bed in the Rose Room. Put these on. It's where Miss Baker will stay tonight."

"B-But Mrs. Henley, all the guest beds h-have clean sheets—"

155

Mrs. Henley's eyes narrowed. "Don't be impertinent with me, Emily. I'll take you straight to the kitchen."

"Yes, Ma'am," Emily sighed, wondering how she'd get it all done.

"Madame Godwin didn't tell me she was having a houseguest until this morning. I want these sheets on that bed before Miss Baker arrives." She raised a finger. "Not one wrinkle or…"

"I-I understand, Ma'am."

"Finish your vacuuming, then change the bed."

Mrs. Henley spun on her heel like a drill sergeant and disappeared down the stairs to begin dinner. Emily brushed a damp strand from her face as she restarted the Kirby and pushed the heavy cleaner down the hall. It was already two o'clock. She'd have to hurry or risk a paddling. No punishment had been mentioned by the housekeeper, but her expression assured Emily if she didn't have the Rose Room made up before Madame's guest arrived, Mrs. Henley was going to take that awful paddle to her.

Emily was bent over the bed in the Rose Room, working furiously to draw the bottom sheet taut when Madame Godwin suddenly appeared in the doorway. Emily's damp breasts sagged against the low neckline of her uniform, threatened to fall out of her bodice as she tugged and smoothed the sheet. Knowing how she must look, Emily was mortified. She brushed a damp lock from her hair and kept on with the bed. She did not look up at Madame Godwin or her guest.

"This will be your room, Viola. I'm sure you'll be

very comfortable here—as soon as my lazy maid finishes making the bed. She was supposed to have finished before you arrived."

Viola studied Emily from the doorway. "I shouldn't say this in front of her, but she's a pretty thing. Country girl."

Emily raised her head to look into Viola's pale blue eyes, cool and serene. Viola looked to be Harriet's age, with black hair severely arranged in a tight little knot at the back of her head. Her chic navy suit, glossy black heels, and smart pillbox with netted veil reeked of money. The suit fit her frame perfectly, molding itself over her breasts and the comfortable spread of her hips. Viola studied Emily from beneath her veil. The veil hid everything but her mouth, which was large and full and neatly lipsticked. Not a hair on her head was out of place. Confronted by such a sophisticate, Emily felt like a country bumpkin.

Viola ignored Emily, directed her comments to Harriet. "I saw Penny in town. She mentioned her." Viola stared unabashedly at Emily's dramatic décolletage. "Such an ample bustline for such a young woman."

"She's got an awful lot to learn. Henrietta Christiansen nearly ruined her."

"I understand Leah's involved."

"Very much so."

"I can see why."

"Stand up, Emily. Where are your manners?" Harriet's voice cut through the heavy silence. She remained in the doorway, arms folded beneath her breasts.

Emily forced herself to straighten up and look up at Miss Baker. Hot and flushed, feeling like she was completely naked, she froze in an upright stance as Viola approached. Viola's gloved fingers gently squeezed her upper arm.

"Miss Devreux said you were plump, but I had no idea...." Her eyes swept the milk-fleshed expanse of Emily's breasts and cleavage, then rose to her face, compelling Emily to look into her cold blue eyes. "Your mistress isn't pleased. You were to be done before I arrived—but I'm early." She smiled wickedly. "Pity for you." Viola put her hands around Emily's waist. She nearly succeeded in spanning Emily's pinched-in waist between her extended thumbs and forefingers. The heavy striped cotton creaked in protest as her fingers squeezed harder. "Almost," Viola said over her shoulder. "Think what a tight-laced corset would do for that waistline."

"Just wait until tomorrow night."

Emily shivered as Viola's hands slid upward beneath her arms. Viola held her tightly at the bulging sides of her breasts, then pressed inward, causing Emily's breasts to expand from her uniform like inflating balloons. "Oh, my," Viola whispered. She glanced back at Harriet. "Do you mind?" Harriet smiled and shook her head. Viola's leather-clad fingers quickly unbuttoned the front of Emily's uniform.

Poor Emily was transfixed. Right in front of her mistress she was being undressed like a doll, a plaything. Her plaintive expression did nothing to stop Viola, whose fingers tore at the buttons until Emily's bare breasts fell into her hands. Viola held their soft under-bellies, slapped them lightly, and pinched her nipples until they were stinging and erect. Viola lifted her veil. Her dark-edged eyes trapped Emily, drew her in. Emily stared hypnotically at Viola's glistening scarlet mouth, the lavender blush of her cheeks. Viola's lips parted to expose the pink tip of her tongue. She came closer. Emily's eyes fluttered closed as Viola tilted her head and kissed her.

"That's quite enough, Emily."

Viola laughed softly. "I'm really sorry, Harriet. It's been awhile. I got carried away."

"And this one wasn't going to stop you either."

Emily felt herself being pulled away from Viola. When she opened her eyes Harriet was in front of her, tugging and closing the bodice of her uniform. "You ought to be ashamed of yourself, you lazy thing. Do you honestly think I'd let this happen when there are beds to make?"

Emily felt like a naughty little girl who'd been caught wetting her pants. "I-I tried, Madame. I meant to f-finish before—"

"Don't say another word. It only adds affront to your indolence. Mrs. Henley will expect you in the kitchen right after breakfast tomorrow. Perhaps a long session with her paddle will change your attitude." Harriet closed the last button and straightened Emily's neckline. "Finish that bed, then go straight to your room. I'll be up later."

"Y-Yes, Ma'am," Emily whispered, nearly choking on her words while Viola stood watching with an amused expression. Harriet and Viola left the guest room as if nothing at all had happened.

Emily was sitting on the edge of her bed when Madame Godwin came into her room. She had the clothes brush in her hand. She pulled a sturdy wooden chair away from the wall and sat down, her feet together. "Come here," she said. "You've had this coming for some time. Consider it a prelude to Mrs. Henley's paddle. Lift your skirt."

Emily whimpered as she drew the folds of her heavy skirt above her waist. Harriet worked the waistband of her panties down to the garter snaps holding up her stockings. She frowned at the damp spot and odor emanating from Emily's panties, but said nothing.

"Over my lap, hands on the floor. You embarrassed me. I'm not accustomed to showing my guests to their rooms and finding half-made beds. Mrs. Henley says you were given plenty of time to change that bed."

Emily felt Harriet's bosom expand and settle into her ribs as she lifted her arm and brought the clothes brush down with a single motion. The brush smacked loudly in the tiny room, sending shivers of fat rolling across Emily's thighs. She shrieked in pain at the first imprint. "The next time Mrs. Henley tells you to do something"—Harriet's brush landed again, emphasizing her point—"I want it done immediately!" The brush abruptly punctuated her remark. "Is that clear, young lady?" Two more hard spanks.

"Y-Yes, M-Madame," Emily sobbed, and yielded to the pain.

"And you'd better stop playing with yourself. You're beginning to smell like Annie." The hairbrush flew then, cutting swath after swath across Emily's flaming seat.

Directly beneath the pathetic scene unfolding on the third floor, Viola lay on her back in her slip, listening to the steady smacks and Emily's cries. Her hands were hidden beneath her slip. Her mouth was slack and wet. She stared at the ceiling with a glazed expression, wondering how she could possibly get that girl to her own home.

Emily was confined to her bedroom until after dinner. At seven, Harriet came up, saying it was time to meet her husband, Charles. She arranged Emily's hair, applied rouge and a fresh layer of lipstick to Emily's pursed lips. Twilight was settling over the estate when Harriet led Emily down the leaf-strewn track to the cottage. The wan amber glow of a lamp through the open shutters of the cottage beckoned Emily, reassuring her. Her beating heart began to subside as she followed Madame inside the cottage.

The interior was poorly lit and smelled of pipe tobacco, damp, and wood smoke. The crumbling remains of a fire smoldered in the fireplace. An oil lamp burned softly on the desk, casting a pallid cone of light onto a typewriter. Mr. Godwin was nowhere to be seen. Emily watched her mistress take the oil lamp and open the door that led to the second room. Harriet beckoned to Emily to follow her into the darkened room.

It took her a moment to see Mr. Godwin. His back was to her. He was bent over the foot of the bed in a sleeveless undershirt. His pants and shorts lay around his ankles. The sight sent a chill through her. She could scarcely breathe. His animal-like thrusts, grunts, and slender white legs stabbed at her sensibilities.

Harriet lifted the lamp. The flickering light danced on Mr. Godwin's gleaming back. Like a flashing strobe, the flame caught the male mass of rippling muscle, his hardened buttocks, bulging upper arms. Then Emily saw the naked young man trapped beneath him, helpless, yielding. His ankles were tethered to the bedposts. He lay sprawled beneath Mr. Godwin with his head and arms spread-eagled on the bed. Madame Godwin waited.

She watched the pair's passion build with no discernible expression. Emily held her breath. The boy began to cry. Whether sobbing in anguish or joy, Emily couldn't tell. He lifted his thin hips into Mr. Godwin's thrusting thighs, as if beseeching the older man to drive even deeper. Emily felt terribly moved, privileged to witness the perverse intimacy between the two men. While her heart went out to the boy, she found herself hoping Mr. Godwin would not relinquish his savage grip until the young man screamed for mercy. Mr. Godwin's gasp jarred her senses. She watched his buttocks become taut and accelerate in powerfully swift shoves that drew cries of protest from the young man. In another second it was over.

The young man's body shook. He moaned and stiffened as Mr. Godwin shuddered and emptied himself.

The moment slowed. Emily watched in slow motion as Mr. Godwin bent over the boy, thrust his hips in quick little jabs to work all of his semen into the young man. The boy eagerly accepted the older man's offering, seeming to want even more.

Harriet's hand slipped into hers. Mr. Godwin slowly backed out of the boy. He turned and looked sheepishly at Emily, then at his wife. "Harriet," he said dryly, "your timing is impeccable."

Emily barely heard him, ignored the plight of the naked young man still tied to the bed. Her entire being was taken up with the size of Mr. Godwin's cock. It sprang from his thighs like a great curved cucumber of flesh; engorged, thick veined and slick, it terminated in a bulbous scarlet-hued tip. Beneath it swung his plump scrotum, half covered in dark hair. Mr. Godwin looked much larger than the thing Miss Devreux had forced into her.

Mr. Godwin looked down at himself, then at Harriet. "I could clean up," he offered softly.

"Don't bother, my love" Harriet said. "By the looks of him, your young man wants more of the same. I should think he'll be enough for one night. Besides, you've frightened Emily. She's not ready yet." Harriet put her arm around Emily and led her out of the cottage.

As they made their way along the moonlit path, Harriet said, "Viola has asked for you. You'll spend the night with her."

Emily nodded, dumbly. "Yes, Madame," she whispered, unable to rid herself of the vision of Mr. Godwin's bulging cock.

CHAPTER 10

E mily bathed and put on a clean nightgown before
going down to Viola's room. She was reminded of
pajama parties, sleeping over, and complaining to
Mama she didn't own decent pajamas. Her flannel
gowns had been through the wash so many times they
were nearly transparent. But it was all she had. Smells of
damp and baby powder trailed behind her as she padded
down the darkened stairs. Her heart was thudding by
the time she knocked on Viola's door.

"Come in."

The Rose Room was bathed in the soft light of the
bed lamp. Viola sat upright in bed in a negligee so sheer
Emily could see the outlines of her breasts. Her shining
black hair was down now, fanned out over her shoulders.

165

She looked younger now and prettier, and less severe. She smiled at Emily, patted the bed beside her. Emily didn't move.

"I know you're frightened, but you must learn to trust and obey. I shouldn't want to spank you before Mrs. Henley paddles you tomorrow morning." Emily took a tentative step. "Get into bed. I won't bite you." Viola threw back the coverlet.

Emily slid timidly into bed alongside the older woman. Viola leaned across her to switch off the lamp. In the darkness, Viola's hair swept softly over Emily's face. Viola's body was warm and smelled of Prell and fresh-cut flowers. She put her arms around Emily and drew her into the pliant heat of her breasts. Emily instinctively relaxed and snuggled closer.

"See," Viola whispered, kissing Emily's forehead, "I'm not an ogre. "I'll be with you tomorrow when Mrs. Henley gets out her paddle." Emily began to cry. "I know it hurts. Mrs. Henley is a formidable woman." She kissed Emily's cheek as she smoothed her hair from her face.

"I-It's not fair, Miss B-Baker."

Viola's hand slid over Emily's breast. Her other hand began to caress Emily's thighs. "Who ever said life was fair?"

"I'm frightened "

"You mustn't think about tomorrow."

"That p-paddle—"

"It's simply punishment. It's why you're at Lilac Row. You need a woman's guidance. Now dry those tears

166

and take off your nightgown. I want to have a look at you."

As soon as Emily had shrugged off her nightgown and laid back on the pillow, Viola was on top of her. Emily found herself hard on her back with Viola's bare thighs straddling her face, pinning her to the bed. In the faint light of a waning moon, Viola's sex yawned wide, gleaming like fresh-sliced apricots. The older woman's scent was sharp and clean. Viola's plump breasts, tipped with nipples the size of ripening olives, turned silvery in the moonlight. Emily lifted her head. Her lips brushed Viola's thighs and the moist surface of Viola's sex. Viola lifted Emily's hand to the velvety underbelly of her breast.

"Let go, sweet thing. Bury yourself."

Emily was beside herself, tongue-poking and sucking her way into Viola's wet, tangy crevice. Viola's thighs settled over her, nearly shutting off her air, encouraging her to take Viola into her mouth. Emily did not see the short black whip with its knotted thongs in Viola's hand until she raised her arm and began to lash Emily's hips and thighs. The knotted tendrils frightened more than hurt, like a thousand mosquito bites. An itch that would not go away. The needling points of pain forced Emily's mouth wider, drove her tongue deep into Viola. Viola moved in synchrony with her whip, bucking and thrusting as her ardor increased. Emily could scarcely breathe. She was mesmerized by this woman. Her body stiffened into a sinuous arch, shook with unbridled passion as Viola whipped her into ecstasy. Her open-mouthed screams bubbled into Viola's streaming sex. Viola dropped the whip onto the bed and plunged her weeping sex hard into Emily's mouth. Viola gasped and shuddered as the first orgasm ripped through her.

Emily's fingers spread the slippery petals of Viola's sex. Viola's heat and scent were all she knew, a powerful aphrodisiac that drove her face into Viola's glistening membranes. Her tongue was as hard as Mr. Godwin's cock. Like a projectile, it sought to bury itself in Viola's cleft. Emily moaned, let her mouth fill with the taste of Viola. She lost all sense of time and place. Spasms of pleasure shot through her. She was barely aware of the older woman above her. She slipped over the precipice, falling, falling, knowing nothing now but bright, pure ecstasy...

The next morning, Mrs. Henley and Viola were at the breakfast table when Emily hurried down the back stairs into the white warmth of the kitchen. Rich scents of baking bread, nutmeg and cinnamon, and fresh-brewed coffee filled the room. Mrs. Henley glanced at the clock.

"It's about time you came down. Another five minutes and I'd have been up there."

Viola smiled. "We let you sleep an extra half hour. "It was a long night."

Mrs. Henley's silence assured Emily she did not approve of such goings-on in her house. Rain beat against the kitchen windows, thrumming as evenly as marching soldiers on the porch roof. Emily felt terribly self-conscious in her low-necked denim uniform. Miss Baker showed no signs that she remembered the previous night.

Had it really happened? In the wet morning light, the intimacy of Miss Baker's body seemed vague and unreal.

Mrs. Henley gestured to a place setting. "Sit down, Emily. You cannot start your day without breakfast."

"I-I'm not hungry, M-Mrs. Henley." In fact, with what was going to happen she could not bear the thought of eating breakfast.

"Emily!"

"Y-Yes, Ma'am."

Emily sat across from Viola. Her breasts swelled and rose like rich cream as she sat. Viola stared unabashedly at her, forcing Emily to avert her eyes. She knew Miss Baker sensed her fear of being paddled. The rain beat a steady tattoo on the windowpanes. Drafts of cool air flowed through the warm kitchen, coating Emily's bare upper arms with gooseflesh. When Emily finished, Mrs. Henley set down her coffee mug and rose from her chair.

"I know a young lady who's due for a paddling. Will you stay, Miss Baker? I would appreciate your help."

"Certainly," Viola purred.

Mrs. Henley beckoned Emily to her worktable and butcher block. A pair of leather straps and buckles hung below the top on one side. Two more straps and buckles were fastened to the bottoms of the short, fat legs on the opposite side. Mrs. Henley laid Emily over the table. Viola spread Emily's legs and buckled her ankles to the table legs. Mrs. Henley buckled Emily's wrists to the upper straps.

Unable to move, Emily shivered as her plump

bosom compressed itself onto the tabletop. The table smelled of bread dough, onions, and countless applications of bleach. Mrs. Henley reached up to the copper kettleware above the table and took down her paddle. Viola lifted Emily's skirt and slip, folded them neatly onto her back. Emily shivered as the cool, damp air flowed over her legs.

"Garters too?" Viola asked.

Mrs. Henley nodded.

Viola's hands were warm and soothing as they undid the garters at the backs of Emily's thighs and lowered her panties to her knees. She held its handle in both hands. The look in her eye assured Emily she was going to get it good. The paddle came around with a whoosh. Emily heard Miss Baker catch her breath as the paddle landed with a loud splat on Emily inflated cheeks. Its polished surface sank deep into Emily's flesh. Rippling layers of fat radiated outward from Emily's bottom-cheeks and into her thighs. A bright red imprint marked where the big paddle had landed. Emily tried to lift herself from the table. Mrs. Henley swung the long-handled paddle again, bridging the deep cleft between Emily's crown cheeks, smacking both cheeks and setting Emily's bottom on fire.

"Naughty, lazy, lazy girl!"

Mrs. Henley swung the paddle again in a swishing arc that landed with a smart crack spanning both of Emily's buttocks. Emily jumped in pain.

"That's three…and here's four!"

Mrs. Henley delivered another stinging blow to

Emily's left crown cheek. "And five!" The paddle smacked hard into Emily's right cheek, biting deep into her reddened flesh, turning it an even angrier shade of red.

Emily clawed at the work tablelegs, twisting and shrieking, no longer aware of Miss Baker's presence. Mrs. Henley was all business now. She devoted her full attention to blistering Emily's backside. The paddle smacks and ensuing stabs of pain were Emily's world now. She did not hear Mrs. Henley's lecture on housework and obedience. Miss Baker was forgotten. The two-handled paddle ruled her universe. She groaned and pleaded with the housekeeper to no avail.

"Remember how this feels, lazy girl." Mrs. Henley caught Emily squarely on both cheeks. She whacked Emily again, eliciting a soft yelp. "Remember how the paddle feels. Learn or return."

Emily knew her backside must be swollen and scarlet now. Mrs. Henley began to concentrate on Emily's upper thighs, where she guessed the housekeeper would apply her paddle until they matched her bottom. She lay motionless, sobbing quietly to herself. The paddle slowly emptied her mind. She free-floated on a sea of pain until two pairs of hands loosened her straps, freed her from the table's grip, helped her to her feet. Miss Baker lowered her skirt over her flaming bottom. Up close, Miss Baker's lips were wet, her mouth soft and full. Even through her mask of pain, Emily could see the glint of desire in Miss Baker's eyes, and compassion, too. She wished Miss Baker would take her back upstairs.

Rain peppered the windows. Beneath her in the

cellar, Emily could hear Annie and Molly doing laundry, their lilting voices carrying over the steady hum and swish of the washing machine. For no reason, it occurred to her the wash would have to be hung on the back porch. In this rain it would take forever to dry. She watched Mrs. Henley hang her paddle back on its hook. She turned to Emily, hands on hips.

"Have I taught you anything, lazy girl?"

Emily's eyes overflowed with tears. "Y-Yes, Ma'am," she whispered.

Just then, Harriet came into the kitchen. She looked at Emily, then Mrs. Henley. "Are you through with her, Mrs. Henley?"

"She's had enough punishment for one morning, Madame. I was about to send her up to make beds. I should think she'd do a better job of it today."

"I'd planned on taking her back to the cottage tonight. Do you think she'll be ready?"

Mrs. Henley examined Emily's seat carefully, squeezing Emily's reddened bottom and upper thighs. "She'll be fine by seven. There's no real harm done to a bottom that big. It's not like I gave her the full measure—like Annie's going to get later on in the day."

"It's settled then. She'll see Charles tonight."

Charles was alone at his desk writing when his wife and Emily entered the cottage. He did not seem surprised as he glanced up at Emily with piercing dark eyes and a trace of a smile. Emily thought he was the handsomest man she'd ever seen.

Madame's next words shocked her. "Emily needs a good spanking."

"Has she been a bad girl?"

"Not so much bad as simply lazy."

"Perhaps I can put some spring in her step."

"I'm sure you can."

"What would you like?"

"Mrs. Henley paddled her britches this morning. A leathering will do."

Charles's chair squeaked softly as he rose from his desk. His tall frame filled the room. He approached Emily like a leopard. She stood motionless while he ran his hands over her hips and through her hair. She waited for his hands to touch her breasts, but they didn't. She could see the five o'clock shadow on his cheeks. She could smell his aftershave, the sweet Wildroot scent in his hair. His hands were long and lean, tipped with the nails of a woman. His fingertips caressed her cheek, teased the soft lobe of her ear. And then his lips were on her. He kissed her hungrily, passionately, until she wanted to scream. His lips parted. The tip of his tongue tested her lips. As much as she wanted him, another part of her did not. The inner struggle stiffened her body. When she opened her eyes he was staring deep into them. In the flickering lamplight, she could see the preening tiger beneath. She shivered but did not move when he began to fondle the undersides of her breasts and tease her nipples erect.

Harriet moved behind Emily, drew her arms behind her. The couple led her to a leather horse she hadn't seen on her first visit. Harriet laid Emily over the horse and buckled her limbs to it while Charles got out his strap. Harriet pinned Emily's heavy denim skirt to her back and lowered her cotton panties. Charles stood in the shadows, his strap doubled over in his hand.

He moved into the light. "I've never seen such a derrière. Didn't you say Mrs. Henley paddled her this morning?"

"This very morning."

"What a pity she's going away."

"Don't spare her, Charles. Make that belt sing."

Emily could hear Mr. Godwin inhale deeply as he drew back the strap and brought it around in a whistling arc. With a soft hiss the strap made first contact with Emily's fleshy flanks. The thick leather strap curled and licked its way across her bottom, leaving a bright red swath in its track. Emily moaned. All the pain from her paddling came rushing back.

"Charles, don't hold back!"

Charles grunted his assent. He swung the looped strap harder, catching Emily on her soft upper thighs, leaving a fat, bright ridge. Emily cried out, twisted her hips. He strapped her again. She responded with a pain-filled shriek.

"That's it, Charles. You've found your rhythm." The strap flew, smacking loudly in the small room. "Step up the pace. I want that big bottom belted until it's as red and swollen as it was this morning! Adjust your stance. Put your upper body into each stroke. Perfect. Now her seat is beginning to swell."

"She takes the leather well."

"Too well. Don't hold back. She needs this."

Emily tossed her head, tried to throw herself off the horse. "A-a-e-e-g-h, M-Madame, M-Mr. G-Godwin, I-I'm s-sor-ry."

"You'll be sorrier before my husband is through with you."

Charles landed the leather near Emily's hips. "I've never…strapped…such a lush, fat bottom." Emily twisted and shrieked, yanked her body against the unyielding restraints. "She makes much more noise than Annie or Molly." The strap sizzled across Emily's upper bottom.

Harriet moved alongside the horse. "Stop that shrieking!"

Emily sobbed. "M-Madame,…M-Mr. G-Godwin,… O-o-g-h,…i-it h-hurts!"

"It's supposed to!" Harriet's voice cut through Emily's shrill cries like a knife, silencing her.

The strapping slid into a smooth rhythm, raising welt after welt on Emily's backside. When was he going to stop? She could feel his excitement. Unlike Madame Godwin and Mrs. Henley, who were all business when they spanked her, he seemed to enjoy punishing her. A glow began to spread through her thighs. Her sex tingled, came awake, aching with desire. Mr. Godwin's presence flooded her senses, stirred up strange new feelings. She glanced sideways at her persecutor. There was nothing to do now but please him. Shimmering bolts of ecstasy flowed from her sex into her belly and bottom.

She collapsed onto the damp leather until moments later when the strapping ended.

Mr. Godwin's eyes were darker now, brooding and filled with ardor. "Plump maids were meant to be fucked," he muttered. "First from behind, then between those huge breasts."

"Control yourself, Charles."

Emily lay yielding, perfectly still.

"Take her. Now."

Charles unbuttoned his pants and dropped them to the floor. Emily caught a glimpse of his huge cock springing from his cotton briefs before he disappeared behind her. His cock was huge. Thick and long with a glossy taut head, it quivered anxiously as he spread Emily's striped cheeks. He ignored her shriek of horror as he split her backside. She cried out again as the bulbous tip of his cock met her anus and thrust its way into her. When her sphincter was clamped tightly around the head of his cock, he paused, looked at Harriet.

"Deeper," she ordered softly. "Much deeper."

Emily shuddered and screamed in primal horror as he shoved himself into her. She'd never had anything so large or painful thrust into her backside. His scrotum, nestling and slapping her thighs, was as soft and warm as puppy-skin. He began to move in and out of her. His cock was like a great hot-ridged tool, unyielding as stone. His hands found their way around her waist to take hold of her breasts. He lifted them in his hands, squeezing them hard while he continued to fuck her in a slow, easy rhythm. Emily had no sense of her mistress being present during this time. Mr. Godwin's cock had seized control of her senses. She knew nothing now but the great shuddering thing inside her and the initial spasms deep within his groin. The slight swelling of his cock, the eager thrusts as he stepped into her, the heavy sway of his scrotum against her, told Emily he was close. She closed her eyes then, and buried her face in the soft leather upholstery. She could not admit she was beginning to enjoy what Mr. Godwin was doing to her.

His thrusts grew more aggressive. He felt twice as big. His cock ballooned inside her. She didn't realize she was lifting her inflamed buttocks into his thighs, trying to take even more of him. Harriet saw her response and ordered her husband to finish. With a gurgling gasp, Charles buckled his knees and exploded into Emily. Hot semen spurted, uncontrollably, for what Emily thought was an eternity. His cock swelled and jetted, filling her until she thought she would burst. With a final gasp, he slipped out of her, leaving her anxious and unsatisfied. She hoped he would finish her; but Madame stepped in then, pushing her husband away before she released Emily from the horse.

It was a warm night, the air heavy with lilac and a raucous symphony of crickets. Moonlight dappled and silvered the path back to the house. Madame Godwin was silent, absorbed in her own thoughts. Emily was hardly aware. She was crazy with desire, desperate to satisfy the horrible longing Mr. Godwin had created.

Sensing her confusion, Madame Godwin undressed

her as if she were a child. She brushed out her hair and put her into a nightgown without a word. Emily was sobbing quietly, staring at the ceiling, when Harriet drew up the thin coverlet and tucked it beneath her chin. Harriet leaned over the bed and kissed her parted lips.

Emily's eyes widened. She blurted out, "M-Madame, I-I didn't mean…I-I didn't mean to…I didn't w-want to enjoy Mr. Godwin. I-I didn't…"

Harriet brushed away the tears from Emily's cheek with the back of her hand. "It was simply a part of your training. It won't happen again."

"Must I l-leave Lilac Row?"

"Unfortunately, there is no alternative. You were sent here to be trained. I cannot escape that. Nor can you." Harriet smoothed strands of hair from Emily's eyes. "There is nothing either of us can do."

"M-Madame, what will h-happen to me there?"

Harriet smiled. "You'll be cared for in a special sort of way. There is no cause for worry."

"Wh-When will—"

"In a few days. Now you must sleep. Tomorrow evening you're going to serve at card club."

Emily lifted her head. "In the black silk?"

Harriet nodded as she rose from the bed and switched off the lamp. "Sleep tight," she whispered, and shut Emily's door behind her.

CHAPTER 11

Emily hurried down the stairs, carrying the black silk dress, fresh underwear, and patent-leather heels. She could hear the opera music pouring from the phonograph in Madame Godwin's suite. Madame would be in a good mood. Harriet was sitting by the window reading when Emily came in. She wore leather boots, a long denim skirt, and her favorite black turtleneck sweater. It was misting outside. Inside the suite, it was warm and cozy. A crackling fire threw a flickering patina of light over the lavender walls, driving off the damp. Harriet laid her book down when Emily appeared in the open doorway.

Madame smiled warmly at her, her mind clearly on the music. "Puccini." Emily nodded dumbly, not knowing who she meant. "I adore Italian opera, but Puccini is the master. His soaring arias." Harriet looked away as the diva slid up to a high C, bathing the room in shimmering vibrato.

"Have you bathed?"

Emily shook her head. She'd never been alone with Madame in her suite before.

"You can bathe here." Harriet gestured to her bedroom. "You can relax, Emily. There will be no housework—and no punishment—this afternoon. Go draw your bath. I'll be in shortly."

Emily was confused by Harriet's expansive manner. She had no idea what was in store as she tiptoed across the deep carpeting and into Madame's elegant bathroom with its black-and-white mosaic-tiled floor and Victorian claw-footed tub. After starting the bath, she took off her uniform and underwear. The elegant surroundings made her uncomfortable. Why was she even here, she asked herself as she pinned up her hair and stepped carefully into the deep, steaming tub. Madame's lilac-scented soap was rich and smooth, luxurious on her skin. Oblivious to the rain now streaming down the bathroom window, Emily closed her eyes and slipped beneath the hot soapy water. She did not hear Madame Godwin come into the bathroom.

"Are you enjoying your bath, Emily?"

Emily's eyes fluttered open. Looking down at herself, she saw the sponge between her drawn-up legs. Its hard little ridges had invigorated the engorged folds of her sex. A scarlet hue of shame stained her cheeks.

"I know what you were doing, you naughty girl." Harriet shook her head and made tsking sounds. "Stand up, it's time I got you out of that tub."

Emily wore a stricken look as she rose to her feet. Harriet took a thick towel from a stack beside the tub, wrapped it around Emily's shoulders, and began to towel her dry. Madame Godwin's thin smile made her seem more like an aunt or older sister than the mistress of Lilac Row. Harriet dropped the damp towel on the floor and wrapped Emily's hair turban-style in a fresh towel, before returning her to the bedroom. Emily spotted the loose-laced ivory waist cincher on the bed, the hard-edged outlines of its stays visible beneath the elegant fabric.

"I'm going to turn you into an old-fashioned Gibson girl," Harriet said, holding up the stiff undergarment. "Stand at the bedpost while I lace you. The cincher will make that adorably small waist even smaller. Hang onto the bedpost while I lace you in."

Emily stood at the bedpost with her back to Harriet, while Harriet wrapped the stiff, abbreviated corset around her bare waist. She felt the laces being drawn in, tightened, then Harriet's knee thrusting itself into her still-swollen bottomcheeks. "This allows me to draw the laces as tight as they should be." The corset walls stiffened as the cords tightened, squeezing her sides and breasts upward. Her bosom swelled like twin white hemispheres above the hard upper edge of the cincher until she thought her bosom would brush her chin. Her hips and bottomcheeks filled out dramatically as Madame drove every bit of flesh from her waist. She imagined what she must look like and blushed furiously. When the laces were finally tightened and tied, Harriet spanned Emily's shrunken waist with thumbs and fore-fingers. "You're less than twenty-two inches. What is your regular waist?"

"Twenty-five—twenty-six," Emily whispered, think-ing her breasts must have gone up a cup size as well.

"Miss Devreux and Miss Baker will be delighted with your new shape. You're not wearing panties tonight." Harriet said.

Emily went white. She turned her head. "M-Madame, wh-why?"

"I'd forgotten you haven't served at card club. Miss Devreux, Miss Baker, and my sister, Frances Cartwright, are coming to Lilac Row for our monthly night of cards. And you, my dear, are going to serve us tonight."

Emily stared into the outdoor gloom. Annie had mentioned Madame Cartwright; a no-nonsense woman, stricter even than Madame Godwin. She and her five daughters ran a laundry in the city. Annie said Madame Cartwright was a formidable and very successful business woman. And Annie was terrified that Madame Godwin would make good on her threats to send her to her sister.

Emily stood as still as a sentry while Harriet fastened a clean garter belt around her hips, then rolled a pair of seamed nylons up her legs, straightening the seams, before fastening their dark tops to the dangling garters. She helped Emily into her heels, which were so tall Emily could hardly stand. Harriet dropped the black silk dress over Emily's head. As she closed the back of the bodice, the black silk drew tight around Emily's waist, stiffening the strategically placed shelf of starched white linen beneath Emily's breasts. Emily might as well have been wearing a bra. Her breasts were completely exposed as well as trapped, snuggled tightly between her plump upper arms and supported from beneath by the linen shelf. Her inflated breasts were forced into each other to create a stunning cleavage that ran from the tops of her breasts to their bottoms. The milky white texture of her breasts contrasted dramatically with the wine-dark flesh of her aureoles and nipples, which were aimed like projectiles straight away from her body.

Harriet sat Emily down at the dressing table. While Emily stared blankly at her bare breasts in the mirror, her mistress brushed out her hair and put it up in lush maple swirls. Harriet layered lipstick onto Emily's pursed lips, followed by a thick rouging of her cheeks and heavy lines of mascara around her eyes. Emily was transformed into a silent-film star, dark eyed and wet lipped. Her breasts plumped and rearranged themselves as she rose from the table onto her slender heels. Harriet stood back. She arranged and resettled Emily's breasts as casually as if she were plumping a pair of pillows, before taking Emily downstairs.

Viola was helping Mrs. Henley set up the card table when Emily came down the stairs. Viola's eyes widened, but Harriet's gaze silently warned her to say nothing. A moment later, the doorbell rang.

"Emily, answer the door."

Harriet smoothed a strand of hair from Emily's face, then released her with a reassuring squeeze of her arm. "You're absolutely lovely, Emily. You mustn't look so frightened." The doorbell rang again, jangling Emily's nerves as she went to the door.

Frances Cartwright, Harriet's sister, was taller and not as attractive as Harriet. She filled the doorway with her presence. Five daughters and years of hard work in her laundry had taken their toll, softening and rounding her shape. She was heavy through the hips and bosom, with a round face and small blue eyes. Her hair was died a deep black and pulled away from her face into a stubby ponytail. She wore a plain brown dress, sensible pumps, gloves, and a silly little velvet hat. She stood staring at Emily from beneath her dripping umbrella. Emily stared back, unable to move under the woman's gaze.

"Are you going to let me in, young lady, or must I push my way into the house."

"I'm sorry, Madame," Emily muttered, and stepped back, conscious only of the bobbling of her breasts. "Madame Godwin and Miss Baker are in the living room," she offered, taking Madame Cartwright's umbrella. She shook with embarrassment and shame when Frances Cartwright turned her cold blue eyes on her. Frances opened her mouth but nothing came out. Emily could only assume her uniform had rendered the older woman speechless. Frances brushed past Emily into the living room.

"Harriet, how dare you? It's disgraceful. If one of my daughters did that I'd horsewhip her."

Harriet pecked her sister's cheek. "Frances, indulge

me. Besides, I have something for you later. Would you like something hot? You look wet and chilled."

Emily admired the way her mistress smoothed her sister's feathers. "Do you mean a girl for my laundry?" Frances asked, looking sideways at Emily.

"Exactly, dear sister."

Frances worked her round face into a smile. "In that case, Harriet, she can bring me a cup of tea."

Penny arrived while Emily was in the kitchen with Mrs. Henley. The four women were in the living room when Emily carried the heavy tea tray. She could feel the women's eyes following her as she set the tray on the coffee table and poured the tea. Madame Cartwright was everything Annie had said; mean-spirited, cold, dangerous. A woman who would dominate those around her, and severely punish those beneath her. She was completely unlike her sister. Even Miss Baker deferred to her. It was a relief to be dismissed and sent back to the kitchen where she helped Mrs. Henley with the hors d'oeuvres. "Watch your step with Frances Cartwright," Mrs. Henley warned. "She's a spiteful woman—and her daughters are every bit as nasty…."

Frances threw out a card, thumping it onto the table. "Is she an obedient girl, Harriet?"

"She will be. Florence Bertram nearly ruined her."

Frances folded her cards. "Let me take her home tonight. My daughters would love to…to meet her." Her eyes glittered.

"Absolutely not. I bid three spades."

185

"Why not? You've lent others to me."

"Those girls weren't going to Leah."

"Leah? She's going to Leah?"

"Yes, and don't look so surprised. She's a sweet girl. I don't want your girls muddying the waters."

"I'll try to take that remark as I hope you intended it."

Harriet sighed. "Whose play?"

"Mine," Penny volunteered.

"Who were you going to send, then?"

Harriet threw out a card. "Annie. Dreadful, incorrigible Annie. Would you consider her?"

Frances's bosom sagged. "Of course," she murmured, looking primly from Viola to Penny. "I shall make preparations tonight and be back tomorrow."

"Mrs. Henley will love you for it. She's at her wit's end with that girl."

Frances smiled expansively. "I'm sure we can rectify her behavior in short order."

Later that evening, Emily and Annie were doing the dinner dishes. Emily waited for Mrs. Henley to leave the kitchen. She leaned to Annie and whispered, "I heard Madame Godwin say you're going to Madame Cartwright's."

Annie turned white. "Emily, are you sure? Madame is bad enough, but those five daughters…they're like a pack of wolves." She sobbed silently over the sink while Emily held her. Mrs. Henley came into the kitchen. "Annie, go on up to your room." Emily watched tight-lipped as Annie disappeared up the stairs. Mrs. Henley shook her head. "It's a shame it comes to this. Madame Cartwright is all business. She is not known for her compassion. Annie has been there before. She knows what she's in for. You would not want to spend one day in her laundry."

"Why is Annie—"

"Because she needs Madame's Cartwright's discipline. Now get out of that dress and into bed. And don't forget to brush your teeth."

"Yes, Ma'am," Emily whispered, and hurried up the back stairs, grateful she wasn't being sent to Madame Cartwright.

She went to bed, knowing she'd played herself and her daring dress to the card club like a brazen whore. She'd hidden behind Madame Godwin's skirts when she knew the other three wanted to see her upended and whipped. Thankfully, her mistress had not budged, refusing to punish her. By the time Madame Cartwright, Miss Baker, and Miss Devreux had left, she'd begun to enjoy her role as a human centerpiece. When the house had settled down for the night, she heard Annie's shrieks and the crack of Mrs. Henley's paddle echoing through the darkened halls. How cruel it seemed. Yet, it also made sense. Poor Annie. Perhaps Madame Cartwright would be good for her.

The next morning Mrs. Henley fixed oatmeal and brown sugar, swimming in fresh cream, for Emily. Something was in the air. And Mrs. Henley wouldn't say. Before Emily had finished her breakfast, Mrs. Henley surprised her a second time.

"Madame wants you to spend the day in your room, resting. Annie and Molly will make the beds, do the wash."

"Mrs. Henley, I can make beds—"

"Do as I say, girl!" Mrs. Henley's voice hardened as she glanced at her paddle hanging above the worktable. Emily flew up the back stairs to her room, wondering what had gotten into the housekeeper. An hour later, Annie stuck her head into Emily's room. "I know a girl who's going to leave us soon. Shortly after me."

"Annie, you're a brat! Don't say that—please."

"May I come in?"

"If you promise not to tease me."

"I'm sorry. I guess I'm just envious. You get to leave. Molly is stuck here. I'm going to Madame Cartwright's. I wish I could be sent to Miss Talons."

Emily sat up. "I don't know—I have no idea. Madame Godwin says I'll be happy there, but she won't elaborate."

"Do you mind if I sit on the bed?" Emily beckoned. Annie bounced down next to her. She eyed Emily's stunning display of breast and cleavage. "You're so voluptuous. Molly and I should be so lucky. Look at you—practically bursting from that uniform. I'm as flat as a pancake."

Emily took Annie's hand. "You're a pretty girl, Annie. Much prettier than me. I'm as big as a cow. I wish I was slender with your curly hair."

Annie smiled sideways at her. "I appreciate that. I really do. But we both know why you're leaving."

Emily leaned toward Annie, kissed her lightly on her lips. "Perhaps Madame Godwin will send you to join me. I'd like that."

"Oh, Emily, do you honestly think she ever would?"

"She might."

Annie glanced at the door. "I hear Mrs. Henley in the hall."

As Annie hurried from the room she was caught by the housekeeper. Frances Cartwright appeared behind her, a heavy wash paddle in her hands. While Emily watched horrified, Mrs. Henley produced a length of clothesline. The two women twisted Annie's arms behind her, lashing them tightly to her body. During the struggle, one of Annie's breasts came out of her uniform. Madame Cartwright, as calmly as could be, replaced it in Annie's low bodice, before she and Mrs. Henley rudely hurried their trussed captive down the hall. Emily moved to the window. A pale blue van with its rear doors open stood in the drive. A gilt sign was emblazoned on its side.

CARTWRIGHT LAUNDRY

SHIRTS—LINENS—ALL WASH

She watched the two women toss the tightly bound maid into the back of a van. Annie sank facedown into a cushiony pile of laundry bags. Emily shut her eyes as Madame Cartwright and Mrs. Henley climbed into the van. She could not bear to watch as Madame Cartwright lifted her wash paddle. But she could not shut out the abrupt whaps of the paddle and Annie's screams. When the paddling finally stopped and she opened her eyes, Madame Cartwright was emptying a laundry bag. Mrs. Henley was tying a huge pair of pink panties around Annie's head, drawing the gag tight between her parted lips. Stunned, Emily watched the two women lower the empty laundry bag over Annie, then upend the bag and stuff the pile of sheets back into the bulging bag. Mrs.

Henley tied the heavy bag closed and helped Madame Cartwright throw it back onto the pile. When the van doors had been shut, Madame Cartwright drove away with Annie as if she were so much dirty wash.

The rest of the day passed slowly. Depressed over Annie's departure, she tried to lose herself in *Forever Amber.* But it didn't work. She finally laid down the book and drew up her legs. For the next hour she teased herself from one silvery orgasm to another. Afterwards, she fell asleep, her hands between her thighs. Mrs. Henley woke her at five.

"Shame on you! Had I known how you'd spend your day off, I'd have tied your arms and legs to the bed." Mrs. Henley jerked down Emily's skirt. "You've just time for a quick bath. Madame wants to see you in her suite."

"Madame? Why would she—"

"Probably to whip you for putting such crazy ideas into Molly's head. Now get out of that bed and into the bathroom." Emily received a hard swat from the housekeeper as she slid out of bed. "Put on a clean uniform before you go downstairs."

After her bath, Emily brushed and arranged her hair before going down to Madame Godwin's suite. A flickering oil lamp similar to the one she'd seen in the cottage burned next to Harriet's chair.

"I've been expecting you. Did you enjoy being a lady of leisure?"

"Y-Yes, Ma'am. Though it felt odd not to be doing housework."

Harriet smiled. "You'll get used to it." She was dressed in gleaming boots, a long black leather skirt Emily hadn't seen before, and a sheer maroon chiffon blouse that did nothing to hide the fullness of her breasts. She beckoned to Emily.

"Come here and turn around. I want to have a look at your bottom." Emily stiffened as Harriet unceremoniously lifted her denim skirt and lowered her panties. "I'm delighted. Your backside is pink, but sufficiently recovered for my cane."

Emily turned her head. As she was about to speak, the faint but shrill sounds of Molly's cries echoed through the hallway.

"Do you know what that is, Emily?"

"Yes. It's Molly."

"Do you know why Mrs. Henley is punishing her?"

Emily hesitated. "N-No, Ma'am."

"Today, Molly asked if she might leave Lilac Row. She implored Mrs. Henley—begged to be sent away! Who would put such thoughts in that girl's head?" Emily turned scarlet. "Answer me!"

"I-I did, M-Madame. I see n-now it was wrong to encourage her." Her lower lip quivered.

"You'll pay for that indiscretion. Molly is my concern —not yours. Face me." Harriet's long white hands flew down the front of Emily's uniform. Before the front was open to Emily's waist, Emily's plump breasts had sprung from the bodice. Emily stood helplessly in front of her mistress in panties and nylons. "This was to be your night, Emily. A night you would not forget."

Emily stared at Harriet. She had no idea what her mistress meant.

"I had not planned on correcting you so vigorously on your last night at Lilac Row. Two women will be here tomorrow to take you away. You will not see me again. You will be the sole property of Miss Talons and The Ecole."

Tears filled Emily's eyes. "Madame, must I leave? Please, cane me, but—"

Harriet shook her head. "You have no say in the matter. Tomorrow you are going to Miss Talons. And that is final."

"Your husband…what if I let him?…"

"Charles has nothing to do with this. You'll not see him again. What he did last night was part of your training. You enjoyed it, didn't you?"

"N-No, Madame. It hurt too much."

"Don't lie to me, Emily. Come into the bedroom. Lay facedown on the bed."

Emily whimpered like a child as she extended her legs and arms to the corners of the bed. Harriet took a pair of pillows from her closet.

"Lift your hips."

Harriet thrust the stacked pillows beneath Emily's elevated hips. As Emily settled into the pillows, Harriet tied Emily's wrists and ankles to the bedposts. Emily tried to move, found she was securely bound to the bed. She looked imploringly at her mistress as Harriet moved alongside the bed. She jerked Emily's panties, ripping them open. Emily could smell the musky scent emanating from her thighs.

Harriet's voice was as rich as molten caramel. "Already, Mrs. Henley has worked wonders, rounding out your bustline and bottom. Miss Talons will put those attributes to special use."

Emily flushed scarlet. She twisted her head sideways. Her eyes were wet and glistening. "Am I just an object?" she whispered.

Harriet did not answer the question.

She disappeared into her dressing room where she removed her leather skirt and blouse and strapped a fat leather cock around her hips. The pseudo cock bobbed just like her husband's. Over her underwear and projecting cock, she threw a long satin cape, clasping it at her throat before she reentered the bedroom. Emily lay on the bed, unmoving. The lush, layered flesh of her bottomcheeks shone in the flickering light.

Emily watched her mistress open a drawer and take out a long, slender cane. Harriet stood over her, holding the cane across her body. Her shimmering cape flowed from her shoulders and over the smooth rounded curves of her breasts. The tips of her nipples shone like tiny gleaming points of light beneath the satin. Her eyes were hidden in dark shadow.

Emily melted like soft butter over the hot crust of fresh-baked bread. She was ready to please her mistress. A crisp fold of the pillowcase beneath her found its way into the raw edges of her sex. The cotton ridge grew damp as it met the petals of her sex. She lifted her head and whispered, "I'm ready, Mistress."

Harriet's cape sighed as it slipped from her shoulders. Emily's mouth opened when she saw the bulging cock rising from Harriet's thighs. Before she could cry out, the cane flashed and arced across her bottom. Harriet became a goddess, towering over Emily. Her swaying breasts tipped with long slender nipples were packed into flesh that could barely contain them. Her belly was flat and sleek, her arms long and sinuous. Emily barely saw the leather thing she knew was going to enter her after the caning.

Cane met flesh, erupting Emily's senses into a fiery burst of tears and a shower of stars. She opened her mouth to scream. Darkness settled over the room. On the western horizon the sky was drowning in a bath of mauve, pink, and orange. Emily twisted and mewed, rolled her hips into the pillows while the cane descended again and again, crisscrossing her beet-red flanks. Her shrieks floated through the open window into the dark, moon-washed sky.

She did not hear Harriet whisper, "And the best, my dear, is yet to come."

BOOK II
The Ecole

CHAPTER 12

E mily emerged naked from of the bathroom in a cloud of steam, her head shrouded turban fashion in a thick bath towel. Her damp shape and stark white limbs gave her the look of an alabaster sculptor. Mrs. Henley was waiting for her. Emily looked startled at the hairbrush in her hand.

"Take the towel off your head, Emily," the housekeeper said patiently. "I'm going to brush your hair."

Emily's heart was pounding, but she stood quietly while Mrs. Henley pulled the ebony hairbrush through her hair. The big brush glided effortlessly through the conditioned silken strands. "I'm going to miss you. I must say I've grown quite fond of you."

"I'll miss you, too," Emily whispered. Her hair

rippled through the housekeeper's hands like a burnished waterfall, splashing over her bare back and arms in a lustrous sheen of maple gold. It was an intimate moment for both women with no need to speak.

Mrs. Henley divided Emily's hair into three long thickets, drawing them back and away from the sides of her face. The housekeeper plaited the three strands into a single hank that was as thick as Emily's wrist before tapering down her back. When she was finished, the housekeeper secured the braid with a satin bow. The tips of the bow brushed the crowns of Emily's bottom, making her feel like a little girl again. Mrs. Henley fastened a stiff new garter belt around Emily's waist, drawing the belt too tight.

When she tried to protest, Mrs. Henley said, "No sagging stockings at the Ecole."

Mrs. Henley spoke as if she knew the Ecole staff personally, but everyone, even Molly, knew that was not the case. The housekeeper might have seen Miss Talons, but she was not on a familiar basis. She helped Emily into her seamed nylons, smoothing and straightening them before attaching them to the dangling garters. Hands on hips, Mrs. Henley took a long look at her maid. "I think Miss Talons will be pleased with the likes of you."

Emily glanced down at the swollen globes of her breasts. "Mrs. Henley...couldn't I wear a bra? I jiggle s-so."

"I agree, but Madame Godwin insists it's a shame to stuff such a lavish bosom into a brassiere."

Emily's heart sank. Every time she moved, her unsupported breasts swayed and jiggled, shaming her, reminding her how big she was. Mrs. Henley produced a pair of glistening patent-leather high heels. "I hope you can walk in these. Madame Godwin picked them out of the Frederick's catalog. They must be five inches high." The ridiculous height of the heels strained Emily's calf muscles, adding inches to her height. For the first time she stood taller than Mrs. Henley.

The housekeeper took out a lavender silk dress. She had to stretch to drop the dress over Emily's head. As the dress settled over her, the housekeeper began to button its front. The silk clung to the plump outlines of Emily's unsupported breasts. By the time Mrs. Henley had closed the bodice, Emily's bosom and semierect nipples stood out in stark relief. Emily looked from the mirror to Mrs. Henley.

"M-Mrs. Henley, isn't it...too tight through the bust?"

"Miss Devreux has tailored it to Madame's wishes. I cannot, will not get in the middle of that. It's probably appropriate for the Ecole."

Confused, Emily turned back to the mirror. She looked like a harlot. Mama had called them tarts. Hot girls who stood outside the saloons, showing off their legs. She hated the dress. It made her uncomfortable. Mrs. Henley and Madame Godwin ought not to make her wear this dress—especially since she was going away. Scarlet with shame, she frowned at her reflected image. Mrs. Henley gave her arm a reassuring squeeze.

"You look just fine, sweetie. Believe me. Where you're going, there won't be any boys to notice."

Emily wanted to scream. Defiance bubbled and rose inside her. She could hear its roar in her head. Suddenly, she didn't care. "Mrs. Henley! This dress makes me look...horrible. And this bow...it's for a little girl!" She planted her palms indignantly on her hips. Her eyes sparkled with anger. "Mrs. Henley, I don't like this dress, and I don't need a bow in my hair."

Mrs. Henley's hairbrush came out of her apron pocket, catching Emily by surprise as it smacked her backside, stinging her through the thin fabric. Emily was as shocked by her outburst as Mrs. Henley. "I declare. Miss Emily has acquired a mind of her own. If you're going to act like a child, I'll treat you like one." Mrs. Henley sat down on the bed, her hairbrush beside her. "Come here! I never thought I'd be spanking you today."

Emily melted. "M-Mrs. Henley, n-n-o, p-please...not today,...not n-now—"

"I said come here, and I meant it. You've gone too far." Emily dropped her arms in resignation and went to the housekeeper. "Lift your skirt, Miss Smarty-mouth."

Emily sighed and turned her back to Mrs. Henley. She slowly raised her skirt over her waist, exposing her snow-white cotton panties and dark-seamed hose, whose seams ran straight from the backs of her heels over the smooth arcs of her calves and up to her thighs. She watched helplessly over her shoulder while Mrs. Henley slid her thumbs under the taut band of her garter belt and found the elastic band of her panties. The house-keeper drew Emily's panties down to the dark tops of her nylons. As Emily's seat was bared, her defiance melted into a blur of tears. She was crying when Mrs. Henley took her over her lap. Emily's pale white bottomcheeks lay across Mrs. Henley's broad lap, neatly framed by the strips of garter and dark tops of her nylons. Emily's seat had become the perfect target for Mrs. Henley's hairbrush.

The older woman took her time with Emily before lifting her hairbrush. Emily thought she must be studying the ridges and welts from Madame's caning the night before. Surely, the marks would bear out the severe punishment she'd received, and that would alleviate what Mrs. Henley was going to do to her now.

"I heard Madame Godwin caning you last night. You were making so much noise everyone in the house heard it." Emily's heart sank. The flat tone of Mrs. Henley's voice told her what was coming. "By the time I'd gone to bed, I could tell the mood in Madame's suite had changed. Your shrieks became swoons and sighs. I know perfectly well what she was doing to you. You lost your virginity, didn't you?"

Emily's body shook with her sobbing as she nodded.

"It only happens once in a girl's life. I'd be glad it was Madame Godwin and not some young man who cares nothing for you."

Mrs. Henley ran her palm over Emily's lower thighs. "Still warm, but nearly unmarked. The clear skin of a young woman. Believe me, you won't look like that when I'm finished. This may be your last day at Lilac Row, but you're still in my charge, Emily."

The hairbrush descended noiselessly. Emily shrieked as the smooth flat of the brush landed with a splat on her tensed bottom. Mrs. Henley lifted the brush and brought it down again, and again. The housekeeper devoted most of her spanking to Emily's untouched lower thighs. She gave Emily a rapid and thorough spanking that turned Emily's seat and thighs a glowing red. When the maid was back on her feet, the house-keeper waited for Emily to kiss her, a ritual she was made to perform each time Mrs. Henley spanked her.

"I'm sorry, M-Mrs. Henley. I shouldn't have lost my temper."

Mrs. Henley touched Emily's cheek, wiped away a tear. "You'll be taught control at The Ecole. The staff there is quick to correct willful, disobedient girls. Punishment, I'm told, is swift and severe. Madame is worried you won't respond, and will shame her."

Emily blushed brightly. It hadn't occurred to her she might embarrass Madame Godwin. And what about the more unpleasant prospect of being punished by women she didn't even know? Would they be mean to her, more cruel than Mrs. Bertram or that awful woman, Madame Cartwright? Would correction be done in private? She tried to smile through tear-stained eyes. Her voice was firm again, controlled.

"You mustn't be concerned, Mrs. Henley. I'll be a good girl. A perfect student. I'll do as I'm told and make you and Madame proud of me."

"It's best that you do. Learn suppliance and submit-tal. You'll always need a woman's hand to guide you.

Once you accept that, Emily, your life will be serene and pleasant. Madame would not send you to the Ecole if it wasn't in your best interests."

Emily relished the reassuring touch of the housekeeper's hand. "Mrs. Henley, I'm terrified at being sent from here. Can't I stay at Lilac Row?" As she hugged the housekeeper, her fear flowed silently into Mrs. Henley's stolid warmth. Strong hands brushed the hair from her forehead. Mrs. Henley pulled a handkerchief from her sleeve and dried Emily's eyes. She took Emily into her arms.

"You're afraid. I can understand that. I don't want to let you go. But it's time. Time for you to leave."

"I-I can't imagine leaving this lovely house. I-I don't know what will happen when I leave."

"I'm told the Ecole is highly regimented. There will be no free time. That ought to keep you out of trouble." Mrs. Henley stood up. "It's been a difficult morning. Come downstairs, and I'll fix your breakfast."

"M-Mrs. Henley, will you be with me when Miss Talons comes?"

"Until her assistants arrive. Miss Talons rarely leaves the Ecole now. She wants no one but you present when her assistants take you away."

"H-Has Madame sent other girls from h-here t-to...The Ecole?"

Mrs. Henley smiled. "Very few, Emily. You're in select company."

"That doesn't make it any easier."

"The Ecole will be good for you. Madame and I will

miss you of course, but we have no qualms about turning you over to Miss Talons."

Harriet was waiting for Emily at the foot of the stairs. Emily searched her mistress's expression, but she detected nothing. Not a trace of emotion. No sign of her virginal seduction of Emily the night before. Harriet waited until Emily had reached the bottom of the stairs before she spoke.

"You look sweet in that new dress."

Emily realized with a blush that Madame had been watching the movements of her breasts. They must have made quite a show as she came down the steps. Harriet took her hands and drew her into her arms. "Miss Talons's assistants will be here soon. You must be attentive and obedient. You're an Ecole girl now. That makes you very special." Harriet enfolded Emily in her arms. "Good-bye, sweet girl. You have no idea how much I'm going to miss you."

Harriet turned then, and disappeared up the stairs. She did not look back. Emily's last memory of her mistress was the glint of a tear in the corner of Harriet's eye as her lips brushed Emily's.

Mrs. Henley broke the silence. "Come along, Emily." Emily followed the housekeeper into the kitchen where they ate a silent breakfast. Emily shook when the front doorbell rang. "You stay right where you are. I'll get it."

Mrs. Henley straightened her apron and went to the front door. Emily ran to the window. A long black limousine stood in the gravel drive. Its windows were too dark to see inside. Two tall women came around the front of the limo and up to the house. Their heels thudded importantly on the portico. She heard Mrs. Henley open the front door and welcome the women as if they were the best of friends. The housekeeper sounded affected—intimidated—in the presence of the women.

Mrs. Henley stuck her head into the kitchen. She spoke in a hoarse whisper. "They're here! Fix your dress, wipe your mouth, and come into the foyer."

Poor Mrs. Henley was more nervous than Emily was, perspiring, fawning, and catering to the two women, who seemed not care. They were more amused than flattered by her efforts to please them. She introduced Emily to the women. Renzi and Celeste were their names. Mrs. Henley hurried into the kitchen, saying over her shoulder, "Emily, take the ladies into the parlor while I make a fresh pot of tea."

They were tall women, dressed completely in leather. They wore supple leather capes so thin the leather molded itself to their movements. Gleaming boots disappeared above their skirt hems. Of the two, Celeste was clearly the leader. Renzi didn't make a move without Celeste's subtle nods of approval. Celeste's smile, her sylphlike motions, reminded Emily of a cat. Her lips were full and curved, glossy with lip color. Her heavily shadowed eyes danced over Emily's body, missing nothing of her. She smiled disarmingly as she shrugged out of her long cape. Renzi followed her movements.

"You may take these."

Emily was suddenly weighted down with volumes of soft black leather. The rich scent filled her nostrils, exciting her.

Celeste wore a gleaming black leather dress that wrapped the curves of her hips and thighs like a shrunken sheath. Her dress was high necked and fit tightly over her breasts. Below the neckline, its front was cut open in a diamond pattern over her bosom, exposing a generous amount of her breasts and startling cleavage. Long, skintight black leather gloves covered her arms to her shoulders. Her eyes were dark, outlined in sharp black accent, giving her a wide-eyed stare that intimidated Emily. Her dark brown hair was short, carelessly tossed in a casual arrangement that fit the heart-shaped profile of her face. Her heeled boots were even taller and spikier than Emily's heels. Made of glossy patent leather, they laced from instep to above her knees. Emily wondered if the boot tops reached her thighs.

Renzi remained silent and expressionless, her eyes always on Celeste. Emily thought she must be about her own age. She reminded Emily of faraway places. A thin golden ring dangled from her nostril. Emily couldn't help staring at the grotesque and exquisitely beautiful accessory. Renzi's hair was glossy black and pulled away from her rounded face into a plump chignon so heavy it lay in a woven dark mass at the back of her head. She had an olive complexion and limpid, almond-shaped eyes that were tipped upward at their outer corners. At the slightest provocation, Emily would have kissed that petulant small mouth. The bodice of her dress was nothing more than a tight-laced leather bra-corset. Its V neckline was cut low, offering enticing views of her breasts every time she moved. She wore a thick leather collar around her neck that did not seem to bother her or impinge on her movements. Emily wondered what in the world it was for. Her supple leather skirt was full, gathered into tiny pleats at the waist which flowed smoothly over her hips. Like Celeste, her arms were completely covered with fitted leather gloves. She made Emily feel completely inadequate, and terribly self-conscious of her own silk dress and heels. Renzi held a small leather bag in her hand.

"I was told you were a big girl, Emily, but I must confess, I wasn't prepared for this."

The liquid tones of Celeste's voice sent shivers up Emily's spine. Being seen without a bra in the horrible lavender dress and spindly heels was like nothing now. She no longer cared what she looked like. Celeste was the most beautiful woman she'd ever seen. Her dulcet voice caressed Emily's mind like the brush of a butterfly's wing. "I like your going-away dress. Did Miss Devreux make it special for you?" Emily nodded, struck silent by Celeste's aura. "She's a wonderful seamstress. I have a few things of hers—leather, of course. It's all I ever wear now. Has Madame Godwin left the house?"

"Sh-She's upstairs, in her suite," Emily murmured in a tone she hoped pleased Celeste.

"I know you'd like her to be with you, but that's not possible."

Emily turned scarlet. She could not endure Celeste's limpid gaze. "Of course," she stammered.

In that moment Emily knew she'd fallen completely under Celeste's control. It no longer bothered her she was being taken by these women. The realization thrilled her. She became weak and willing to be whisked away in the long black limo. She could hardly believe her sense of ecstasy. Her insides sang a clear bright song of surrender. Her heart was pounding. She thought of Madame Godwin, the warm weight of her as her cock had entered her. *Surrender*, she thought. She imagined herself bound and prostrate at Celeste's feet, staring up into those lovely eyes and that scarlet mouth....

Mrs. Henley came in with the tea tray. She set it on the coffee table. "I've errands and shopping to do," she said to Celeste. "Is there anything…"

Celeste shook Mrs. Henley's hand. "There is nothing left for you to do, Mrs. Henley. Emily will be quite safe with us. We will take good care of her. Say good-bye, Emily."

Emily turned to the housekeeper. Mrs. Henley suddenly looked older. "G-Good-bye," she whispered. "Thank you for looking after me." She crossed the room to hug and kiss Mrs. Henley.

"Dear child," Mrs. Henley sighed, squeezing Emily's hand. "Be a good girl at the Ecole. Do make us proud of you." Mrs. Henley awkwardly backed away, then disappeared into the safety of her kitchen. A moment later, she heard Mrs. Henley's Volkswagen puttering away from the house.

Emily sensed Celeste's presence behind her. "It will be all right, Emily. Mrs. Henley and Madame Godwin are wonderful women. And they obviously loved and cared for you. We love them as much you do. But every girl has to leave her nest." Emily nodded, her eyes wet with tears. Celeste took her to the fat leather couch where Madame had spanked her so severely. Why was it always warm when she sat there?

"Pour our tea, Emily. Then we must prepare you so we can get underway. It's a long drive to The Ecole."

"Do I need to bring anything? Madame said—"

"The Ecole provides everything." Celeste gestured to the younger woman seated next to her. "I haven't introduced Renzi, one of our advanced students. Miss Talons allows her to leave The Ecole—but only rarely and under my supervision. You will not be permitted to leave for a very long time."

Emily drew in her breath as Celeste's unseen grip gently tightened around her, binding her to her so that she could never come back to Lilac Row. And there was no way she could resist this lovely apparition. Her head felt light as she whispered, "Madame Godwin says The Ecole will be good for me."

"Madame is a wise woman."

Celeste reached out with a leather-clad finger to tease a strand of Emily's hair. "You have lovely light brown hair, full of coppery highlights. When you turn your head just so, the effect is quite striking. I adore that braid. What a pity it will all soon be covered."

"C-covered, like going into a convent?"

Celeste's gloved hand traced a line down Emily's plump upper arm, coming dangerously close to the swell of her breast beneath her arm. "You must not be afraid, Emily. The Ecole will become like a good mother—strict, caring, loving. You're embarking on a journey—an odyssey you were meant to take. You must trust me as much Renzi does."

Emily could see the intense devotion in the younger woman's eyes, her expression of rapture as she looked at Celeste. Renzi's lovely eyes grew wide as she swam in Celeste's gaze. Emily envied the invisible current flowing between the two women.

"Renzi is not American." Celeste said. "She was raised in Arabia, a pasha's harem. Her mother was French. She died shortly after Renzi was born. An older woman in the harem took Renzi in, raised her as if she were her own daughter. And completely spoiled her, I should add." Renzi's eyes fluttered madly as she smiled. "She became the darling of the harem. Everyone, including the old pasha, doted on her. In a word, she was spoiled rotten. Finally, in desperation, he gave her to his eldest daughter to bed and train."

Emily looked puzzled at the quaint expression.

"At the Ecole, we have a saying. 'A young woman's beauty can only be fully understood by another woman.'" Emily blushed furiously at her thoughts as Celeste continued. "We believe the love between two women is a perfectly woven fabric; seamless, warm, and wonderful to wear."

Celeste leaned to Emily. She lightly stroked the nipple projecting from Emily's lavender-covered breast with the tip of her gloved finger. "You have very large breasts, Emily. And lovely upstanding nipples."

Emily stared at the black leather finger, gently teasing her nipple erect. Frozen with shame, she could not look up at her tormentor or down at her breasts, which had arranged themselves like pillows in her lap. Celeste put her hand on her breast, tested its resilience through the silk fabric. "You were meant to join us. Supplication, surrender, submission—and there will be punishment too. All part of the exquisitely intimate Ecole atmosphere. Do you understand?"

Emily's head was so light she thought she might faint. The prospect of surrendering herself to Celeste overwhelmed her as it slowly dawned on her that Mrs. Bertram, Madame, and Mrs. Henley had been preparing her for this moment. She already knew she couldn't let another man touch her. Mr. Godwin had seen to that. Renzi's infatuation was really no different than how she'd felt about Miss Devreux and Miss Baker. She was one of these women.

Celeste continued. "Unable to properly train Renzi, the pasha's daughter sent her to the Ecole. Renzi may be the daughter of an Arabian pasha, but it means nothing at the Ecole. She came to us in Indian silks and Egyptian cotton robes so finely woven you could see right through them. In many ways she's still a child—a child desperate for her mother's breast. See how she looks at you." Emily looked at Renzi, who was half smiling through her embarrassment, her eyes fixed on Emily's breasts. "She will always be a child of sorts. Unfortunately for Renzi, there are no wet nurses or nannies at the Ecole."

"Will Renzi return to Arabia?"

"Perhaps. Most girls, once they're there, never leave the Ecole." Emily barely heard Celeste. Renzi's sweet look, her fascination with Emily's overflowing bosom captivated Emily. Renzi's scarlet mouth opened. Her dark eyes fed shamelessly on Emily's loose bosom, embarrassing and arousing her. She caught herself wondering what it might be like to put that lovely soft mouth to her breast, and nurse the child-woman like the baby she really was. Celeste cut into her reverie with a hard slap to Renzi's leathered thigh.

"Stop staring, or I'll take you over my knee right here in front of our new student."

Renzi blushed and sat back. Her eyes lifted to the ceiling and stayed there.

"Emily, remove your panties. Leave your garters and nylons on." Celeste's voice had turned to ice. Emily stiffened. "I said remove your panties! I am not accustomed to repeating a command."

Emily's eyes brimmed with tears. "C-Celeste, I-I d-don't understand."

"There is nothing to understand, Emily. You do as you're told or I'll punish you." Celeste's eye had narrowed to dark slashes, her mouth a red gash. She did not take her eyes off Emily as Emily reluctantly lifted the hem of her skirt and released her garter belt. She drew her panties down, dropped them to the floor, and stepped out of them. Her eyes were fixed on the gleaming toes of her new heels. Her face was flushed with shame as she drew up her stockings and reattached her

212

garter belt. Renzi picked up Emily's panties and dropped them into her bag.

"Renzi, give me Emily's gloves. The next time she disobeys, I'm going to discipline her."

Discipline me?

The words fell effortlessly from Celeste's lips with no more emotion than if she was telling Renzi what time it was. Celeste had only been in the house minutes. Already she was asserting her absolute authority. With no apparent effort, Celeste had diminished Emily to the status of a little girl. She felt as if she were in front of her mother in wet pants. How would she be corrected? Would this lovely woman do what Mama had—take down her hair, and then her underwear, before spanking her on her bare seat. And put her to bed afterwards? She was sure Celeste sensed her excitement.

Renzi removed a pair of crumpled long leather gloves from her bag. Knowing the gloves were meant to cover her arms reinforced Emily's tenuous connection to Celeste. A bolt of excitement ran up her spine. In those gloves, some of her plainness would be hidden. She eagerly extended her arms. Renzi began to fit one tight-fitting glove over her spread fingers. Celeste did the same thing to her other hand. It was not unlike being mittened by her mother years before. The two women's faces were expressionless as they shrugged the gloves up her arm.

The baby-soft leather molded itself to her hands and arms. Thin leather lacings ran from her palms to the glove tops. The gloves fit so tightly over Emily's fingers, she could scarcely flex her fingers. When the leather reached her shoulders, Celeste and Renzi began to tighten the laces. They worked their way up her arms, tightening the gloves around her arms until the leather became a second skin. Emily's arms were turned into a pair of rigid clubs. Like being bound, she thought. She remembered a movie where the heroine had been bound and gagged with leather straps and hung from ropes. She'd sneaked back to see that same movie several more times. She felt warm and suffused, awkward, almost giddy. The rich smell of the shiny leather covering her arms filled her nostrils. For no reason it made her want to giggle. She wondered if she should thank Celeste for binding her limbs so cleverly. Celeste's command shocked her out of her fantasy.

"Arms behind you—palms together. Thighs together, too."

Emily stared awkwardly at Celeste. The older woman's words frightened her, reminded her of Annie's abrupt, cruel departure in the back of Madame Cartwright's van. She watched with growing awareness as Renzi removed a leather sleeve and a length of soft white rope from her bag. What else lay inside that bag? "Y-You're not going to t-tie me up?…" The look in Celeste's eyes told her that was exactly what Celeste had in mind.

"I wouldn't dream of transporting you any other way," Celeste said softly. "It's how we bring our girls to the Ecole. It is the beginning of your training. You may not understand, but you must trust us completely. There can be no reservations on this point."

"What if I refuse? Madame never—well almost never—tied me."

"You no longer belong to Madame Godwin. You belong to us—the Ecole—now. If you do not obey, Renzi and I will subdue you with force—and there will be punishment as well."

"B-But th-that's k-kidnapping!"

"It's a moot point. I won't waste my time arguing."

Celeste ignored Emily's pleading look. "I ordered you to put your arms behind you. Thighs together too!" Celeste's voice was impatient, demanding.

Frightened by the look in Celeste's eyes, Emily reluctantly put her stiffened arms behind her, palms touching, and kept them there. Renzi knelt and lifted Emily's skirt. Renzi's face was so close to Emily's bare thighs and exposed sex, she could feel the Arabian beauty's moist breath caressing her thigh. Renzi wrapped one length of the white rope twice around Emily's upper thighs and knotted it tightly while Celeste took a padded leather collar from Renzi's bag and fastened it around Emily's neck. As the collar buckle was cinched, Emily began to feel like a slave being readied for market. She glanced down at Renzi, who had expertly knotted the soft line around her thighs, leaving a trailing end, which she tied around Emily's overlapped leather-clad wrists. There was still sufficient length to run the rope up Emily's back where Renzi threaded the rope through a ring at the back of Emily's collar, then returned it to Emily's wrists where she tied it off in a hard knot. Renzi had cinched the rope tight enough to draw Emily's head and chin back, thrusting out her breasts. Emily could no longer look down at her bosom, but she knew her breasts had been lifted, were thrusting now in front of her. Her nipples stood erect with shame, pointing boldly at her captors. With her arms securely fastened behind her, her head up and back, and her thighs pinned, it was virtually impossible to move except in tiny shuffling steps. Walking was made even more difficult by her spiky heels.

She cried out but was helpless to stop Celeste and Renzi as they lowered her to the carpet and onto her side like a slab of beef. Renzi knelt on Emily's upper calf while she bound Emily's ankles with another length of the white rope. Renzi left a foot of loose rope between Emily's feet, hobbling her so that she could stand and walk in hobbled fashion. Emily noticed Renzi was watching her. The slant-eyed Arabian beauty had the sweetest smile on her face. She didn't seem in the least bit ashamed to truss Emily. In fact she seemed to be enjoying it.

After Emily was on her feet again, Celeste produced another length of the rope. She wrapped it around Emily's leather-clad arms and began to draw her arms together behind her at the elbows. The imperious lady drew on the rope until Emily's elbows were nearly touching. As supple as Emily was, touching her elbows behind her was uncomfortable, but not terribly painful.

"You'll get used to it," Celeste whispered in her ear as she tied the final knot.

Emily's pose was aggravated by the tight fit of the

leather gloves covering her arms. Her breasts were thrust out, hardening her nipples until they pressed through her dress front. When Celeste ran a gloved finger over the hardened bulges, teasing them until they stung, Emily could only stare at her captor.

The beginnings of pleasure mingled with her shame, spreading through her body as Celeste relentlessly fondled her engorged nipples and breasts. Renzi watched, unmoving, her lips wet and parted. Emily could see pure envy in the Arabian's eyes. But Renzi did nothing. Because Celeste would not allow her. Emily was beginning to understand Celeste's power. It was overcoming her as well. She felt as helpless as a newborn.

Celeste moved in a circle around her, studying her bound body. She paused behind Emily to lift the back of her dress above her waist, exposing her garters and swollen bottom. Emily's mouth opened in protest when Celeste's leather-clad hand glided over her crown cheeks. Spanked muscles and flesh protested painfully as Celeste's hand squeezed her. Her fingers slid between Emily's thighs, stopped inches from her sex. There was nothing Emily could do. She could scream, but that would surely mean punishment. She waited tensely. Was Celeste going to touch her sex? She felt Celeste's hand relax. Her fingers returned to the plump arcs of her bottom. Celeste's fingers were cool and soothing. Emily could not help responding to this woman's touch. Her eyes fluttered closed.

Celeste spoke in whisper. "Did Mrs. Henley spank you this morning?" Emily nodded. "Why?"

Emily shuffled her feet. "I didn't like my dress. It's too tight."

"Did you tell her that?"

"Y-Yes."

"How did she punish you?"

"H-Hairbrush."

Celeste smiled. "You deserved it for your impudence. By the looks of you she did a thorough job. She knew what was best for you. Now the Ecole has assumed that responsibility. From now on we will care for and punish you when you need it. Sometimes you'll wish you were here again, under Mrs. Henley's hairbrush. Ecole discipline is much more rigorous than the domestic variety you're used to."

"Y-Yes, Ma'am," Emily whispered, filled with a strange excitement at the prospect of being punished by this woman. Celeste was so unlike Madame and nothing like Mrs. Henley. She was beautiful and possessed with an inner wellspring of strength that reached out to Emily.

Celeste ran her hand over Emily's silk-covered breasts. "Lovely," she whispered. Emily had never felt anything as tender as that gloved hand gliding across her breasts. It was the first time any woman had touched her breasts so perfectly naturally. It was as if Celeste owned her now, body and soul. Susan had never touched her like that. She found it impossible to visualize her old girlfriend. Her mind was too crowded with Celeste and her beauty.

"It's time we left," Celeste said.

"Yes, Ma'am," Emily murmured.

Celeste took another length of the white rope from Renzi's bag. Renzi smiled at her mistress and crossed her wrists behind her. Emily watched wide-eyed. "Wh-Why does Renzi need to be tied up?"

"For her own good. Besides, as you can see, she enjoys her bondage. As you will too in time."

Celeste quickly tied Renzi's crossed wrists behind her. Emily noticed Celeste did not restrain Renzi at her elbows like she'd done with her. She opened her mouth to ask, then thought better of it. Celeste inserted a thick leather pad into Renzi's wide-open mouth, completely filling it and propping open her jaw. She wrapped a leather strap and buckle over Renzi's mouth and around her head, drawing it tight enough to nearly close Renzi's lips before buckling the strap at the back of Renzi's skull. Renzi's eyes glazed over. Emily wasn't sure if it was a reaction to the elaborate gag or to the pleasure she derived from being bound and gagged. Celeste donned her own cape and threw Renzi's cape over the Arabian girl's shoulders.

She led Renzi and a shuffling Emily onto the porch and out to the parked limo. The back door stood open. Celeste guided Emily's head into the cavernous back seat. Emily was acutely conscious of Renzi's presence behind her as the hem of her skirt rose to expose her bare seat and sex when she bent to enter the car. Inside the car a small dome light shed a narrow cone of light over the interior. The seats were upholstered in rich black leather. Everything else was covered in gray velour. A blacked-out partition window cut off Emily's view to the front. As she slid across the seat, the cool surface of the leather cushions met her bare bottom, adding to the sting of the spanking and reminding her she wore no panties. She blushed at the thought. She'd never left home before without her underwear.

Celeste's voice startled her. "Ankles against the seat, Emily."

The strap at the back of her head prevented Emily from looking down, but she could feel Celeste's hands attaching thin leather straps to her ankles and buckling them to the bottom of the seat.

Celeste glanced up at her captive. "We wouldn't want to lose you on the drive to the Ecole."

"N-No," Emily whispered, overcome with a sense of being completely out of control, and with no desire to fight back. She knew she could—had to—trust Celeste. The pressure of the leather straps hugging her ankles wasn't painful. Celeste had done a skillful job of tightening them so that she couldn't move. Celeste attached Renzi's ankles in a similar manner, before getting into the limo herself. Emily sat in the middle, squeezed between the two women. Their leather-clad hips were pressed tightly into hers. She could feel their warmth through the thin fabric of her dress. Emily moved her head slightly, as much as the strap and collar would allow, to glance at Renzi. Renzi's eyes were closed, her head thrown back against the leather seat. She appeared to have fallen asleep.

Celeste leaned so close her warm breath painted Emily's cheek. "You'll learn to do the same, little one."

Emily nodded, ashamed at the affectionate term.

"I see I've embarrassed you. You shouldn't be. In many ways you are a little girl. Now close your eyes, lean back, and do not move a muscle."

Celeste reached into a side pocket of the door. She took out a pair of cotton pads, a roll of white tape, and a flesh-colored scarf. Emily could see none of these. Her eyes were tightly shut. They fluttered open as Celeste laid cotton pads over them and secured the pads with two strips of the tape. Emily tried to make a sound as Celeste wrapped the flesh-colored scarf over her eyes and tied it snugly at the back of her head, but Celeste warned her to be absolutely silent or risk severe punishment. Emily whimpered and closed her mouth. No light could find its way beneath the tightly taped eye pads. She was completely blind. The blackness frightened her, made her feel queasy. She fought the urge to bolt, tried not to test her bonds; she was settling her stiffened back uneasily into the cushions when her nostrils were suddenly pinched hard, cutting off her air.

She screamed instinctively. As quickly as her mouth flew open, Celeste stuffed a thick wad of folded leather into her mouth, cutting off the shriek still rising in her throat. With an almost inaudible moan, the shriek died in the leather wadding. She stiffened when Celeste finally released her nostrils and fresh air flowed deep into her lungs. In the next minute she felt the leather begin to swell and fill the inside of her mouth, preventing her from closing it.

Celeste patted Emily's thigh. Though Emily couldn't

see her, she could imagine Celeste's dark eyes looking at Emily with an obviously amused expression. "I'm sorry to have surprised you like that, little one, but it was the only way I could gag you without you making a horrible scene. This is how you will be kept from now on, so you might as well get used to it."

Emily tried to wiggle her hips in defiance but was too well tied in place to do much of anything. Celeste tied another flesh-colored strip around Emily's head to retain the leather gag. The strip slipped between her lips as Celeste knotted it tight. Sightless, speechless, and bound, Emily could still sense Celeste's pleasure at what she'd done. She was completely defeated. Helpless to resist. And Madame and Mrs. Henley had let her go. Did Madame Godwin have any idea it would come to this?

Exhausted, she felt Celeste's hands easing her forward to thread another of the soft ropes around her elbows, then around her body just below her breasts. Celeste drew the rope tight, pulling Emily's elbows and arms tight against her back so that her arms were pinned to her sides and back, completely eliminating any movement of her upper body. Confused and frightened, Emily wondered if this was more punishment. It seemed to demand her complete surrender. She felt her limbs growing pleasantly numb. There was no longer any pain from her restraints. As she sagged back into the seat and Celeste's gloved hand began to tease the strands of her hair, she knew she was caught. Trapped like a buzzing fly in a spider's web. The metaphor thrilled and frightened her.

The big limo sped smoothly through the countryside. Emily could not hide the fact she was becoming more aroused now, and less afraid. Whatever lay in store for her at the school they called the Ecole might turn out to be better for her than those horrid denim low-necked uniforms, and Mrs. Henley's paddle and hairbrush. She would miss Madame Godwin. A lovely woman. Already she was fading to a wistful memory. "It was time," Madame had said. "Time to spread your wings."

"Sweet child," Celeste whispered, and began to caress Emily's breasts and thighs through the thin fabric of her lavender dress.

CHAPTER 13

E mily woke slowly. Moving from sleep to consciousness, she stared into absolute darkness. She was still
tightly bound and vaguely aware of someone's
warmth and movements next to her. She struggled to
understand where she was. She caught a woman's scent—
familiar, not sweet or cloying, but fresh and clean.
Where was she? Everything seemed different. Understanding, mixed with an ineffable sadness, washed over
her as she slowly rose to the surface.

Lilac Row. It was a distant memory. Had it ever
happened?

She could remember Madame Godwin's kiss, being
bound by women in black. She could not move, didn't
care. Dreamy and warm, she felt herself slipping back

into drowsiness. "I'm going away," she thought. "And I don't expect to return."

Her transformation from domestic to submissive filled her with uneasiness and a sense of longing. Beneath her dread lay a pure rush of pleasure and expectation she'd never known. Wetness seeped from her thighs and onto the leather seat beneath her as she reluctantly yielded to Celeste and the Ecole. Celeste's fingers were in her hair, caressing the hard finish of her braid. Her gloved hands glided over her face, cupped the weight of her breasts, and stroked her thighs. Had Celeste really kissed her? She couldn't remember. The muted hum of the limousine was all she knew. Everything else was drenched in black.

The squawk of a radio startled her. She heard the click of a microphone key as Celeste murmured questions and orders. Was Celeste even aware of the bound prisoner next to her? A few moments later, she sensed the car had slowed, heard the crunch of gravel beneath the tires. The limo swung through a turn, forcing her into Renzi, who did not move as she leaned into her. The limo squeaked to a gentle stop. The click of the microphone in its receptacle was the last sound she heard before the door swung open. The car was suddenly filled with cool fresh air that smelled faintly of damp stone.

The car shifted as Celeste slid out to unstrap Renzi. The Arabian whispered something naughty, giggling at Celeste's warnings to be still or she'd be punished. Emily looked down, unseeing, at a pair of hands undoing the straps that held her ankles to the seat. Another pair of arms gently guided her legs out of the car. Being cradled in four strong, warm arms was a new and delicious experience. Sightless, completely helpless, Emily had to trust her captors. She found herself reveling in her vulnerability. She knew these were women. The way they held her, the way they smelled, the soft brush of their bodies helping her from the limousine were unmistakable. Beyond the young women, she heard Celeste, hovering over her brood of girls like a mother hen.

A sharp smack. Paddle or cane on leather? Renzi's muffled shriek could be heard through her leather gag. "Take her inside. I want her whipped, well whipped. We'll see if she giggles tonight."

Emily listened to the crunch of gravel as the women led Renzi away. Celeste led her inside. It was much cooler there. She heard the shuffling of feet, echoes and sighs that were as vaporous as whispers, wafting gently through the darkness covering her eyes. At Celeste's command, one of the young women removed the scarf around her eyes. Another peeled away the tape that held the cotton patches.

Emily blinked, and found herself in a large vaulted chamber that reminded her of a medieval great room. Smoky torches threw dim, flickering light over the soaring space. The wood-ribbed ceiling high above her was almost hidden in smoky mists. The walls were mortared stone, cold looking and damp, partially covered with faded tapestries. Leaded-glass windows set high in the walls let in measured amounts of the late afternoon sunlight. Renzi was gone. Emily wondered what would happen to her. Celeste and two young women stood nearby, watching her with amused expressions. The two girls wore coarse dark hose, ankle-high boot-slippers, and black leather skirts that barely covered their thighs. Both girls wore black silk blouses so sheer that Emily could see right through the diaphanous material to their jiggling bosoms.

"Welcome to the Ecole," Celeste said. "I'm sorry about your blindfold, but for security reasons it's the only way we transport our new girls."

Celeste beckoned for the two young women to leave. "Go now," she said. "Before Mother happens along and finds you dawdling here." The girls smiled and curtseyed to Celeste before hurrying away. Emily looked at Celeste. "Your gag. Is it bothering you?" Emily nodded vigorously. "I won't remove it. You must keep it over your mouth. You'll learn to live with it, along with being perpetually bound. How else could we train you for your work?"

Emily had no idea what Celeste meant. And Celeste did not seem disposed to talk any more about it. She looked up and around her and was struck by the eerie quiet of the place. There were faint sounds. The barest shreds of voices, whispers, and shrieks, distant and unreal. They might have been the cries of girls being punished or simply the wind moaning through the overhead spaces. Interspersed, she heard the muted rhythmic smacks of punishment implements. Paddles? Leather strops? She had no way of knowing. Perhaps it was

Renzi being punished for her naughtiness. She didn't know, and to her surprise, didn't care. She was no longer frightened by these things.

Her eyes were drawn upward to great wheeled iron chandeliers whose torches were fastened in a circular pattern to the perimeters of the spoked iron wheels. Each iron wheel hung from heavy chains that disappeared into the overhead darkness. The torches ringing the wheels burned steadily. Their oily smoke streamed upward to the smutty dark ceiling, casting amber pools of light downward onto the flagstone flooring. A female figure hung a few feet below each wheel. Suspended by short lengths of chain and padded leather cuffs at their wrists and ankles, the young women hung facedown by their extended limbs. Emily could see the swells of their breasts and hips beneath the skintight leather that completely covered their bodies and heads. The taut black leather dehumanized them, made them look like inanimate objects rather than living breathing young woman. The young women were in no danger of being harmed by the burning torches, but Emily thought they must be terribly uncomfortable, spread-eagled in space.

Celeste said, "They've been turned into overhead torchlights, and rather attractive ones don't you think? I particularly like the way the burning torches above them backlights their leather profiles."

Emily stared up at the girls. They hung motionless, sightless, and completely immobilized.

"You seem drawn to them. And I can understand why. Miss Talons has turned them into faceless decorations.

They will remain up there until she decides to do something else with them. As to eating and sleeping, there are maids who see to them. They sleep when the torches are extinguished."

Emily could not take her eyes off the girls' shapes.

"They get used to it. Have you noticed our wall torchbearers? They sleep on their feet. Which isn't that difficult given how stiffly Miss Buxton has trussed and bound them." Emily's collar prevented her from turning her head. She had to swing her entire body to follow Celeste's gloved finger to a series of niches built into the stone walls. Emily was surprised. Until now, she hadn't noticed the motionless shapes set into the walls, each one as motionless as a statue, and each supporting a single torch. They were clad in skintight leather suits just like the ones covering the girls overhead. Their faces were covered with thin sheets of leather that allowed their features to show through. Emily wondered how they could breath.

Sensing her question, Celeste said, "There are tiny holes beneath their nostrils. Each girl is tightly laced and bound in several layers of leather. Even before they are strapped into their niches at their necks, pinched waists, and ankles, I can assure you they cannot make the smallest movement. Their unsightly arms are well hidden, being tightly bound behind them, crossed and out of sight. Very attractive, don't you think? Miss Buxton does wonderful work."

Emily didn't respond. She could hardly believe what she was seeing. The girls' torches were attached to the

230

tops of long iron poles that rested on the floor between their feet. The poles canted away from their bodies and were secured to the young women at their shoulders and breasts with thick harnesses. The flickering light from their torches cast an eerie glow over the girls' leather-clad breasts and thighs, throwing their soft curves into sharp relief. It began to dawn on Emily what coming here might mean. Her days as a housemaid were over.

Celeste smiled at her concern. "You needn't worry. You're much too plump and endearing to be made into a torch girl. It will be up to Miss Talons, of course. My guess is you will be transformed into an objet' d'art, or something useful. You may be sent to Miss Buxton's shop, but not to become a torch girl. In the meantime, we will train you in the art of absolute servitude and submission. Madame Godwin has done her job well. But you must be taken further. We will take you the rest of the way." Celeste caressed Emily's thickly braided hair as she spoke.

She turned her body to the distant clatter of a cart and the shuffle of footsteps on the stone flooring. A tall, thickset Negress in a long black leather skirt rode through an archway into the chamber in a roughly made two-wheeled wooden cart. As regal as a queen, she stood at the front of the cart, holding reins in one hand, a long, slender buggy whip in the other. A stout leather strap hung over one hip. Emily was struck by how much the black woman looked like Mrs. Bertram, even wore her belt the same way! From the waist up the Negress was completely bare. In the pale, smoky light, her smooth ebony skin shone as if it had been oiled. She was a formidable woman; thick waisted, broad shouldered, and wide hipped. Her breasts were larger than Mrs. Bertram's, and so heavy they sagged like a set of swollen buttocks below her waist, quivering and rolling drunkenly from side to side as the cart approached. Fat, rubbery-looking nipples protruded from the bottom of each breast.

A pair of young women were harnessed to the cart. They wore tight-laced leather helmets, collars, and breast harnesses. Silver bridles sagged from the corners of their mouths. The bridles were kept in place with ball-like, tightly fitted gags that gave the girls startled, openmouthed expressions. Reins ran from their mouths back to the Negress. Except for their leather helmets and tall boots, the girls were completely naked. Their arms were sewn behind them into slender leather sheaths just like the one that drew Emily's arms together from her elbows to her palms. One of the girls was a flaming redhead, and as slender as a boy. The other was brunette, and nearly as buxom as Emily, with heavy thighs and breasts that bounced vigorously as she high stepped across the open floor toward Emily and Celeste. The Negress lifted her whip, cracking and whipping the girls' backsides.

"Lift those boots, my girls! Prance like cart-girls!"

The Negress was still raising fresh welts as the team slowed. Emily could see the whip marks on both girls' buttocks and thighs. The brunette's wide seat had received more punishment than the redhead's. The

Negress tugged suddenly on the reins, slowing her team as she neared Celeste. The girls obediently slowed and stopped. It wasn't at all warm, but the girls' bodies were sheened with sweat. They stared straight ahead, would not look at Emily.

The Negress nodded politely at Celeste. "Good afternoon, Mother," Celeste said. "This is our new girl, Emily." The Negress's liquid mahogany eyes turned to Emily. Emily could have swam in the depths of those great soft eyes. Mother's lips opened slightly as she appraised Emily.

"A-a-e-e-g-h, she's plump alright. Take real long stroppings." Mother's voice was rich and melodious. "I say she go to Miss Buxton—de upholstery shop."

Celeste shrugged. "You're probably right."

From where Emily stood, without being too obvious, she could see into the back of the cart. A young woman lay on her side on the rough flooring, tightly bound with hemp. The coarse rope had made nasty grooves in the pale white flesh. Her knees were drawn up to her chest, her folded arms trapped between her breasts and thighs. A thick leather gag was tied over her mouth. Her buttocks and thighs had been well striped. She was not wearing a helmet. Her long flowing blonde hair had spread like a golden avalanche onto the floor of the cart. The girl looked up at Emily with such tender blue eyes, Emily's heart melted. She wished she could kiss and comfort her.

Celeste went to the cart. She pinched the girl's breast until the girl screamed beneath her gag. "She's only been with us a week. Wasn't she sent down to the kitchen?"

Mother smiled, showing twin rows of straight white teeth. "She barely lasted de week. Cook, she whipped dis one daily...." She shrugged in resignation.

"What was her duty?"

"Soup and broth flavoring. Was a good one too, by Cook's account. Nice and spicy pussy." Mother's laugh was low and mellifluous, setting her huge shining breasts in motion. "I tell you, Celeste, it's a shame. She make wonderful soup."

Emily caught the glance that passed between the two girls harnessed to the cart. "Eyes straight!" Mother shouted, and raised her whip. The thin black whip tendrils snapped out at the girls so quickly Emily lost sight of the whistling tip as it laced the girls' bottoms, tracing a spidery pattern of fresh welts. Emily empathized with the girls, was grateful she didn't have to face this woman with the strange accent, arms the size of bread loaves, and the largest breasts she'd ever seen.

"Where are you taking her?" Celeste asked..

Mother's lips parted in a devilish smile. "To my quarters, den Miss Buxton. She want her for de lavatories. When dat woman and I finish wid dis one, she wish she'd stayed in de kitchen wid Cook and flavored de soups."

The Negress' words sent a chill through Emily. Her demeanor was maternal, yet rigid and terrifying. Emily's feelings for the bound girl wavered. Perhaps it really was her fault. Perhaps the girl hadn't done what Cook expected of her. Wasn't that why they were here? She wondered how a girl could be made to flavor soups. Was she suspended by her limbs above a simmering kettle, bottom and sex hanging in the steam that rose from the bubbling soup? The possibility frightened her. She could imagine Cook stirring the broth beneath her while she dripped hotly and steadily into the kettle. What an awful existence that would be.

Mother's voice brought her back. "You behave, child. You don't want to end up like dis one." She lifted the reins and drove her team away, urging them on with a series of whipping lashes. Her rolling laugh echoed throughout the chamber. Celeste and Emily watched her until the cart disappeared. A moment later, they heard a scream and the slam of a heavy door.

"They've reached Mother's chamber." Celeste said softly. In another moment, Emily heard the first sharp slap of the leather strap. The girl shrieked again. Emily shuddered as Celeste took her arm. "Come along. Miss Talons is waiting."

Unable to speak with the swollen gag filling her mouth. Emily listened as Celeste, in a rare moment of candor, talked openly of the Ecole. She led Emily through a labyrinthian series of torchlit corridors until the sounds of the leathering and the kitchen-girl's cries had faded into shredded tendrils and sighs.

"Don't move or back away if Miss Talons touches you, Celeste said. "She may kiss you on the lips and fondle your breasts. It's her way of welcoming you."

CHAPTER 14

A narrow, twisting set of stone steps led to Leah Talons' quarters high in the stone bastion. Hobbled and bound, struggling to keep up with the leash running from her collar to Celeste, Emily had to struggle to climb the stairs and keep up with Celeste, who hurried her along unmercifully. Out of breath and exhausted, Emily stumbled into Celeste when she paused at a door set into a landing.

Celeste turned on her. "That will cost you, Emily." She dragged Emily to a nearby wooden bench and sat down. She took Emily over her lap, drawing up her skirt with one hand. Letting Emily down on with the other. Emily's mistake earned her a flurry of hard spanks on her bare seat with Celeste's tightly gloved hand. The leather stung Emily's bottom nearly as much as Madame Godwin's clothes brush. Her pleas and cries echoed down the stairs and beyond. The door flew open. A young woman with a cherubic face and a horrendous pout looked out at them. Her expression changed when she saw Celeste.

Celeste glanced up while continuing to spank Emily. "Never mind, Chloe. Go on about your business."

"Yes, Ma'am," Chloe responded, and shut the door, but not before smiling wickedly at Emily and her plight.

Emily was sobbing when she struggled off Celeste's lap. Her big bottom was reddened and on fire. "I hope you learned something from that. You never touch one of us. It is a sign of disrespect."

"I-I understand," Emily blubbered, wondering why it was such a terrible thing.

Celeste knocked softly on the door.

Chloe was not happy at being interrupted again. Her blonde hair was damp from exertion. It lay in a tight mass of curls around her face. She wore a belted satin tunic that barely reached her thighs. Its draped front lay open over her breasts and pale red nipples She held a short thonged whip in her hand. She glanced at Emily, then back at Celeste with wondrous blue eyes. The girl seemed grudgingly afraid of Celeste, cowering like a puppy in the older woman's presence.

Celeste ignored the girl. She pushed the door open and went in. It was a smallish room, with a round floor plan and two narrow windows that looked out over rolling wooded countryside. Hidden in shadow against the wall was another young woman mounted on a narrow saddlelike device Emily had never seen before. A stout wooden post was set into the floor. A narrow cross member with curving, upturned ends was mounted on top of the post. The cross member was padded with a thin layer of leather. The girl was astride the padded cross member, riding it like a saddle. Unfortunately for her, the padded saddle between her thighs was no more than an inch wide. And her feet, which were lashed to the sides of the upright post, did not reach the floor.

A skintight leather hood hid the bound girl's face. Emily could see the bulging gag beneath the girl's mask. Other than knee-high leather boots and gloves that covered her arms, the girl was stark naked. Her arms were pinioned behind her in a laced-up leather sheath. A wide leather strap spanned her waist. It had been cinched in until the girl had no waist left. Her bound arms were buckled to the back of the belt, pinning them to her back. A second strap ran from the waist belt to the back of the girl's hood, pulling her head back and up so that she stared unseeing at the ceiling. Her stiff upright stance and bound posture thrust her breasts forward in the most provocative and unintended pose.

Emily could imagine how ashamed and hurt the poor girl must feel. All of her body weight was focused where her sex met the leather padded cross member. The girl had to keep her thighs clamped tight to the saddle or the saddle would make its way into her sex. Emily glanced at the blonde cherub. Chloe didn't seem in the least concerned about the bound girl's plight. Emily's sex ached at the thought of being put there. Chloe had been busy with her whip. There were tendrils, marks, and welts covering the bound girl's breasts, arms, buttocks, and hips. The blonde cherub stood hipshot, waiting impatiently, like a hungry animal, to get back to her whipping. She flicked the tendrils of her whip into her open palm. Emily was stunned. The little bitch couldn't wait to get back to work.

"Is Mistress Talons here?"

Chloe nodded. "Yes, Ma'am."

"Tell her I'm here, and do it quickly, before I take that whip from you, and use it on you." Celeste's voice never changed in pitch, but Chloe jumped. "Move, or I'll send you to the laundry!"

Before Chloe had opened the door that led to Leah's chambers, a high soprano voice cut through the pregnant silence.

"Is that you, Celeste?"

"Yes, Leah."

"Come in. Come in."

"As Celeste led Emily into Miss Talons' private quarters, Emily heard the first snap of the whip as it met the girl's welted flesh. Chloe closed the door behind them.

Leah Talons' boudoir made Emily forget about the girl on the saddle. The room was large, comfortably furnished, and drowsy with heat. A log fire roared in a fireplace large enough to swallow Emily. Heavy indigo drapes sealed off the tall narrow windows. A human chandelier hung from the domed ceiling. Like the others Emily had seen, this one was spread-eagled on chains from a fancy wrought-iron wheel. Unlike the others, this girl was naked and hung on gleaming golden chains. A leather gag kept her mouth open. She stared unblinking at them until Emily wondered if she was alive. The unsteady light from the torches above her illuminated the painted panels of erotica and punishments that covered the inside of the dome. The scenes depicted women doing depraved things to other younger women. Breasts were whipped raw. Long-shafted cocks were driven into sexes and bottoms. Several girls rode narrow saddles and wheels with nothing to protect their sexes. Other hapless captives were being unmercifully strapped with doubled belts and long slender paddles. Emily saw young girls made to kneel with their faces tightly strapped to older women's thighs. Emily's head swam. There was too much to take in.

Inert, faceless female shapes were arranged around the perimeter of the bedroom. Each one was completely clad in leather and strapped tightly to the stone wall. Burning iron torches canted inward to Leah Talons's bed. Two young women knelt against the wall opposite the bed. Like the chandelier and wall torches, they were bound in laced leather suits with their arms crossed and bound behind them. Unseeing, unmoving, the pair had been positioned to face each other. A carved dressing table and mirror rested on their padded shoulders. Another shapely nonentity knelt on all fours in front of the dressing table. Thick white furs were spread over her back, covering most of her black leather outline. Emily was struck by the rigid immobility of the living furniture, how immutable they were. There wasn't a single motion. Not a sound. She thought she could see the lazy swell of a breast as the table breathed. But she couldn't be sure. For all practical purposes, these young women were nothing now but furniture. She remembered Madame Godwin's couch. It had swelled like that. *Omigod*, she thought. This might happen to her. It made her want to scream.

Celeste touched her arm. Emily stared at her as if she were crazy.

Leah Talons watched them from her bed. Spectacular in scale, the bed dominated the room. It was framed in polished ebony. Carved posts at each corner supported a brocade canopy. The coverlet and top sheet of cream-colored silk were folded down neatly at the bottom of the bed. The bottom sheet was wrinkled and mussed, unable to conform to the rounded contours of the overstuffed mattress.

Leah studied Emily with smoldering greenish blue eyes so radiantly perceptive that Emily thought her new mistress could see right through her. Miss Talons had a small and red mouth. Just now it was pursed in concentration. Her skin was clear, nearly transparent. She had the complexion of a child. The front of her gown had fallen open to reveal finely sculpted full breasts tipped with tiny red nipples. Emily imagined Chloe's curly blonde head snuggled to Miss Talons' breast, her lips around one of those hard little nipples.

Miss Talons was everything the oil painting had depicted and more. The brush strokes could not have caught the air she projected of being in complete control. Her presence overwhelmed Emily, made her want to kneel at the feet of this noble woman. An attendant knelt on the bed next to Miss Talons, brushing the lustrous strands of her mistress's auburn hair. Hair so soft it flowed in lustrous waves through the maid's hands like sheening waves. The uneasy light altered the color of Miss Talons' hair, from scarlet to molten caramel. Emily shuddered when Leah lifted her finger and beckoned.

"Don't stand there, child. Come here. Under the torches. I want to see those breasts I've heard so much about. No, don't open her front, yet, Celeste. I'll do it myself. Now turn her to the firelight. Splendid. She's every bit as buxom as Harriet and that dreadful Mrs. Bertram said she was. Look at that tiny waistline. She puts the rest of us to shame. Turn her around. I want to see her bottom." Celeste pinched Emily's buttock hard with her gloved hand as she spun Emily around, lifting her skirt. "Oh, my word. One doesn't often see such deliciously plump backsides. Shows what a rich diet will do for a girl. Did you just spank her?"

"Yes. She was slow coming up the stairs."

Leah's eyes narrowed. "She'll get more than a spanking before I'm done with her." Emily's eyes filled with tears, which streamed in shimmering lines down her cheeks. Celeste turned her around to face Leah. Emily's tears made Leah smile. "Look at those crocodile tears,

Celeste. As if she were about to be whipped. Bring her to me." Leah touched the arm of the maid on her bed. The maid slipped off the bed, leaving the hairbrush behind.

Celeste urged a reluctant Emily toward the bed. Emily hesitated. Something about the bed frightened her as much as Leah did. There were fluttery movements beneath the sheet. Leah smiled, patted the sheet.

"Sit her next to me."

Bound as Emily was, Celeste had to help her sit. The leather mattress was too warm and too soft, had an inner vibrancy. Something moved—deep inside the mattress. It flexed beneath her weight. Leah dismissed Emily's frightened look. She ran the long-nailed tips of her fingers up Emily's arm. With no warning, Leah's fingernails pressed hard into the soft flesh of Emily's upper arm. Emily squealed in pain, tried to pull herself away. Leah pressed deeper, retaining Emily in her vice-like grip. A tiny bit of blood trickled down Emily's arm. Emily began to whimper. Still gripping Emily's arm, Leah began to fondle the swollen contours of her breasts. She squeezed Emily's breasts and nipples until more tears streamed down Emily's cheeks. Emily felt like a bauble in a child's hands while Leah examined her until she no longer felt the bright pain of Leah's nails piercing her flesh.

"She's wonderfully ample!" Leah said to Celeste, oblivious to Emily's pain. "I should think she's suited for…" She paused. "I'll have to think what to do with her." With the unbridled enthusiasm of a little girl, she released Emily's mottled, blood-flecked upper arm and attacked Emily's braid. Emily was reminded to sit quietly while Leah loosened the satin bow. As the ribbon came free, Emily's thick braid slowly unraveled, tumbling, spreading over the bed. Emily shifted her weight. The bed responded beneath her.

"Why, it must reach her thighs," Leah said excitedly, tearing the braid into crimped wavy strands.

She picked up her hairbrush and began to pull it through Emily's hair. The bristles crackled as they were drawn through Emily's hair, snapping her head back with each powerful stroke. In the pallid light, Emily's hair shone like polished bronze, was shot through with raspberry highlights.

"She reminds of me Charles Dana Gibson's pen-and-ink sketches. Gibson girls, all bust and hips. No waistline at all." Leah mused. "Do you remember them, Celeste?" She idly twisted the long, thick hank of Emily's hair in her hands before arranging it in shimmering coils on top of Emily's head. "It's a shame," she murmured to herself, "having to put this one away. But Miss Buxton has been relentless. What can one do?" She beckoned to her maid. The maid drew several long pins from her own hair. Leah took the pins, thrust them deep into Emily's hair to secure the shimmering layers.

"Gibson would want to draw this one."

Emily stared straight ahead, not knowing how to respond to this powerful woman who alternated between childish mean-spiritedness and maternity.

Emily moaned softly when Leah began to unbutton her dress. Strained by the weight of her breasts, the lavender silk fell away before Leah had half opened the dress. Emily could have sunk into the floor as Leah took her breasts in her hands. Scarlet with shame, all she could think of was how big she was compared to the petite girl on the saddle next door. Leah placed her hands beneath Emily's arms. She squeezed Emily's ribs, gently compressing Emily's breasts into a luscious display of creamy white cleavage.

"Did Madame commission something special for you to wear?"

Emily nodded, her eyes wide and dark with fright.

"We'll dress you more conservatively here."

Emily wondered what that meant as she glanced up at Celeste. In that instant she forgot Leah's words and knew Celeste wanted her. It was a stunning revelation—that anyone as beautiful as Celeste could feel the slightest desire for the likes of her. Caught up in Celeste's eyes, she barely felt Leah pulling up her dress and laying a hand over her sex.

"Why, the bitch is in heat! Her thighs are wet. And look at those nipples." Leah pinched Emily's extended nipples until Emily screamed silently behind her gag. "They're as hard as acorns. You naughty, naughty girl." She turned to Celeste. "Do you suppose she'd stay this hot if I sent her to Miss Buxton?"

Celeste smiled faintly at the question.

"I know what I'll do with her. It's settled. She's going to Miss Buxton."

Celeste's expression changed. "I thought...perhaps you'd leave her with me."

"No, Celeste. She's going to Miss Buxton. Miss Buxton needs her more than you." Without so much as another glance at Emily, Leah picked up her hairbrush and beckoned to her maid. The maid slid eagerly back onto the bed, pushing Emily aside. She took the proffered brush and began to brush Leah's hair.

Confused and disappointed, Emily was shocked at how Miss Talons dispatched her as casually as she might shoo a cat off her bed. There was nothing to do but follow her leash back down the narrow twisting stone stairs and an endless array of damp corridors. Water dripped from vaulted ceilings, puddling on the stone floors, sending shivers down Emily's spine as she tried to avoid the shallow pools.

Torches held by leather-clad females strapped into stone niches lit the way. At the corridor crossings, naked girls hung by their arms from black iron rings set high into the walls. These girls were blindfolded and gagged, their ankles fastened to rings in the floor. They were made to face the wall, as if offering their swollen bottoms for even more punishment. As Emily and Celeste approached, the girls anxiously lifted their heads, then dropped them again when they saw Celeste. Celeste hurried past them, ignoring them. She spoke to Emily over her shoulder.

"Once these girls were Miss Talons' chambermaids. They wore the Ecole's finest silks and fragrances. Some of them were even taken into Miss Talons' bed. They have fallen from her graces. Perhaps they were not attentive, or thought more of themselves than their mistress. A wrong glance, a single word would be enough to ingratiate themselves. They are in disgrace, and completely under Mother's jurisdiction. She will punish them in ways you could not imagine."

There were no sounds now but the soft moan of air flowing through the corridors and the steady drip-drip of water. The damp air weighed heavily on Emily. Already, the atmosphere and philosophy of the Ecole were soaking into her psyche, assimilating her, altering her forever. She could sense the change. Part of her struggled. Guilt and shame and desire fought and spun wildly through her subconscious, threatening to pull her apart in a tangled swirl of emotions. Celeste's jerking on her leash brought her back, reminded her where she was. She shut out her thoughts and hurried to catch up with Celeste.

CHAPTER 15

The room reminded Emily of a cloistered convent cell. Bare wooden floor. A cabinet against the stone wall. No bed. No chairs. A tall stand with narrow saddle—like she'd seen in Miss Talons' ante-room. Celeste smiled at Emily's expression.

"For naughty Ecole girls," she said.

Emily's eyes widened in response. Unable to speak, her eyes welled with tears at the prospect of riding that thing. At least, she thought, Celeste was removing her gag. Even with her jaw extended, Celeste had trouble fishing the sodden swollen leather from her aching jaw. Emily didn't speak. Celeste hadn't said she could, and she wasn't going to risk another punishment this soon.

"You won't be here long," Celeste said. "You're spending tonight with me."

Celeste looked into her eyes with such a wonderfully sad expression, and Emily weakened, forgot about being punished. It hurt to utter her first words since leaving Lilac Row. "Wh-Who is Miss B-Buxton? That girl…" She glanced at the saddle. "Miss Talons' bed…I f-felt it move."

"Yes. I saw it, too. They will be well punished tonight before Miss Talons goes to bed."

"Will I be?…" Emily broke down.

Celeste took in her arms. She put a finger to Emily's trembling lips. "Shame on you for even asking. You'll find out soon enough. Tomorrow morning you're going to see Miss Buxton."

Emily cried to herself while Celeste removed her collar and the ropes binding her arms. Feeling the ropes fall away was a frightening experience. Having spent the entire day in bondage, she felt naked and insecure. A subtle anxiety lapped at the edges of her mind.

Miss Buxton?

Celeste opened Emily's lavender dress. Emily flushed hotly as Celeste took her face in her leather-clad hands. The kid absorbed the heat in her cheeks. Captivated by Celeste's glistening lips, she closed her eyes and forgot about tomorrow. Celeste kissed her, smothering her with her soft lips. Celeste's hand was on her thigh, lifting her skirt, entering her with a gentle, unexpected squish. Emily's eyes flew open. Celeste's breasts, firm and unyielding beneath their glossy leather prison, crushed into hers. She rose on her toes to guide herself onto Celeste's fingers, timing her thrusts to Celeste's liquid fingers.

Emily screamed.

While holding tightly to Celeste's warmth, she screamed her sadness and fear, her awful need for Celeste's approval. The orgasm was over so quickly she wondered if it had been a dream. Celeste's slippery fingers withdrew, leaving a smoldering, aching void. Her eyes pleaded with Celeste, implored her to continue.

"That's enough," Celeste said, holding up her gloved fingers, wet now with Emily's desire. "Lick them clean," she ordered.

Emily's heart beat furiously at the raised glove. Clinging hopelessly to the afterglow, she opened her mouth and began to suck Celeste's glistening glove. The older woman did not stop her as she sank to her knees. Still sucking like a baby, she closed her eyes and put her hands to her thighs. Her lips were a tiny O around Celeste's finger. Her hands fanned over her thighs. She didn't stop until she'd pleasured herself again and again. She never felt Celeste's finger slip from her mouth. When she opened her eyes, Celeste was standing over her with a shiny leather garment.

"Feeling better, you naughty girl?"

Emily stared up at Celeste. Her eyes cloudy with fading desire. "I-I'm s-sorry," she whispered. "I couldn't help it. Are you going to punish me?"

Celeste nodded. "A turn in the saddle and a good whipping."

"C-Celeste…Ma'am…"

"Don't question me, Emily!" Celeste held up the bodysuit with its dangling laces. "Australian kid," she said. "The finest, most supple leather in the world." She removed Emily's garter belt, hose and heels, leaving her naked and shivering. "You'll be warm in a minute." She took a box of talcum powder from the cabinet, dusted the sweet scent over Emily's bare skin.

She steadied Emily as Emily tried to insert her legs into the suit.

"Celeste, it's too tight."

"Push hard. The powder will help."

Emily plunged a leg into the suit. The leather legging compressed tightly around her calf and then her thigh. It felt warm and comfortable. She inserted the other leg, then wriggled into the upper half of the suit. She guided her fingers through the loops that would prevent the taut sleeves from riding up her arms while Celeste drew up the lacings at the back of the suit. As the suit tightened around Emily, her breasts rose beneath the leather like shining dark moons. Looking down at herself, the effect was stunning.

"Omigod," she whispered. The nubby surfaces of her aureoles and half-erect nipples shown clearly though the kid.

"Lovely," Celeste said, teasing Emily's nipples. "We'll expect you to keep them nice and hard. Otherwise…" Celeste's gloved fingers pinched Emily's nipples hard, stinging and hardening them beneath the skin-soft leather. Emily's heart beat a tattoo. "You needn't be ashamed. Miss Buxton wants big-busted girls."

The leather suit fit Emily like a body corset, pinching everywhere, even snuggling itself between the outer folds of her sex. Celeste's hands were all over her body, drawing and smoothing the leather until there wasn't a wrinkle. To Emily's surprise, the leather felt wonderful against her skin. Celeste opened the cabinet. When she turned around, she held a bamboo cane in her hands. A smile flitted over her face. "I don't suppose you've ever experienced one of these. They're a staple in English schools. Headmistresses use them to punish their naughty young ladies."

Emily stared at the cane as Celeste approached her. The tip of the cane nudged Emily's breasts and belly, poked at her nipples, then dropped to her thighs. Celeste probed her leather-clad sex while running her other hand over the shining contours of Emily's hips. Her glove squeaked as it fondled Emily's bulging bottom. Emily didn't dare move while Celeste toyed with her. Her neck hair stood up as Celeste's hand slid deep into the thick pile of her hair. Celeste fondled the layered coils, loosening, twisting. Her fingers were like snakes in her hair.

Turning her head earned her a stroke across her buttocks. The sting of the cane forced her to shriek, which earned her several more strokes. Her hair loosened and tumbled to her shoulders.

"You just don't learn, do you?"

"I-I don't understand," Emily wept.

"You are to stand perfectly still in my presence. Didn't Madame Godwin teach you anything?"

Emily nodded and whimpered.

"Go to the dressing stand! Kiss the saddle." The

padded leather shone dully in the late afternoon light. "Kiss it, and be quick!"

Blinking away her tears, Emily bent to the saddle. The leather was damp to her lips and smelled tartly of girls who'd ridden it before. Her head reeled as Celeste pushed her facedown onto the saddle.

"Don't be shy. Inhale the leather. Taste it. Revel in the feminine scent. Soon it will be your world."

"N-N-o-o, p-please," Emily whispered. "I-I can't. M-My M-Mama would—"

The cane whooshed, striking her twice in quick succession. She'd been holding her breath, hoping, praying, until the cane and then Celeste's gloved hand pushed her mouth down onto the leather.

"Suck the leather, Emily. As if you were starved for female nourishment. I want to hear your slurps, your wet sucking."

Emily reluctantly opened her mouth and began to lick the narrow saddle. The tangy scent and flavor inundated her senses. She barely felt the cane on her backside, lacing one stripe after another over her plump cheeks. Her arms lifted to the ends of the saddle. She clung to it, head down, sucking, whining, moaning as the cane worked its magic on her leather-covered bottom. It was an exquisite experience. Shame fueling desire. As her desire grew, so did her shamelessness, until she was lost in a swirl of punishment and pleasure. She nearly lost consciousness before Celeste stopped the caning and positioned her burning, swollen seat on the now-wet saddle.

Emily hadn't noticed the layered fold of leather covering her sex. Celeste reached between her thighs and opened the fold so that her sex emerged to ride directly on the saddle. Under the full weight of her body, the slippery surface of the narrow saddle instantly made its way into her sex. She gave out little gasps as waves of pain-filled ecstasy washed over her.

"Be still," Celeste ordered. "You're being punished. I don't want to hear another sound."

Emily blushed. How could she ever have enjoyed this? What depths had she sunk to? If Mama found out, she'd disown her. Swaying unsteadily on the saddle, she watched Celeste beneath her, lashing her ankles to the post. Her feet hung several inches above the floor. She could feel her own wetness merging with the other girls'. She rocked back and forth as Celeste knotted her bindings. Each undulation sent shivers through her.

"Arms behind you. Palms pressed tightly together. Do not move or speak."

Emily fought back scalding tears. The saddle perch was precarious at best. And now she had to sit with her arms bound behind her. Celeste slipped a loose leather sheath over Emily's arms, then drew the laces tight until Emily's arms were compressed into a long tapering triangle.

Every motion of her body allowed the saddle to sink deeper into her sex, turning her thighs to liquid. She wept onto the saddle, soaked it, and didn't care. Overlapping waves of hurt and pleasure rippled through her body. She bit her lip to remain silent. She tried not to

255

moan, tightening her hips and thighs in a vain effort to stop the intrusion. Celeste delivered two whistling strokes to her backside. Emily shrieked. She rocked forward, nearly fell from the mount.

"Stay straight!"

"I-I'm sorry, C-Celeste."

"Disobedient girl!"

Celeste caned her again. "I warned you not to make a sound!" Emily's legs stiffened. She teetered awkwardly on the narrow saddle. Her hips writhed with the cane strokes, but she did not utter another sound.

Celeste applied a half dozen more cane strokes then put it down. She took Emily's jaw in her hand and squeezed it until Emily's mouth was strained open. A trickle of drool ran down Celeste's glove as she peered into Emily's mouth. "What a tiny mouth for such a big girl," she said, rummaging in the cabinet, examining several straps before she found one that fit Emily. The strap was made of brown rubber, wide and thick with a buckle at its end. A bullet-shaped bulb was molded to the middle of the strap. Emily stared at the thing, wondering how that huge bulb was going to fit into her mouth.

Celeste took Emily's jaw again, squeezing it unmercifully. "Open wide," she ordered. Emily's jaw jerked open. "What a good girl."

As Celeste shoved the compliant rubber bulb into Emily's open mouth, Emily began to drool. Saliva ran from the corners of her mouth. Celeste wrapped the rubber strap around her head, stretching it, buckling it tight at the back of her head. The taut strap forced the bulb deeper into Emily's mouth, depressing her tongue, completely filling her mouth. She bit hard into the rubber, found it resilient but unyielding. The tapered rubber tip caressed the back of her throat. She wanted to scream but couldn't make a sound. Tears of frustration streamed down her cheeks.

Celeste watched her with a pitiful expression. "Crying makes it worse. Accept the gag. You'll wear one from now on, every waking minute. I'm going to finish your punishment now. I'll wager not even Mrs. Bertram ever punished you like this."

Celeste picked up her cane and began to lash Emily's backside so fiercely, tiny screams leaked from beneath Emily's airtight gag. The Ecole mistress delivered two dozen flaming strokes to Emily's seat and upper bottom before moving to Emily's front. Emily's eyes grew dark and wide as Celeste applied the whistling cane to her breasts. Emily shook as the thin instrument sank into the soft contours of her breasts, jiggling and stinging, imparting another track with each new stroke. Her nipples came next. She almost toppled off the saddle as the cane attacked her erect nipples. A slashing stroke over her belly caught her off guard.

"Hold still!" Celeste screamed, her eyes bright and filled with excitement. She lifted the cane and lashed Emily's breasts again. "I'll show you what happens when you don't obey your mistress!" Emily was dizzy with fright. Celeste was screaming. "You're a whore! A fat bitch who knows nothing of Ecole discipline. I'll teach you about the Ecole, Emily Johnson. I'll teach you until you scream for mercy, and then scream for more of my cane!"

The cane flew incessantly, stinging, whipping Emily's flesh. She was whipped on her sheathed arms, her back, her hips, her belly and thighs until her whole body was a mass of bruises and welts. By the time Celeste stopped and threw the fractured cane into a corner, Emily felt nothing.

Breathing heavily, Celeste took a pair of gleaming black leather boots from the cabinet. They had stiletto heels and small silver rings at their insteps. The lacings ran from instep to the boot top. It would be an arduous job to lace them. Celeste untied Emily's ankles from the post. While Emily perched precariously on the saddle, Celeste slipped the boots over Emily's legs. Emily was momentarily revived. She had no idea the Ecole would allow her to wear such elegant and expensive boots. They fit her feet perfectly. They were quite stiff, but conformed easily to the curves of her calves. She teetered as Celeste laced the boots tight, first at her calves, then up her thighs. The boots stiffened her legs, so that they hung as uselessly as her sheathed arms behind her. Their tops stopped just short of her sex. If she squeezed her thighs, the boot leather rose and creased the edges of her swollen sex, dulling the pain of the saddle.

Celeste helped her off the saddle and onto her feet. The tight-laced boots supported her. She found she could stand on the six-inch heels without wobbling, in spite their height. The leather saddle's surface gleamed brightly. Looking at it, Emily realized she'd left something for the next girl. The thought pleased her.

"The boots add a certain something," Celeste said. "Hobbling will make you even more adorable." Emily took a tentative step. "Don't move. You'll go right back onto the saddle." Celeste took a short length of silver chain from the cabinet. She snapped the ends of the chain to the rings at Emily's insteps. The chain was shorter than her first hobble, forcing her to walk with tiny mincing steps.

"Now, I'm going to tight-lace you into an old-fashioned corset. Miss Talons and I swear by them. They're wonderful for training full-figured girls like you. It's too bad Mrs. Bertram didn't use one on you."

Emily decided not to tell Celeste that Mrs. Bertram had threatened to put her in a corset. Mrs. Bertram would have, if she hadn't been sent away. Celeste took the corset from the inside wall of the cabinet. She held it up to Emily. It was made of stout black steer hide, stiffened with sewn-in steel stays. Instead of the usual lacings up the back, this one had three buckles across its front.

"A figure like yours needs more than silk corset strings to cinch you in."

A thick, wide strap hung from the corset's front. Emily thought it must pass between her thighs to buckle over her seat to the back of the corset. Another strap ran up the back of the corset, which would terminate in a buckle at the padded collar. Celeste wrapped the thick-walled garment around Emily's waist and drew the three buckles tight at its front. The corset fit tightly beneath her breasts and over her hips, shrinking her waist dramatically, and forcing her breasts up and over the rim. Celeste stood back, studied her, then drew in the waist buckle another notch. The corset was so tight now, Emily could not bend her spine. Celeste ran the bottom strap between Emily's thighs, buckling it to the back of the corset. The belt was wide and soft, and completely covered her sex.

"This will put a stop to those naughty boot tops," Celeste said as she drew the belt snug.

Emily stood as stiffly now as a statue while Celeste closed her collar and buckled the strap running from corset to collar. This strap was short enough to pull her head back and up, locking her gagged mouth into a defiant chin-up pose. She looked sideways, imploringly, silently, at her captor, while Celeste stood back to study her, her hands resting on her hips.

"What a pretty sight. Helpless as a baby. Look at those arms. Unsightly!"

Celeste produced another belt which she used to attach Emily's sheathed arms to a metal ring at the back of the corset. Emily experienced a moment of agonizing fear as Celeste tightened the belt around her arms. She found herself wrapped in an unrelenting leather prison. Her eyes widened when she saw the soft leather helmet in Celeste's hands. Helpless to stop her, Emily moaned as the helmet was pulled down over her head, blinding her, sealing off her gag. To her relief, there were two tiny holes to breathe through. Celeste pulled her long hair from beneath the hood and ran it through an opening in its back, before tightening the laces at the back of her head. When she was finished lacing the helmet, it fit skintight over her face.

Blind and stiffly bound, unable to speak, she could do nothing while Celeste brushed her hair until it was soft and feathery, sheened with copper and gold highlights. Celeste twisted the long hank into a thick bun and secured it at the base of Emily's hood. The coppery bun was as large as a grapefruit, resting on Emily's collar.

Emily could hear the soft shushing of Celeste's slipper-boots as she slowly circled her. She did not know Celeste had the cane in her hand and was ready to strike. The cane flew with a whisper, striking Emily's bottom so hard she took a halting step forward, stumbling on her spiky heels and the silver chain that kept her ankles together.

"How did that feel, my pet?"

Emily could only stare straight ahead into the darkness. She wanted to tell Celeste she would obey—she would be the perfect Ecole student. Celeste cracked her again, twice, in quick succession. Emily fought to breathe as Celeste warmed to her task, striking Emily's leather-clad bottom again and again, setting her buttocks on fire. The cane flew until Emily lost count of the cutting strokes.

"Did you feel those, my pretty plump doll?"

Emily imagined Celeste's expression. Her eyes

would be glittering, her red mouth wet with desire. Unable to see or move or respond in any way, Emily forced a long scream into her gag. Her body shook with frustration and terror. Her hair slowly came undone, compelled by the smacking force of Celeste's cane. Celeste finally stopped the horrible caning.

Emily heard her step away, the clatter of the cane in the closet as she put it away. Celeste was suddenly behind her, sliding out the comb that held the remnants of Emily's bun in place. Emily felt her hair uncoil and burst into a golden cascade that fell to her shining and now-swollen seat. Celeste moved in like a tigress. Emily could hear her measured breathing, feel her gloved hands running through her hair, stroking and crushing it, raising it to her lips. Celeste gathered up Emily's hair, artfully coiling it back into a bun.

"You do have lovely hair," Celeste whispered. Her hands slid from behind Emily to fondle the smooth leather skin covering Emily's breasts. Her fingers ran over Emily's nipples, found them shrunken and soft. "I told you to keep those nipples erect. Failure means punishment—severe punishment."

The very thought of being punished once more startled her nipples erect again. As her nipples gently probed their leather prison, she thought of the mysterious Miss Buxton and what the woman might have in store for her. She felt Celeste snap a silver chain to her collar and lead her from the dressing chamber.

CHAPTER 16

Emily had no idea where she was or where she was going. Without a word, Celeste hurried her downward, through damp-smelling corridors to another part of the Ecole where the air smelt warm and dry. Celeste abruptly pulled her up short with the silver leash. Breathing heavily after the long walk, Emily waited patiently and blindly. She heard the rasp of a key in a lock. The squeak of a door. Celeste led her into a chamber that smelled faintly but distinctly of Celeste. Celeste backed her against the wall where she fastened Emily's arms and ankles so that she could not move. And then Celeste was gone, locking the door behind her, hurrying away without a word as to whether or not she was coming back.

Emily found herself alone for the first time since

arriving at the Ecole. What seemed like hours passed. She had no idea, really. A key slid into the door and clicked. Blinded by her leather hood, she knew it was Celeste. The soft shuffle of her boots, the scent of her, preceded her presence into the chamber. Celeste undid the straps that held her to the wall, moved her into the center of the chamber where she undid Emily's hair. Emily had no idea why Celeste seemed so taken with her hair. Her new mistress seemed to derive real pleasure in letting it down and putting it up. Celeste's ministrations, her punishments, were beginning to make Emily feel like an object, a toy in the older woman's eyes. Celeste's hands slithered through the twisted strands of her hair, pulling her head back sharply with each pass.

Celeste loosened the laces at the back of her hood. As the helmet slid off her head, she opened her eyes and saw Celeste, smiling at her. Celeste had changed. She wore a long leather skirt with a slit up the side, and a loosely laced leather bodice so supple the outlines of her nipples could be seen through the leather. The bodice was cut low to expose a generous amount of cleavage and breasts. Her eyes glittered as she looked at Emily.

"Can you guess where you are?"

Emily twisted her whole body in an attempt to shake her head.

"You're in my quarters now. They're not as ostentatious as Miss Talons's, but I prefer more militant furnishings."

Emily's eyes wandered around the room. Its stone walls were hidden behind heavy woven tapestries. The floor was planked, hard and smooth beneath her boots. A pair of narrow arched windows opened onto the rolling hills, blurred now in the falling shades of violet twilight. There was a large, unassuming bed strewn with pillows. A leather-bound steamer trunk stood at its foot. A painted armoire angled across a corner. Hanging from the dusty ceiling were ropes and pulleys that frightened her. A pair of torches stood against the walls. Like the others, these were tightly bound into stiff leather suits. Each one was strapped in place to the wall behind. Blinded by their hoods, the motionless bodies were faceless sentries. Their iron torch-bearing poles threw a pale flickering pall over the room. Celeste threw open the armoire's doors.

"Come into the center of the room, Emily. I want to brush your hair."

Emily's hobble chain made soft clinking sounds as she crossed the room. Celeste removed a long-handled, intricately carved ivory hairbrush from the armoire. In spite of her fear, Emily was struck by the exquisite beauty of the brush. Celeste began to brush out her hair with long sweeping strokes. In the soft yellow torch-light, Emily's hair shone with flickering points of light, shimmering and slithering down her back and over her bottom, swaying with the motions of her body. Celeste unbuckled the gag strap and slipped the rubber plug from her mouth. As Emily breathed in fresh air and fought to swallow the flat taste of the wet rubber in her mouth, she noticed a heaping bowl of fruit and cheeses and a gag like her own on the table by the bed. The fruit reminded her she hadn't eaten since morning. Was that new gag meant for her?

"How do you feel now with your gag removed? Is it better, or are you more comfortable with your mouth being filled?" Celeste asked. Emily found it impossible to speak. Celeste smiled, touched Emily's lips with her finger. "You're afraid to speak. That's good. You're learning. But, you may speak now."

Emily worked her jaw. "I-It feels strange.... As if I'm not…"

"Supposed to speak? Did you enjoy your mouth being stuffed?"

"Wh-Why, y-yes," Emily whispered, surprised that Celeste had so easily read her thoughts.

"Being silenced is wonderful. A full mouth is even better. I thought you'd enjoy it."

Celeste offered the bowl of fruit and cheeses to Emily. "I want you to eat. You must be starving. We cannot afford to take off a single pound from that body of yours. Miss Talons would not be pleased. Miss Buxton even less so."

Emily stood awkwardly, waiting to be fed, her eyes dancing at the mounded fruit and cheeses. "M-Miss Celeste,…"

"How insensitive of me. You can't feed yourself."

Emily opened her mouth like a hungry baby bird. Celeste stuffed fruit and cheese into her mouth until the fruits' juices were running down her cheeks. Celeste wiped Emily's mouth dry.

"That should hold you until tomorrow—and Miss Buxton. I have another surprise for you."

Celeste led Emily beneath a pair of leather-covered steel hooks, hanging a few feet above their heads. Celeste pulled the hooks down and inserted them into steel eyes on the sides of Emily's collar. She arranged the padded hooks so that they lay comfortably against the sides of Emily's head.

"Don't move, Emily. I'm going to make an adjustment."

Emily watched Celeste open a control panel at the head of the bed and press a button. An overhead motor clicked and whirred, straightening the ropes hooked to Emily's collar, gently lifting her off the floor. She hung now in her padded collar several inches off the floor. She squeezed her eyes shut as she began to turn. She was surprised. Being suspended wasn't that uncomfortable. Her body weight was distributed from her collar to the strap down her back to the strap between her legs, which was drawn up now between her thighs and buttocks. Still, she thought, I do not deserve to be hung like a side of beef.

It isn't fair. No! It's not fair!

When she opened her eyes, Celeste was looking at her with a wicked smile. Celeste's expression silently and poignantly assured her it made no difference what she thought. As Celeste came to her, she unlaced the front of her soft leather bodice. She slipped out of it and dropped it to the floor. Emily jerked in her harness, causing the taut soft-leather strap between her thighs to catch the edges of her sex. Celeste stood unsmiling in front of her, bare to the waist, her ivory skin gleaming in the pale light. She was a voluptuous woman with wide hips that moved easily beneath the taut leather skirt. Her waist matched Emily's. Her breasts were large and firm, tipped with plum-colored nipples springing from raspberry fields. No longer caring, possessed by her captor, Emily's lips parted. Celeste responded by caressing and lifting her own breasts to Emily. Emily nearly fainted at the prospect of touching and kissing such beauty. Her suspended body shook with desire.

"M-Miss C-Celeste," she croaked. Her mouth was so dry she could hardly speak. "I-I…"

"You want these."

It was a simple statement of fact that Emily could not have denied. Celeste's black gloves were like spiders' legs covering the milky textured flesh of her breasts. Her distended nipples peeped between her fingers. Emily blinked in response. She was flushed from her hairline to the tips of her breasts. Waves of heat engulfed her. She gave in. "I-I…adore y-you, M-Miss Celeste. Honestly, I…worship you." She lowered her eyes to Celeste's slippers. "I am yours," she whispered so softly Celeste barely heard her.

Celeste kissed her on her lips. "You mustn't be ashamed, Emily. It's your raison d'être. Why you are with us now. You must devote your being to pleasing Miss Talons and me, and tomorrow, Miss Buxton."

Emily's eyes filled with tears. Bound, impossibly suspended in space, she could not imagine how to please. The prospect of failing loomed like a specter. "I-I don't know…."

"I'll teach you."

Celeste stood on her toes. As gently as a mother caressing her child, she took Emily's face in her hands. She closed her eyes, kissed Emily passionately. Her tongue nibbled at the edges of Emily's lips while her hands moved to Emily's breasts. She gently teased Emily's breasts and nipples until Emily was awash in pleasure. In an attempt to work the strap between her legs into her sex, she lifted a hobbled leg, catching Celeste's shin with the tip of her boot. Celeste stood back to gaze at Emily, spinning slowly in her ropes.

Her voice was flat. "You haven't learned a thing! I should have thought you'd learned from the dressing stand."

Emily burst into tears, appalled that she'd failed so soon. "I-I'm s-sorry," she wailed. "I d-didn't mean to…upset you."

"You wretched girl! You no longer exist for yourself. You are here for one reason. To be transformed into an objet d'art, another bauble for Miss Talons' collection. You can never leave. And you must learn obedience! Let me show you something."

Celeste swung the armoire doors open. Inside, nearly hidden behind the hanging array of punishment implements, a motionless figure stood in the cabinet. She was clad from head to toe in a faceless tight-laced leather suit. Her rigid pose reminded Emily of an Oscar statuette. She was a big girl, as large as Emily through the hips and bustline, and about the same height.

"This is where I store my girls. She's been in there

for days, waiting for your arrival. Is this what I must do with you, too? There's plenty of room in there for you."

Emily swayed from her ropes, her eyes focused on the girl in the armoire. The prospect of being shut away reminded her of what Madame Godwin used to do with Annie at Lilac Row. Had Madame Godwin learned this punishment method from Celeste and Miss Talons? Mrs. Bertram would have appreciated Celeste's ultra-strict training methods—and her extensive collection of punishment implements. How many of the devices in that cabinet had been used on the poor thing standing in the armoire?

"I-I'll try to b-behave," Emily whispered, blushing scarlet at the realization that the girl in the armoire could not move or see through her laced hood, but she could certainly hear what was going in this room. Celeste removed a thick leather belt from the armoire. She doubled its ends in her hand, then closed the armoire doors.

"Leather on leather. A superb combination, don't you think? It's especially nice when the strap is well oiled, which this one is." Emily eyed the glistening leather with a horrified expression as Celeste raised the shining loop of strap to her lips. "Kiss the leather. Show me how you respect and revel in the smack of it on your backside. Beg me to belt you until you scream for mercy."

Emily burst into tears. She shrieked out, "What has Madame G-Godwin done to me?"

"She's put you where you belong." Celeste thrust

the belt into Emily's face. "Kiss it, I said." Emily shut her eyes, grimaced, and delivered a delicate kiss to the looped belt. "Kiss it as if you cannot live without it. Kiss it like you kissed the saddle." Emily kissed it again. This time her lips opened and she took a bit of the leather into her mouth, sucking like a baby on its coarse texture.

"That's my girl," Celeste purred, backing away and kneeling to anchor Emily's ankles to a small iron ring set into the floor. When she rose, she set her feet apart in a balanced stance. The leather curled and snapped as she drew back her arm and delivered the first blow to Emily's leather-clad bottom. The oily, wet leather smacked noisily, sending droplets flying. Neither the thin leather covering her backside, nor the thick strap between her legs, could alleviate the pain. The belt burned, forcing a cry from her lips. Celeste ignored her outburst. As she continued to belt Emily, time slowed. In the dimly lit room the soft curling hiss of the strap and the noisy smacks on her thighs and bottom merged, driving Emily into a state where she knew nothing but the belt and Celeste's hard measured breathing.

Celeste strapped Emily until the belt was nearly dry and Emily's bottom was covered with slick. Emily hung sobbing, quivering, drained of all protest. There would be no more promises. No more shrieks. She was being fulfilled. Hurting beyond comprehension, she found herself accepting, even beginning to relish her new persona.

Celeste touched Emily's lips, traced their outlines with a leather-covered finger. "Had enough?"

"I-I'll do whatever…you say."

"We'll see if you're so compliant tomorrow when I take you to Miss Buxton's upholstery shop."

"Upholstery sh-shop…. Why?… What?… I-I don't understand"

"I think you do, Emily. I think you know you're to be molded and bound, and made into furniture. Another fine piece of leather furniture from Miss Buxton's upholstery shop. She's as good at furniture making as Miss Devreux is at making clothes."

"Oh, God,…Celeste, please,…don't m-make me…"

"Silence! Miss Buxton can hardly wait to get her hands on you. She's known for weeks you were coming. Unless I miss my guess, after being properly fattened and shaped, you and the one in the armoire will be joined at the hip and bound into a fine new whipping horse." Celeste tossed her head at the armoire.

Emily's eyes widened as she remembered Madame Godwin's plump, fat couch. How it moved when she sat. And Miss Talons' bed—soft, pliant. She screamed. Kicked against the strap that held her feet to the floor. Her body shook with fright and anger. "N-N-o-o!" she shrieked. "I won't do it!"

"Yes, you will. And you'll do it willingly, because it's best for you." Celeste did not raise her voice. She sounded like a patient mother whose child was throwing an awful tantrum. "Perhaps, this will convince you."

She returned to the armoire and took out a long, slender rod. Its metal surface gleamed in the dim light. Her eyes darkened. "Look at those nipples! They're like tired little soldiers." She prodded the leather covering Emily's semierect nipples with the tip of her rod. "They must be kept erect. Miss Talons and Miss Buxton expect it." Emily turned ice cold as Celeste slowly circled her, the rod clutched in her gloved hand. With a whistling arc the rod whistled and caught Emily across her hip. Emily's body flexed sideways as the rod cut deep.

"Miss Buxton will put you on a special diet. She'll make you even bigger before turning you into a piece of furniture. She relishes fattening up her stuffings before binding them into her furniture." The rod sighed, cut another bright swath of pain across Emily's buttocks. "Did that hurt? It will be nothing by the time I finish with you."

The pain was terrible. She tried not to cry. At each stroke, she bit her lip, hoping it would be the last. Miss Buxton. Why was Miss Talons doing this to her? She hadn't disobeyed. She'd done everything the women asked. How could she be discarded? She'd disappear without a trace. Celeste didn't seem to care as she vigorously applied the slender rod to her front and back for several more minutes. When she finally stopped, Emily's buttocks, thighs, and breasts were ablaze with bright, searing pain.

Celeste walked around Emily, tracing the tip of her rod over Emily's striped breasts. In spite of the pain, the tip of the rod sent tiny electric bolts of pleasure shooting through her body. Celeste thrust one of her hands beneath the taut leather strap covering Emily's sex. One at a time, she slipped a pair of chrome balls beneath the strap and into Emily's sex. The strap would keep the balls high in her sex. She could feel the outer lips of her sex parting to admit the balls, and closing again after the balls had slipped inside. Trapped inside her, her thighs quivered helplessly. The balls responded with tiny clicking, sliding motions that set her insides on fire.

Celeste patted the thick strap over Emily's sex. "You will wear the balls from now on. Tomorrow, Miss Buxton will permanently place the balls before you are...transformed. The balls will keep you nice and damp, nipples erect, in a proper state of mind."

"W-Will I ever be released?"

Celeste caressed Emily's cheek. "How droll. No, you won't be released. There is no release from The Ecole. You will become Miss Buxton's property. There *is* no way back."

"B-But there must be...."

"There is no way back, Emily. No way."

Emily let the awful finality of the Celeste's words sink in before she screamed, an awful crescendo of pain, resignation, and unrealized expectations. Tears flowed down her cheeks, splashing onto the shiny leather covering her breasts.

"Mrs. B-Bertram,...M-Madame G-Godwin," she whispered to a blurred image of Celeste. "O-o-o-h," she screamed softly, and turned her tear-stained cheeks back to Celeste. "Wh-What have you done to me?" The words rose like a bubble in her throat. She already knew the answer. She hung from the twin ropes, unmoving. Staring straight ahead, not thinking. When the rod struck her again, across her seat, she smiled through bright tears at her captor. The chrome balls moved ever so slightly.

"I deserved that, Celeste," she murmured. "I need to be punished."

Celeste smiled her feline smile. "A good whipping, and then to bed, little one."

"Yes, Celeste."

The rod flew, blanking out her consciousness.

Later, in the cool darkness, revolving slowly, filled with a measure of pain and pleasure she'd never known, Emily slept. Celeste was gone. The door creaked, awakening Emily. The door slowly opened behind her. A white-robed figure came into the room, carrying a limp leather suit.

Celeste?

Renzi floated into view. A soft white vision in a gauzy robe so sheer Emily could see right through it to Renzi's breasts and the patch of dark covering her sex. Her ebony hair was brushed out into a thick curling mass that fluttered about her shoulders. She smiled at Emily.

"Did you think I wasn't coming back? I had to see you before...well, before you go to Miss Buxton."

She went to the table, picked up the fresh gag Celeste had laid out. As she lifted the gag to Emily's mouth, Emily compliantly opened wide and took the fat rubber bulb without a whimper. Renzi kissed Emily on her cheek, then fastened the wide rubber strap around Emily's head, drawing it tight at the back of Emily's head. She coiled and knotted Emily's long hank of hair into a bun and secured it to the back of Emily's head.

"It's your bedtime, Emily. You should spend at least one night in one of these. I think you'll like it." She held up the suit. It was similar to the one Renzi wore, with lacings up its back. But this one was made of heavier leather and had only one leg.

How in the world will I be put into that?

Renzi unlaced and pulled off Emily's boots. She set them to one side and began to work the tight-fitting body shell up and over Emily's legs, trapping, compressing her legs into a single stiffened entity. Emily swayed gently, like a muted set of wind chimes. She gasped through her gag when her head disappeared beneath the new hood. She could feel Renzi's hands as she began the tedious job of tight-lacing the shell from Emily's ankles, over her swollen buttocks to the back of her head. When Renzi was finished, Emily could imagine herself tightly cocooned, like the poor thing waiting silently in the armoire. Renzi stuffed and laced her thick bun of hair into its own leather ball, allowed it to rest on the back of the suit. Emily's only connection to the outside world was a pair of tiny breathing holes in the face of the suit. Her breasts were rounded and flattened now by the press of the suit. Inside the suit, aside from the pain of the caning, she was reasonably comfortable.

Renzi patted Emily's swollen bottom. "Good night, sweetie. Sleep tight."

Blinded and gagged, unable to move, Emily found her sense of hearing was heightened through the leather over her ears. She heard Renzi close and lock the door as she left. Then she was alone again with the girl in the armoire. From somewhere deep in the bowels of The Ecole she thought she heard a brief scream. It might have been the night wind or Mother disciplining one of her maids. A heavy unbroken silence settled over the room. Warmed by the double layer of leather covering her, exhausted by the rigors of her first day at The Ecole, Emily drifted off to dream of Celeste. She had no idea how much time had passed when she was wakened by a muted giggle and Celeste's throaty response.

Renzi was back—and in bed with Celeste.

Unable to see, she knew. Jealousy and abandonment stabbed at her gut. Was she to be set aside, trussed like beef, while Renzi made love to her mistress? After what she'd gone through, the inequity of it stunned her. The wet sounds of Renzi's mouth at Celeste's breasts, the playful and not-so-playful spanks that emerged from beneath the bedclothes, filled the room. Emily's thighs instinctively tensed, turning the balls inside her. But their movements couldn't satisfy her. She wanted the warmth of Celeste, the cool scent of her shining hair, her thighs pressed to hers. Awake now, and quivering with desire, Emily desperately tried to turn herself in the direction of the bed. Whispered sighs, punctuated with sharp, open-handed spanks, moans and passionate cries, the faint sounds of a girl in the throes of a whipping drifted through her consciousness, satiating and dulling her senses until she could stand no more. She finally fell back into an anxious sleep.

In the hour or so before dawn, the air had turned cool and damp. The clasping leather warmed Emily like a down-filled comforter. She woke at the hand on her shoulder, heard the hum of the invisible motor. The ropes holding her jerked, settled her gently to the floor. Unseen hands released the hooks at her collar. Those same hands lifted her and carried her to the bed. Soft bodies slipped into bed on either side of her, quickly unlacing the bosom of her suit. She didn't recall an opening there, but now it seemed as if it were so. Open palms gently kneaded scented oil into her exposed breasts and nipples until they shone like pearlescent moons.

Renzi leaned over her and whispered something in Arabic as she took Emily's distended nipple between her lips. Emily was as compliant as a rag doll as Renzi rolled her onto her stomach and gently lifted her hips, elevating her bottom above the sheets. Somehow Renzi had found her way beneath her. Renzi's mouth was clasped to her breasts, sucking so hard her nipples screamed in protest. Out of nowhere, Celeste's shining metal rod came down suddenly, startling her, exposing her breasts to Renzi's open mouth, twin rows of even white teeth. Renzi's mouth closed. Biting teeth tore the bloody nipple from her breast. She barely felt the cut of the rod as it lashed and ripped the leather from her bottom. An abyss opened, pulled her down at heart-stopping speed into an endless cold blackness.

When Celeste came for Emily the next morning, Emily woke to find herself suspended in her cocoon.

She remembered little of her dream. It had been the most exquisite, terrifying, and pain-filled night of her life. As Celeste loosened the shell's lacings and exposed her head to the light, Emily remembered. She saw Renzi's straight white teeth, scarlet, glistening with her blood. Working her head forward against the unyielding strap at her back, she managed a quick sideways glance down at herself. Her breasts were still covered, rising like twin swells on a sleek black sea. Both nipples stood up proudly, prodding through the leather skin. There were *no* lacings—*no* openings for Renzi's biting mouth.

"I love you, Celeste."

"You look famished. First I'll feed you, and then we're going down to Miss Buxton. She's been asking about you."

CHAPTER 17

Miss Buxton paused at a nearly completed sofa. "No! No! No! The leather must be drawn perfectly tight before you sew the seam." Miss Buxton spanked her assistant. "Rip it out. Start over."

The assistant straightened up and turned to her mistress. She spoke slowly, choosing her words with care. "It's not me, Miss Buxton. The stuffing won't lay still."

"I see. Then, we must be firm. Take charge of our work."

Miss Buxton took a heavy paddle from the post near the workstation. Holding the paddle in both hands, she spread her legs and began to beat the fat, leather-clad thigh bulging through an open seam in the seat of the sofa. "This is how we stop such nonsense." The paddle smacks reverberated throughout the shop. The exposed thigh shivered and receded with each successive application. Miss Buxton delivered two dozen strokes to the exposed bulge before she paused to wipe her brow. She rehung the paddle.

"If it moves again, give it another dose. Now, sew up that seam. I'll be back to inspect your work." The assistant thanked her and bent over the sofa, embarrassed she hadn't thought to take the paddle down herself. With her long slender needle and thread she worked quickly to close the unsightly gap. Miss Buxton moved on, her tiny red mouth pursed in silent frustration. She was short in stature and dark eyed; had a deceptively sweet air about her. Her heavy bustline, matronly hips, and soft features put off the girls Leah Talons sent to her. Beneath her grandmotherly facade lay a woman of steel, a perfectionist and craftswoman who worshipped Leah Talons and everything she stood for. She wore her graying hair in a soft knot and covered with a folded bandanna. Unlike the other members of the Ecole's staff, Miss Buxton eschewed leather garb. She preferred long denim skirts and blouses, heavy work aprons, and soft leather boots to ward off the damp that was always present in the upholstery shop she ran for Leah.

The upholstery shop was located in a large window-less chamber on the lowest level of the Ecole, directly opposite the laundry. Air shafts and fans provided inadequate ventilation. The air was always heavy with the mingled smells of tanned leather, dyes, damp, and the laundry next door. The work areas were unevenly lit by torch stands made in Miss Buxton's shop. The arched brick ceiling was too low for overhead torches, which upset Miss Buxton. She complained to Miss Talons that her assistants needed more light for their work. A skilled upholsterer and furniture builder, Miss Buxton crafted what she called full-figured furniture for Leah and a select few of Leah's friends. Not a single piece of furniture left her shop without her approval.

About the time the upholstery-shop assistant was closing the sofa, Emily was hurrying after Celeste. She was gagged and hobbled, but at least, she thought, Celeste hadn't put her into the helmet. Being able to see made it much easier to traverse the rough stone flooring and uneven steps. Celeste took her through twisting corridors and down several sets of narrow steep stairs before they reached the lowest level, and Miss Buxton's shop.

"Don't make a single move unless Miss Buxton orders you," Celeste warned. "One move without her permission and she'll use you to test a new spanking horse."

The soft clink of Emily's hobble chains turned several assistants' heads as she was paraded to the back of the shop where Miss Buxton stood with an assistant. Being led like an animal was terribly embarrassing for Emily. Yet none of Miss Buxton's pretty young assistants took more than a passing interest in her tightly bound and collared plight.

Celeste's voice turned oily in Miss Buxton's presence. "Fiona, I'm not interrupting?…"

"Don't be silly, Celeste. It's always nice to see someone from up there. You ought to visit us more often."

Celeste looked around the shop. "This place is too damp and gloomy."

"You ought to work down here six days a week." Miss Buxton turned her gaze to Emily. "So this is my new one." Emily froze as Miss Buxton fixed her with cool gray eyes and squeezed her upper arm. "Nearly plump enough. Though I'm sure you hadn't noticed." She looked coyly at Celeste.

Celeste ignored the remark. "I wish I could take credit for this one. Florence Bertram found her. Harriet Godwin trained her."

"Mrs. Bertram's a bitch, but I can't complain. She's been good to me. And Leah's sent me two plump morsels in as many days. My cup runneth over." She began to laugh, a deep belly laugh that lifted and rolled her mountainous breasts beneath the bib of her apron.

Celeste cleared her throat. "Quite honestly, Fiona, if I had my way—"

"She wouldn't be here. Well, my dear Celeste, we both know your loss is my gain." She smiled broadly as she squeezed Emily's breasts, put her hands around Emily's waist and squeezed with such strength Emily cried out.

Miss Buxton stepped back. She glared at Emily. "Do that again, Missy, and I'll tan your hide! Is that clear?"

Emily stared into Miss Buxton's open expression

and nodded. Celeste looked around the shop, inhaled deeply. "As much as I dislike coming all the way down here, this place does fascinate me. Do you mind if I look around?"

"I'll give you a tour."

Miss Buxton gestured to an area of partially uphol-stered beds, tables, and chairs. "These are workaday projects. There are no special shapes or stuffing required here. The stuffings are simply fattened, shaped, and molded to suit the needs of the piece."

Emily stared, disbelieving, at the projects. Bodies in all shapes and sizes, clad in skintight leather suits just like hers, were being fitted and stuffed and sewn into furniture. She watched an assistant paddle-spank a swollen leather-clad bosom into place, finally resorting to pushing the breasts in with the flats of her hands until another assistant with needle and thread had sewn the bosom into the back of a chair. Emily could see the leather expanding and receding as the cover was sewn closed. The sight of the young woman's breasts disap-pearing into the chair made her dizzy with desire.

"How wonderful that is to watch, Fiona." Celeste breathed. "Closure is such an erotic and organic process."

"Like being returned to the womb," Miss Buxton said.

Emily held her breath. She was shocked at the sight.

"May I see where you train and fatten your stuff-ings?"

Miss Buxton led Celeste and Emily to a dimly lit

section of the shop. As Emily's eyes adjusted to the semi-darkness, her body stiffened against the taut leather straps that held her head back and her sheathed arms behind her. She swayed dizzily on her tall heels. What Celeste called stuffings were strapped into a long row of padded iron frames. Some of the featureless figures sat bolt upright. Others were tied head down over an upside-down V-frame. Others lay side by side in horizontal frames.

Ignoring Emily's wide-eyed stare, Miss Buxton explained. "Iron frames are used to mold the stuffings into the positions they will eventually and permanently assume. Those that are head down with their bottoms in the air will stuff our whipping horses. Those strapped into upright chair frames will become just that. Fine chairs for milady's delicate derrière. The stuffings stretched out on bed frames will become mattresses in all sizes and grades of firmness."

Twisting her body sideways, Emily could see the girl nearest her. She was strapped into a tall iron chair frame. Her head was pulled back, strapped tightly to the frame behind it. A rubber gag like the one Emily wore ran around her head beneath her leather hood. Her arms were buckled and bound to her thighs. She could not see Emily, but Emily was sure she knew she was there.

"Furniture training is rigorous and unrelenting. A stuffing that dares move in training is severely whipped until she learns to hold her position without twitching a single muscle."

Emily thought of Miss Talons' bed. The motions she'd felt and seen. What of them?

"What do you feed them while they're here?" Celeste asked.

"Several times a day we force-feed rich, heavy meals. We want them to gain, substantially, in the shortest amount of time."

"I understand your need to fatten them." Emily knew the question was to make her uncomfortable. "But, what if they're not hungry?"

"Oh, they eat. They eat well. They know better."

"They look terribly well fed, plump and sleek."

"They should," Miss Buxton said, proudly. "What with their special diet and being bound for weeks or months in these training frames, it isn't long before they become languorous. Plump piggies, we call them."

"Overripe piggies," I should say."

"Exactly. I like your choice of words. And they become wonderfully compliant. As they ripen, they mold themselves right to their frames. When their breasts and upper arms have swollen to bursting, their nipples are the size of plums, and their lower bodies have turned to overstuffed pillows, then and only then will I approve their transfer to actual furniture frames. By that time, they are so sluggish they are barely able to move. We take great care not to chafe that soft, taut flesh when we transfer them."

The chair-bound girl, Emily had noticed earlier, slowly turned her head to Miss Buxton and the sound of her voice. Emily could see her belly flexing against the leather belts that held her to the chair frame. Miss Buxton also saw the movements. She gestured to an assistant. The young woman drew a short black tendrilled whip from her waist and began to whip the girl's leather-covered breasts. Miss Buxton and Celeste watched with interest. Emily was horrified. "That one simply will not learn. She'll carry those welts into the wingback chair she's going into."

Celeste turned to Miss Buxton. "Does it ever bother you when you…you transform them?"

"Dear me, no. I'm too busy making furniture to think about that. A long time ago I learned to turn a deaf ear to the silly mewings of stuffing. Down here, they are just so much material; stuffing and batting to be fattened, molded, bound, and sewn into my furniture. When the last stitches have been sewn, all the cushions are closed, and I examine each piece before it leaves my shop. By that time I couldn't tell you which stuffing has been sewn into which piece."

"How do you select the material for torches?"

"I use the tallest, strongest ones. Their arms are tightly bound behind them, and their backbones are stiffened with iron rods. We leave them like that until they can stand for days without a whimper. Then we lace them into wet rawhide cocoons, which over a day or two shrink to encapsulate them. Lighter ones are done the same way for use in the suspended torches. Leah decides where the torches will be sent. Where their light is needed."

"Rigid, sightless, faceless; they're really quite pathetic."

"Yes, but there's a certain beauty in that. Knowing what's bound beneath the surface of my furniture can be quite moving, and for some it can be much more than that."

"Yes, I can see what you mean."

"My greatest challenge comes when Leah orders a new piece. These items must be perfect in every way. We import the finest leathers from Morocco, and use the most supple stuffings we can find. Only those with the fleshiest thighs, softest bottomcheeks, and largest breasts are chosen. I have an order from Leah for a new whipping horse. It's for her friend. These horses require matched sets of stuffing. It can take months to find the right pair of shapes, bottoms, and thighs. They must fairly ripple with lard."

Celeste smiled.

"I prefer to use shapes that are naturally plump, but you know Leah doesn't like to be kept waiting."

Celeste looked at Emily. "Doesn't this one meet your requirements?"

Miss Buxton lifted her hand. "Let me finish. I had begun double-feeding two of my thinner shapes to fatten them quickly. Last night, you delivered exactly what I needed. Today you bring this one—the other half. I now have the stuffing to construct Leah's new horse."

Celeste hid her disappointment with a smile. "I'm glad," she said.

Miss Buxton turned to Emily. "Come along. It's time we got you started." Miss Buxton took Emily's leash from Celeste as if she were leading a dog. Miss Buxton looked at Celeste. "Do you want to be here when…I could have you summoned."

Celeste eyes blurred. "N-No. I don't…I'd rather not."

"It's painless—as long as she cooperates."

"I know. How long before?…"

Miss Buxton shrugged. "She's supple enough. By the looks of her, she ought to fatten and shape quickly. I should think she'd be a suitably fat piggie and ready to transfer in several more weeks."

"Take care of her, Fiona."

"You know I will."

Celeste hurried away without saying good-bye. Emily burst into tears. Miss Buxton jerked Emily's leash. "Enough, young lady! Down here your tears will only earn you a good paddling."

Miss Buxton led Emily away and gave her to an assistant. The assistant removed Emily's corset and buckled her head down over a padded A-frame made of iron angles and bars. Emily found herself being bound in place next to her permanent partner, the girl in the armoire. Since both girls were gagged, there could be no communication between them. Not even a glance to mark their inexorable coupling.

Time passed slowly. There were meals. Passivity. More meals. Nothing between the hands that woke her and the hands that fed her. She lost all track of time. Had no idea what time or day it was. One day strong hands lifted her and her partner from the iron frame. Instead of being fed and returned to the frame, she felt herself being lifted, swung, and transported away from the frame she'd grown to love.

"Why?" she murmured into the rubber plug that filled her mouth. No one answered.

She was too full and lazy to care, or wonder. She had no strength to stretch or yawn—no idea where she was being taken. Hands and slings guided and settled her into another place, softly padded, conforming, as familiar as before. No different than where she'd been. The press and warmth of her partner soothed her.

I don't even know her name or what she looks like, she thought numbly.

Busy hands wove wide straps around her, binding her tightly to the padding beneath her and the wood-smelling frame. Her partner drew in a deep breath. She heard and felt the repetitive smacks of a thick paddle. Another layer of padding was laid over her, woven around her. She could smell the stiff, heavy layer of leather when it came. Long needles stitched and bound the black skin tightly over her, compressing the padding between her thighs, forcing her down into the frame, filling her sex with warmth, finally isolating her completely from her partner. When the last bit of leather had been stitched into place, everything was soft and velvety black. The rich smell of newly tanned leather drenched her senses. Her sex wept with joy. She was home at last.

Before falling into a dreamless sleep, she thought she heard a woman's voice. Felt the press of her hands on the leather somewhere above her. "Very nice," the voice said. "Harriet Godwin will be pleased."

Emily struggled with the name. Harriet...Harriet G-Godwin. It echoed in her mind like a forgotten phrase. The snatch of a song. Lilac Row... It was so familiar. Finally, she could not remember. Nor did she care. She did not remember anything after that....

You've heard of the writers
but didn't know where to find them

Samuel R. Delany • Pat Califia • Carol Queen • Lars Eighner • Felice Picano • Lucy Taylor • Aaron Travis • Michael Lassell • Red Jordan Arobateau • Michael Bronski • Tom Roche • Maxim Jakubowski • Michael Perkins • Camille Paglia • John Preston • Laura Antoniou • Alice Joanou • Cecilia Tan • Michael Perkins • Tuppy Owens • Trish Thomas • Lily Burana • Alison Tyler • Marco Vassi • Susie Bright • Randy Turoff • Allen Ellenzweig • Shar Rednour

You've seen
the sexy images
but didn't know where to find them

Robert Chouraqui • Charles Gatewood • Richard Kern • Eric Kroll • Vivienne Maricevic • Housk Randall • Barbara Nitke • Trevor Watson • Mark Avers • Laura Graff • Michele Serchuk • Laurie Leber • John Willie • Sylvia Plachy • Romain Slocombe • Robert Mapplethorpe • Doris Kloster

You can find them all in
Masquerade

a publication designed expressly for the connoisseur of the erotic arts.

MASQUERADE BOOKS

VANESSA DURIÈS
THE TIES THAT BIND
$6.50/510-7
The incredible confessions of a thrillingly unconventional woman. From the first page, this chronicle of dominance and submission will keep you gasping with its vivid depictions of sensual abandon. At the hand of Masters Georges, Patrick, Pierre and others, this submissive seductress experiences pleasures she never knew existed....

M. S. VALENTINE
THE CAPTIVITY OF CELIA
$6.50/453-4
Colin is considered the prime suspect in a murder, forcing him to seek refuge with his cousin, Sir Jason Hardwicke. In exchange for Colin's safety, Jason demands Celia's unquestioning submission.... Sexual extortion!

AMANDA WARE
BINDING CONTRACT
$6.50/491-7
Louise was responsible for bringing many prestigious clients into Claremont's salon—so he was more than willing to have her miss a little work in order to pleasure one of his most important customers. But Eleanor Cavendish had her mind set on something more rigorous than a simple wash and set. Sexual slavery!

BOUND TO THE PAST
$6.50/452-6
Anne accepts a research assignment in a Tudor mansion. Upon arriving, she finds herself aroused by James, a descendant of the mansion's owners. Together they uncover the perverse desires of the mansion's long-dead master—desires that bind Anne inexorably to the past—not to mention the bedpost!

SACHI MIZUNO
SHINJUKU NIGHTS
$6.50/493-3
A tour through the lives and libidos of the seductive East. No one is better that Sachi Mizuno at weaving an intricate web of sensual desire, wherein many characters are ensnared and enraptured by the demands of their long-denied carnal natures.

PASSION IN TOKYO
$6.50/454-2
Tokyo—one of Asia's most historic and seductive cities. Come behind the closed doors of its citizens, and witness the many pleasures that await. Lusty men and women from every stratum of Japanese society free themselves of all inhibitions....

MARTINE GLOWINSKI
POINT OF VIEW
$6.50/433-X
With the assistance of her new, unexpectedly kinky lover, she discovers and explores her exhibitionist tendencies—until there is virtually nothing she won't do before the horny audiences her man arranges! Unabashed acting out for the sophisticated voyeur.

RICHARD McGOWAN
A HARLOT OF VENUS
$6.50/425-9
A highly fanciful, epic tale of lust on Mars! Cavortia—the most famous and sought-after courtesan in the cosmopolitan city of Venus—finds love and much more during her adventures with some of the most remarkable characters in recent erotic fiction.

M. ORLANDO
THE ARCHITECTURE OF DESIRE
Introduction by Richard Manton.
$6.50/490-9
Two novels in one special volume! In *The Hotel Justine*, an elite clientele is afforded the opportunity to have any and all desires satisfied. *The Villa Sin* is inherited by a beautiful woman who soon realizes that the legacy of the ancestral estate includes bizarre erotic ceremonies.

CHET ROTHWELL
KISS ME, KATHERINE
$5.95/410-0
Beautiful Katherine can hardly believe her luck. Not only is she married to the charming and oh-so-agreeable Nelson, she's free to live out all her erotic fantasies with other men. Katherine's desires are more than any one man can handle—luckily there are always plenty of men on hand, reading and willing to pleasure her!

MARCO VASSI
THE STONED APOCALYPSE
$5.95/401-1/mass market
"Marco Vassi is our champion sexual energist."—VLS
During his lifetime, Marco Vassi praised by writers as diverse as Gore Vidal and Norman Mailer, and his reputation was worldwide. *The Stoned Apocalypse* is Vassi's autobiography; chronicling a cross-country trip on America's erotic byways, it offers a rare glimpse of a generation's sexual imagination.

ROBIN WILDE
TABITHA'S TICKLE
$6.50/468-2
Tabitha's back! The story of this vicious vixen—and her torturously tantalizing cohorts—didn't end with *Tabitha's Tease*. Once again, men fall under the spell of scrumptious co-eds and find themselves enslaved to demands and desires they never dreamed existed. Think it's a man's world? Guess again. With Tabitha around, no man gets what he wants until she's completely satisfied—and, maybe, not even then....

MASQUERADE BOOKS

ERICA BRONTE
PIRATE'S SLAVE
$5.95/376-7
Lovely young Erica is stranded in a country where lust knows no bounds. Desperate to escape, she finds herself trading her firm, luscious body to any and all men willing and able to help her. Her adventure has its ups and downs, ins and outs—all to the undeniable pleasure of lusty Erica!

CHARLES G. WOOD
HELLFIRE
$5.95/358-9
A vicious murderer is running amok in New York's sexual underground—and Nick O'Shay, a virile detective with the NYPD, plunges deep into the case. He soon becomes embroiled in an elusive world of fleshly extremes, hunting a madman seeking to purge America with fire and blood sacrifices. Set in New York's infamous sexual underground.

CLAIRE BAEDER, EDITOR
LA DOMME: A DOMINATRIX ANTHOLOGY
$5.95/366-X
A steamy smorgasbord of female domination! Erotic literature has long been filled with heartstopping portraits of domineering women, and now the most memorable have been brought together in one beautifully brutal volume.

CHARISSE VAN DER LYN
SEX ON THE NET
$5.95/399-6
Electrifying erotica from one of the Internet's hottest and most widely read authors. Encounters of all kinds—straight, lesbian, dominant/submissive and all sorts of extreme passions—are explored in thrilling detail.

STANLEY CARTEN
NAUGHTY MESSAGE
$5.95/333-3
Wesley Arthur discovers a lascivious message on his answering machine. Aroused beyond his wildest dreams by the acts described, Wesley becomes obsessed with tracking down the woman behind the seductive voice. His search takes him through strip clubs, sex parlors and no-tell motels—and finally to his randy reward....

AKBAR DEL PIOMBO
DUKE COSIMO
$4.95/3052-0
A kinky romp played out against the boudoirs, bathrooms and ballrooms of the European nobility, who seem to do nothing all day except each other. The lifestyles of the rich and licentious are revealed in all their glory.

A CRUMBLING FAÇADE
$4.95/3043-1
The return of that incorrigible rogue, Henry Pike, who continues his pursuit of sex, fair or otherwise, in the most elegant homes of the most debauched aristocrats.

CAROLE REMY
FANTASY IMPROMPTU
$6.50/513-1
Kidnapped and held in a remote island retreat, Chantal—a renowned erotic writer—finds herself catering to every sexual whim of the mysterious and arousing Bran. Bran is determined to bring Chantal to a full embracing of her sensual nature, even while revealing himself to be something far more than human....

BEAUTY OF THE BEAST
$5.95/332-5
A shocking tell-all, written from the point-of-view of a prize-winning reporter. And what reporting she does! All the secrets of an uninhibited life are revealed, and each lusty tableau is painted in glowing colors.

DAVID AARON CLARK
THE MARQUIS DE SADE'S JULIETTE
$4.95/240-X
The Marquis de Sade's infamous Juliette returns—and emerges as the most perverse and destructive nightstalker modern New York will ever know. One by one, the innocent are drawn in by Juliette's empty promise of immortality, only to fall prey to her deadly lusts.

ANONYMOUS
NADIA
$5.95/267-1
Follow the delicious but neglected Nadia as she works to wring every drop of pleasure out of life—despite an unhappy marriage. A classic title providing a peek into the secret sexual lives of another time and place.

NIGEL McPARR
THE TRANSFORMATION OF EMILY
$6.50/519-0
The shocking story of Emily Johnson, live-in domestic. Without warning, Emily finds herself dismissed by her mistress, and sent to serve at Lilac Row—the home of Charles and Harriet Godwin. In no time, Harriet has Emily doing things she'd never dreamed would be required of her—all involving the erotic discipline Harriet imposes with relish.

THE STORY OF A VICTORIAN MAID
$5.95/241-8
What were the Victorians really like? Chances are, no one believes they were as stuffy as their Queen, but who would have imagined such unbridled libertines!

TITIAN BERESFORD
CINDERELLA
$6.50/500-X
Beresford triumphs again with this intoxicating tale, filled with castle dungeons and tightly corseted ladies-in-waiting, naughty viscounts and impossibly cruel masturbatrixes—nearly every conceivable method of erotic torture is explored and described in lush, vivid detail.

MASQUERADE BOOKS

AMARANTHA KNIGHT

THE DARKER PASSIONS: THE PICTURE OF DORIAN GRAY
$6.50/342-2

Amarantha Knight takes on Oscar Wilde, resulting in a fabulously decadent tale of highly personal changes. One young man finds his most secret desires laid bare by a portrait far more revealing than he could have imagined....

THE DARKER PASSIONS READER
$6.50/432-1

The best moments from Knight's phenomenally popular Darker Passions series. Here are the most eerily erotic passages from her acclaimed sexual reworkings of *Dracula*, *Frankenstein*, *Dr. Jekyll & Mr. Hyde* and *The Fall of the House of Usher*.

THE DARKER PASSIONS: THE FALL OF THE HOUSE OF USHER
$6.50/528-X

The Master and Mistress of the house of Usher indulge in every form of decadence, and initiate their guests into the many pleasures to be found in utter submission.

THE DARKER PASSIONS: DR. JEKYLL AND MR. HYDE
$4.95/227-2

It is a story of incredible transformations achieved through mysterious experiments. Explore the steamy possibilities of a tale where no one is quite who—or what—they seem. Victorian bedrooms explode with hidden demons!

THE DARKER PASSIONS: FRANKENSTEIN
$5.95/248-5

What if you could create a living human? What shocking acts could it be taught to perform, to desire? Find out what pleasures await those who play God....

THE DARKER PASSIONS: DRACULA
$5.95/326-0

The infamous erotic retelling of the Vampire legend. "Well-written and imaginative, Amarantha Knight gives fresh impetus to this myth, taking us through the sexual and sadistic scenes with details that keep us reading.... A classic in itself has been added to the shelves." —*Divinity*

THE PAUL LITTLE LIBRARY

PECULIAR PASSIONS OF LADY MEG/ LOVE SLAVE
$8.95/529-8/Trade paperback

Two classics from modern erotica's most popular author! What are the sexy secrets *Lady Meg* hides? What are the appetites that lurk beneath the surface of this irresistible vixen? What does it take to be the perfect instrument of pleasure—or go about acquiring a willing *Love Slave* of one's own? Paul Little spares no detail in these two relentless tales, guaranteed to thrill and shock even the most jaded readers!

THE BEST OF PAUL LITTLE
$6.50/469-0

Known throughout the world for his fantastic portrayals of punishment and pleasure, Little never fails to push readers over the edge of sensual excitement.

ALL THE WAY
$6.95/509-3

Two excruciating novels from Paul Little in one hot volume! *Going All the Way* features an unhappy man who tries to purge himself of the memory of his lover with a series of quirky and uninhibited lovers. *Pushover* tells the story of a serial spanker and his celebrated exploits.

THE DISCIPLINE OF ODETTE
$5.95/334-1

Odette was sure marriage would rescue her from her family's "corrections." To her horror, she discovers that her beloved has also been raised on discipline. A shocking erotic coupling!

THE PRISONER
$5.95/330-9

Judge Black has built a secret room below a penitentiary, where he sentences the prisoners to hours of exhibition and torment while his friends watch. Judge Black's brand of rough justice keeps his lovely young captives on the brink of utter pleasure!

TEARS OF THE INQUISITION
$4.95/146-2

A staggering account of pleasure and punishment. "There was a tickling inside her as her nervous system reminded her she was ready for sex. But before her was...the Inquisitor!"

DOUBLE NOVEL
$4.95/86-6

The Metamorphosis of Lisette Joyaux tells the story of a young woman initiated into an incredible world world of lesbian lusts. *The Story of Monique* reveals the twisted sexual rituals that beckon the ripe and willing Monique.

CAPTIVE MAIDENS
$5.95/440-2

Three beautiful young women find themselves powerless against the debauched landowners of 1824 England. They are banished to a sexual slave colony, and corrupted by every imaginable perversion.

SLAVE ISLAND
$5.95/441-0

A leisure cruise is waylaid by Lord Henry Philbrock, a sadistic genius. The ship's passengers are kidnapped and spirited to his island prison, where the women are trained to accommodate the most bizarre sexual cravings of the rich, the famous, the pampered and the perverted.

MASQUERADE BOOKS

ALIZARIN LAKE

SEX ON DOCTOR'S ORDERS
$5.95/402-X
Beth, a nubile young nurse, uses her considerable skills to further medical science by offering incomparable and insatiable assistance in the gathering of important specimens. Soon, an assortment of randy characters is lending a hand in this highly erotic work.

THE EROTIC ADVENTURES OF HARRY TEMPLE
$4.95/127-6
Harry Temple's memoirs chronicle his amorous adventures from his initiation at the hands of insatiable sirens, through his stay at a house of hot repute, to his encounters with a chastity-belted nympho!

JOHN NORMAN

TARNSMAN OF GOR
$6.95/486-0
This controversial series returns! Tarl Cabot is transported to Gor. He must quickly accustom himself to the ways of this world, including the caste system which exalts some as Priest-Kings or Warriors, and debases others as slaves. A spectacular world unfolds in this first volume of John Norman's Gorean series.

OUTLAW OF GOR
$6.95/487-9
In this second volume, Tarl Cabot returns to Gor, where he might reclaim both his woman and his role of Warrior. But upon arriving, he discovers that his name, his city and the names of those he loves have become unspeakable. Cabot has become an outlaw, and must discover his new purpose on this strange planet, where danger stalks the outcast, and even simple answers have their price....

PRIEST-KINGS OF GOR
$6.95/488-7
Tarl Cabot searches for the truth about his lovely wife Talena. Does she live, or was she destroyed by the mysterious, all-powerful Priest-Kings? Cabot is determined to find out—even while knowing that no one who has approached the mountain stronghold of the Priest-Kings has ever returned alive....

NOMADS OF GOR
$6.95/527-1
Another provocative trip to the barbaric and mysterious world of Gor. Norman's heroic Tarnsman finds his way across this Counter-Earth, pledged to serve the Priest-Kings in their quest for survival. Unfortunately for Cabot, his mission leads him to the savage Wagon People—nomads who may very well kill before surrendering any secrets....

RACHEL PEREZ

AFFINITIES
$4.95/113-6
"Kelsy had a liking for cool upper-class blondes, the long-legged girls from Lake Forest and Winnetka who came into the city to cruise the lesbian bars on Halsted, looking for breathless ecstasies...." A scorching tale of lesbian libidos unleashed, from a writer more than capable of exploring every nuance of female passion in vivid detail.

SYDNEY ST. JAMES

RIVE GAUCHE
$5.95/317-1
The Latin Quarter, Paris, circa 1920. Expatriate bohemians couple with abandon—before eventually abandoning their ambitions amidst the intoxicating temptations waiting to be indulged in every bedroom.

GARDEN OF DELIGHT
$4.95/3058-X
A vivid account of sexual awakening that follows an innocent but insatiably curious young woman's journey from the furtive, forbidden joys of dormitory life to the unabashed carnality of the wild world.

DON WINSLOW

THE FALL OF THE ICE QUEEN
$6.50/520-4
She was the most exquisite of his courtiers: the beautiful, aloof woman who Rahn the Conqueror chose as his Consort. But the regal disregard with which she treated Rahn was not to be endured. It was decided that she would submit to his will, and learn to serve her lord in the fashion he had come to expect. And as so many knew, Rahn's depraved expectations have made his court infamous....

PRIVATE PLEASURES
$6.50/504-2
An assortment of sensual encounters designed to appeal to the most discerning reader. Frantic voyeurs, licentious exhibitionists, and everyday lovers are here displayed in all their wanton glory—proving again that fleshly pleasures have no more apt chronicler than Don Winslow.

THE INSATIABLE MISTRESS OF ROSEDALE
$6.50/494-1
The story of the perfect couple: Edward and Lady Penelope, who reside in beautiful and mysterious Rosedale manor. While Edward is a true connoisseur of sexual perversion, it is Lady Penelope whose mastery of complete sensual pleasure makes their home infamous. Indulging one another's bizarre whims is a way of life for this wicked couple, and none who encounter the extravagances of Rosedale will forget what they've learned....

SECRETS OF CHEATEM MANOR
$6.50/434-8
Edward returns to his late father's estate, to find it being run by the majestic Lady Amanda. Edward can hardly believe his luck—Lady Amanda is assisted by her two beautiful, lonely daughters, Catherine and Prudence. What the randy young man soon comes to realize is the love of discipline that all three beauties share.

KATERINA IN CHARGE
$5.95/409-7
When invited to a country retreat by a mysterious couple, two randy young ladies can hardly resist! But do they have any idea what they're in for? Whatever the case, the imperious Katerina will make her desires known very soon—and demand that they be fulfilled... A thoroughly perverse tale of ultimate sexual innocence subjugated and defiled by one powerful woman.

MASQUERADE BOOKS

THE MANY PLEASURES OF IRONWOOD
$5.95/310-4
Seven lovely young women are employed by The Ironwood Sportsmen's Club, where their natural talents are put to creative use. A small and exclusive club with seven carefully selected sexual connoisseurs, Ironwood is dedicated to the relentless pursuit of sensual pleasure.

CLAIRE'S GIRLS
$5.95/442-9
You knew when she walked by that she was something special. She was one of Claire's girls, a woman carefully dressed and groomed to fill a role, to capture a look, to fit an image crafted by the sophisticated proprietress of an exclusive escort agency. High-class whores blow the roof off in this blow-by-blow account of life behind the closed doors of a sophisticated brothel.

....

TAU'TEVU   N. WHALLEN
$6.50/426-7
In a mysterious land, the statuesque and beautiful Vivian learns to subject herself to the hand of a mysterious man. He systematically helps her prove her own strength, and brings to life in her an unimagined sensual fire.

COMPLIANCE
$5.95/356-2
Fourteen stories exploring the pleasures of ultimate release. Characters from all walks of life learn to trust in the skills of others, hoping to experience the thrilling liberation of sexual submission. Here are the many joys to be found in some of the most forbidden sexual practices around....

....

THE CLASSIC COLLECTION
PROTESTS, PLEASURES, RAPTURES
$5.95/400-3
Invited for an allegedly quiet weekend at a country vicarage, a young woman is stunned to find herself surrounded by shocking acts of sexual sadism. Soon, her curiosity is piqued, and she begins to explore her own capacities for cruelty.

THE YELLOW ROOM
$5.95/378-3
The "yellow room" holds the secrets of lust, lechery, and the lash. There, bare-bottomed, spread-eagled, and open to the world, demure Alice Darvell soon learns to love her lickings. In the second tale, hot heiress Rosa Coote and her lusty servants whip up numerous adventures in punishment and pleasure.

SCHOOL DAYS IN PARIS
$5.95/325-2
The rapturous chronicles of a well-spent youth! Few Universities provide the profound and pleasurable lessons one learns in after-hours study—particularly if one is young and available, and lucky enough to have Paris as a playground. A sexy look at the pursuits of young adulthood.

MAN WITH A MAID
$4.95/307-4
The adventures of Jack and Alice have delighted readers for eight decades! A classic of its genre, Man with a Maid tells an outrageous tale of desire, revenge, and submission. This tale qualifies as one of the world's most popular adult novels—with over 200,000 copies in print!

CONFESSIONS OF A CONCUBINE III: PLEASURE'S PRISONER
$5.95/357-0
Filled with pulse-pounding excitement—including a daring escape from the harem and an encounter with an unspeakable sadist—Pleasure's Prisoner adds an unforgettable chapter to this thrilling confessional.

....

CLASSIC EROTIC BIOGRAPHIES
JENNIFER
$4.95/107-1
The return of one of the Sexual Revolution's most notorious heroines. From the bedroom of a notoriously insatiable dancer to an uninhibited ashram, Jennifer traces the exploits of one thoroughly modern woman.

JENNIFER III
$5.95/292-2
The further adventures of erotica's most daring heroine. Jennifer has a photographer's eye for details—particularly of the masculine variety! One by one, her subjects submit to her demands for sensual pleasure, becoming part of the now-infamous gallery of erotic conquests.

....

RHINOCEROS

KATHLEEN K.
SWEET TALKERS
$6.95/516-6
Kathleen K. ran a phone-sex company in the late 80s, and she opens up her diary for a very thought provoking peek at the life of a phone-sex operator. Transcripts of actual conversations are included.

"If you enjoy eavesdropping on explicit conversations about sex... this book is for you."   —Spectator

Trade /$12.95/192-6

....

THOMAS S. ROCHE
DARK MATTER
$6.95/484-4
"Dark Matter is sure to please gender outlaws, body-mod junkies, goth vampires, boys who wish they were dykes, and anybody who's not to sure where the fine line should be drawn between pleasure and pain. It's a handful."   —Pat Califia

"Here is the erotica of the cumming millennium.... You will be deliciously disturbed, but never disappointed."   —Poppy Z. Brite

MASQUERADE BOOKS

NOIROTICA: AN ANTHOLOGY OF EROTIC CRIME STORIES
$6.95/390-2
A collection of darkly sexy tales, taking place at the crossroads of the crime and erotic genres. Thomas S. Roche has gathered together some of today's finest writers of sexual fiction, all of whom explore the murky terrain where desire runs irrevocably afoul of the law.

ROMY ROSEN

SPUNK
$6.95/492-5
Casey, a lovely model poised upon the verge of supercelebrity, falls for an insatiable young rock singer—not suspecting that his sexual appetite has led him to experiment with a dangerous new aphrodisiac. Casey becomes an addict, and her craving plunges her into a strange underworld, where the only chance for redemption lies with a shadowy young man with a secret of his own.

MOLLY WEATHERFIELD

CARRIE'S STORY
$6.95/485-2
"I had been Jonathan's slave for about a year when he told me he wanted to sell me at an auction. I wasn't in any condition to respond when he told me this..." Desire and depravity run rampant in this story of uncompromising mastery and irrevocable submission.   A unique piece of erotica that is both thoughtful and hot!

"I was stunned by how well it was written and how intensely foreign I found its sexual world.... And, since this is a world I don't frequent... I thoroughly enjoyed the National Geo tour."   —bOING bOING

"Hilarious and harrowing... just when you think things can't get any wilder, they do." —Black Sheets

CYBERSEX CONSORTIUM

CYBERSEX: THE PERV'S GUIDE TO FINDING SEX ON THE INTERNET
$6.95/471-2
You've heard the objections: cyberspace is soaked with sex. Okay—so where is it!? Tracking down the good stuff—the real good stuff—can waste an awful lot of expensive time, and frequently leave you high and dry. The Cybersex Consortium presents an easy-to-use guide for those intrepid adults who know what they want. No horny hacker can afford to pass up this map to the kinkiest rest stops on the Info Superhighway.

AMELIA G, EDITOR

BACKSTAGE PASSES
$6.95/438-0
Amelia G, editor of the goth-sex journal Blue Blood, has brought together some of today's most irreverent writers, each of whom has outdone themselves with an edgy, antic tale of modern lust. Punks, metalheads, and grunge-trash roam the pages of Backstage Passes, and no one knows their ways better...

GERI NETTICK WITH BETH ELLIOT

MIRRORS: PORTRAIT OF A LESBIAN TRANSSEXUAL
$6.95/435-6
The alternately heartbreaking and empowering story of one woman's long road to full selfhood. Born a male, Geri Nettick knew something just didn't fit. And even after coming to terms with her own gender dysphoria—and taking steps to correct it—she still fought to be accepted by the lesbian feminist community to which she felt she belonged. A fascinating, true tale of struggle and discovery.

DAVID MELTZER

UNDER
$6.95/290-6
The story of a 21st century sex professional living at the bottom of the social heap. After surgeries designed to increase his physical allure, corrupt government forces drive the cyber-gigolo underground—where even more bizarre cultures await him.

ORF
$6.95/110-1
He is the ultimate musician-hero—the idol of thousands, the fevered dream of many more. And like many musicians before him, he is misunderstood, misused—and totally out of control. Every last drop of feeling is squeezed from a modern-day troubadour and his lady love.

LAURA ANTONIOU, EDITOR

NO OTHER TRIBUTE
$6.95/294-9
A collection sure to challenge Political Correctness in a way few have before, with tales of women kept in bondage to their lovers by their deepest passions. Love pushes these women beyond acceptable limits, rendering them helpless to deny anything to the men and women they adore.

SOME WOMEN
$6.95/300-7
Over forty essays written by women actively involved in consensual dominance and submission. Pro doms, lifestyle leatherdykes, titleholders—women from every walk of life lay bare their true feelings about explosive issues.

BY HER SUBDUED
$6.95/281-7
These tales all involve women in control—of their lives, their loves, their men. So much in control that they can remorselessly break rules to become powerful goddesses of the men who sacrifice all to worship at their feet.

TRISTAN TAORMINO & DAVID AARON CLARK, EDITORS

RITUAL SEX
$6.95/391-0
The many contributors to Ritual Sex know—and demonstrate—that body and soul share more common ground than society feels comfortable acknowledging. From personal memoirs of ecstatic revelation, to fictional quests to reconcile sex and spirit, Ritual Sex provides an unprecedented look at private life.

DAVID AARON CLARK

SISTER RADIANCE
$6.95/215-9

A meditation on love, sex, and death, rife with Clark's trademark vivisections of contemporary desires, sacred and profane. The vicissitudes of lust and romance are examined against a backdrop of urban decay in this testament to the allure—and inevitability—of the forbidden.

THE WET FOREVER
$6.95/117-9

The story of Janus and Madchen—a small-time hood and a beautiful sex worker on the run from one of the most dangerous men they have ever known—examines themes of loyalty, sacrifice, redemption and obsession amidst Manhattan's sex parlors and underground S/M clubs. A thrillingly contemporary love story, and a uniquely sensual thriller.

MICHAEL PERKINS

EVIL COMPANIONS
$6.95/3067-2

Set in New York City during the tumultuous waning years of the Sixties, *Evil Companions* has been hailed as "a frightening classic." A young couple explores the nether reaches of the erotic unconscious in a shocking confrontation with the extremes of passion.

THE SECRET RECORD: MODERN EROTIC LITERATURE
$6.95/3039-3

Michael Perkins surveys the field with authority and unique insight. Updated and revised to include the latest trends, tastes, and developments in this misunderstood and maligned genre.

AN ANTHOLOGY OF CLASSIC ANONYMOUS EROTIC WRITING
$6.95/140-3

Michael Perkins has collected the very best passages from the world's erotic writing. "Anonymous" is one of the most infamous bylines in publishing history—and these steamy excerpts show why! Includes excerpts from some of the most famous titles in the history of erotic literature.

LIESEL KULIG

LOVE IN WARTIME
$6.95/3044-X

Madeleine knew that the handsome SS officer was a dangerous man, but she was just a cabaret singer in Nazi-occupied Paris, trying to survive in a perilous time. When Josef fell in love with her, he discovered that a beautiful woman can sometimes be as dangerous as any warrior.

HELEN HENLEY

ENTER WITH TRUMPETS
$6.95/197-7

Helen Henley was told that women just don't write about sex—much less the taboos she was so interested in exploring. So Henley did it alone, flying in the face of "tradition" by writing this touching tale of arousal and devotion in one couple's kinky relationship.

ALICE JOANOU

BLACK TONGUE
$6.95/258-2

"Joanou has created a series of sumptuous, brooding, dark visions of sexual obsession, and is undoubtedly a name to look out for in the future."
—Redeemer

Exploring lust at its most florid and unsparing, *Black Tongue* is a trove of baroque fantasies—each redolent of forbidden passions. Joanou creates some of erotica's most mesmerizing and unforgettable characters. One of today's groundbreaking talents.

TOURNIQUET
$6.95/3060-1

A heady collection of stories and effusions from the pen of one our most dazzling young writers. Strange tales abound, from the story of the mysterious and cruel Cybele, to an encounter with the sadistic entertainment of a bizarre after-hours cafe. A complex and riveting series of meditations on desire.

CANNIBAL FLOWER
$4.95/72-6

The provocative debut volume from this acclaimed young writer.

"She is waiting in her darkened bedroom, as she has waited throughout history, to seduce the men who are foolish enough to be blinded by her irresistible charms.... She is the goddess of sexuality, and *Cannibal Flower* is her haunting siren song."
—Michael Perkins

PHILIP JOSÉ FARMER

A FEAST UNKNOWN
$6.95/276-0

"Sprawling, brawling, shocking, suspenseful, hilarious..."
—Theodore Sturgeon

Farmer's supreme anti-hero returns. "I was conceived and born in 1888." Slowly, Lord Grandrith—armed with the belief that he is the son of Jack the Ripper—tells the story of his remarkable and unbridled life. His story begins with his discovery of the secret of immortality—and progresses to encompass the furthest extremes of human behavior.

THE IMAGE OF THE BEAST
$6.95/166-7

Herald Childe has seen Hell, glimpsed its horror in an act of sexual mutilation. Childe must now find and destroy an inhuman predator through the streets of a polluted and decadent Los Angeles of the future. One clue after another leads Childe to an inescapable realization about the nature of sex and evil....

DANIEL VIAN

ILLUSIONS
$6.95/3074-1

International lust. Two tales of danger and desire in Berlin on the eve of WWII. From private homes to lurid cafés, passion is exposed in stark contrast to the brutal violence of the time, as desperate people explore their darkest sexual desires.

MASQUERADE BOOKS

SAMUEL R. DELANY

THE MAD MAN
$8.99/408-9

"Reads like a pornographic reflection of Peter Ackroyd's *Chatterton* or A. S. Byatt's *Possession*.... Delany develops an insightful dichotomy between [his protagonist]'s two worlds: the one of cerebral philosophy and dry academia, the other of heedless, 'impersonal' obsessive sexual extremism. When these worlds finally collide...the novel achieves a surprisingly satisfying resolution...." —*Publishers Weekly*

Graduate student John Marr researches the life of Timothy Hasler: a philosopher whose career was cut tragically short over a decade earlier. On another front, Marr finds himself increasingly drawn toward shocking, depraved sexual entanglements with the homeless men of his neighborhood, until it begins to seem that Hasler's death might hold some key to his own life as a gay man in the age of AIDS.

EQUINOX
$6.95/157-8

The Scorpion has sailed the seas in a quest for every possible pleasure. Her crew is a collection of the young, the twisted, the insatiable. A drifter comes into their midst and is taken on a fantastic journey to the darkest, most dangerous sexual extremes—until he is finally a victim to their boundless appetites. An early title that set the way for the author's later explorations of extreme, forbidden sexual behaviors. Long out of print, this disturbing tale is finally available under the author's original title.

ANDREI CODRESCU

THE REPENTANCE OF LORRAINE
$6.95/329-5

"One of our most prodigiously talented and magical writers." —*NYT Book Review*
By the acclaimed author of *The Hole in the Flag* and *The Blood Countess*. An aspiring writer, a professor's wife, a secretary, gold anklets, Maoists, Roman harlots—and more—swirl through this spicy tale of a harried quest for a mythic artifact. Written when the author was a young man, this lusty yarn was inspired by the heady days of the Sixties. Includes a new introduction by the author, detailing the events that inspired *Lorraine's* creation. A touching, arousing product from a more innocent time.

TUPPY OWENS

SENSATIONS
$6.95/3081-4

Tuppy Owens tells the unexpurgated story of the making of *Sensations*—the first big-budget sex flick. Originally commissioned to appear in book form after the release of the film in 1975, *Sensations* is finally released under Masquerade's stylish Rhinoceros imprint. Tuppy Owens provides an unprecedented peek behind the scenes of a porn legend.

SOPHIE GALLEYMORE BIRD

MANEATER
$6.95/103-9

Through a bizarre act of creation, a man attains the "perfect" lover—by all appearances a beautiful, sensuous woman, but in reality something far darker. Once brought to life she will accept no mate, seeking instead the prey that will sate her hunger for vengeance.

LEOPOLD VON SACHER-MASOCH

VENUS IN FURS
$6.95/3089-X

This classic 19th century novel is the first uncompromising exploration of the dominant/submissive relationship in literature. The alliance of Severin and Wanda epitomizes Sacher-Masoch's dark obsession with a cruel, controlling goddess and the urges that drive the man held in her thrall. This special edition includes the letters exchanged between Sacher-Masoch and Emilie Mataja, an aspiring writer he sought to cast as the avatar of the forbidden desires expressed in his most famous work.

BADBOY

MIKE FORD, EDITOR

BUTCH BOYS
$6.50/523-9

A big volume of tales dedicated to the rough-and-tumble type who can make a man weak at the knees. From bikers to "gymbos," these no-nonsense studs know just what they want and how to go about getting it. Some of today's best erotic writers explore the many possible variations on the age-old fantasy of the dominant man.

WILLIAM J. MANN, EDITOR

GRAVE PASSIONS
$6.50/405-4

A collection of the most chilling tales of passion currently being penned by today's most provocative gay writers. Unnatural transformations, otherworldly encounters, and deathless desires make for a collection sure to keep readers up late at night—for a variety of reasons!

J. A. GUERRA, EDITOR

COME QUICKLY: FOR BOYS ON THE GO
$6.50/413-5

Here are over sixty of the hottest fantasies around—all designed to get you going in less time than it takes to dial 976. Julian Anthony Guerra, the editor behind the popular *Men at Work* and *Badboy Fantasies*, has put together this volume especially for you—a busy man on a modern schedule, who still appreciates a little old-fashioned action. Hassle-free quickies.

MASQUERADE BOOKS

JOHN PRESTON

HUSTLING: A GENTLEMAN'S GUIDE TO THE FINE ART OF HOMOSEXUAL PROSTITUTION
$6.50/517-4

The very first guide to the gay world's most infamous profession. John Preston solicited the advice and opinions of "working boys" from across the country in his effort to produce the ultimate guide to the hustler's world. *Hustling* covers every practical aspect of the business, from clientele and payment options to "specialties," sidelines and drawbacks. No stone is left unturned in this guidebook to the ins and outs of this much-mythologized trade.

"...Unrivaled. For any man even vaguely contemplating going into business this tome has got to be the first port of call."
—*Divinity*

"Fun and highly literary. What more could you expect form such an accomplished activist, author and editor?"
—*Drummer*
Trade $12.95/137-3

MR. BENSON
$4.95/3041-5

Jamie is an aimless young man lucky enough to encounter Mr. Benson. He is soon led down the path of erotic enlightenment, learning to accept this man as his master. Jamie's incredible adventures never fail to excite—especially when the going gets rough!

TALES FROM THE DARK LORD
$5.95/323-6

A new collection of twelve stunning works from the man *Lambda Book Report* called "the Dark Lord of gay erotica." The relentless ritual of lust and surrender is explored in all its manifestations in this heart-stopping triumph of authority and vision from the Dark Lord!

TALES FROM THE DARK LORD II
$4.95/176-4

The second volume of John Preston's masterful short stories.

THE ARENA
$4.95/3083-0

There is a place on the edge of fantasy where every desire is indulged with abandon. Men go there to unleash beasts, to let demons roam free, to abolish all limits. At the center of each tale are the men who serve there, who offer themselves for the consummation of any passion, whose own bottomless urges compel their endless subservience.

THE HEIR•THE KING
$4.95/3048-2

The ground-breaking novel *The Heir*, written in the lyric voice of the ancient myths, tells the story of a world where slaves and masters create a new sexual society. *The King* tells the story of a soldier who discovers his monarch's most secret desires. A special double volume.

THE MISSION OF ALEX KANE

SWEET DREAMS
$4.95/3062-8

It's the triumphant return of gay action hero Alex Kane! In *Sweet Dreams*, Alex travels to Boston where he takes on a street gang that stalks gay teenagers. Mighty Alex Kane wreaks a fierce and terrible vengeance on those who prey on gay people everywhere!

GOLDEN YEARS
$4.95/3069-5

When evil threatens the plans of a group of older gay men, Kane's got the muscle to take it head on. Along the way he wins the support—and very specialized attentions—of a cowboy plucked right out of the Old West.

DEADLY LIES
$4.95/3076-8

Politics is a dirty business and the dirt becomes deadly when a political smear campaign targets gay men. Who better to clean things up than Alex Kane! Alex comes to protect the lives of gay men imperiled by lies and deceit.

STOLEN MOMENTS
$4.95/3098-9

Houston's evolving gay community is victimized by a malicious newspaper editor who is more than willing to sacrifice gays on the altar of circulation. He never counted on Alex Kane, fearless defender of gay dreams and desires.

SECRET DANGER
$4.95/111-X

Homophobia: a pernicious social ill not confined by America's borders. Alex Kane and the faithful Danny are called to a small European country, where a group of gay tourists is being held hostage by ruthless terrorists. Luckily, the Mission of Alex Kane stands as firm foreign policy.

LETHAL SILENCE
$4.95/125-X

The Mission of Alex Kane thunders to a conclusion. Chicago becomes the scene of the right-wing's most noxious plan—facilitated by unholy political alliances. Alex and Danny head to the Windy City to take up battle with the mercenaries who would squash gay men underfoot.

MATT TOWNSEND

SOLIDLY BUILT
$6.50/416-X

The tale of the tumultuous relationship between Jeff, a young photographer, and Mark, the butch electrician hired to wire Jeff's new home. For Jeff, it's love at first sight; Mark, however, has more than a few hang-ups. Soon, both are forced to reevaluate their outlooks, and are assisted by a variety of hot men....

JAY SHAFFER

SHOOTERS
$5.95/284-1

No mere catalog of random acts, *Shooters* tells the stories of a variety of stunning men and the ways they connect in sexual and non-sexual ways. A virtuoso storyteller, Shaffer always gets his man.

MASQUERADE BOOKS

ANIMAL HANDLERS
$4.95/264-7
In Shaffer's world, each and every man finally succumbs to the animal urges deep inside. And if there's any creature that promises a wild time, it's a beast who's been caged for far too long. Shaffer has one of the keenest eyes for the nuances of male passion.

FULL SERVICE
$4.95/150-0
Wild men build up steam until they finally let loose. No-nonsense guys bear down hard on each other as they work their way toward release in this finely detailed assortment of masculine fantasies. One of gay erotica's most insightful chroniclers of male passion.

D. V. SADERO

IN THE ALLEY
$4.95/144-3
Hardworking men—from cops to carpenters—bring their own special skills and impressive tools to the most satisfying job of all: capturing and breaking the male sexual beast. Hot, incisive and way over the top

SCOTT O'HARA

DO-IT-YOURSELF PISTON POLISHING
$6.50/489-5
Longtime sex-pro Scott O'Hara draws upon his acute powers of seduction to lure you into a world of hard, horny men long overdue for a tune-up. Pretty soon, you'll pop your own hood for the servicing you know you need....

SUTTER POWELL

EXECUTIVE PRIVILEGES
$6.50/383-X
No matter how serious or sexy a predicament his characters find themselves in, Powell conveys the sheer exuberance of their encounters with a warm humor rarely seen in contemporary gay erotica.

GARY BOWEN

WESTERN TRAILS
$6.50/477-1
A wild roundup of tales devoted to life on the lone prairie. Gary Bowen—a writer well-versed in the Western genre—has collected the very best contemporary cowboy stories. Some of gay literature's brightest stars tell the sexy truth about the many ways a rugged stud found to satisfy himself—and his buddy—in the Very Wild West.

MAN HUNGRY
$5.95/374-0
By the author of Diary of a Vampire. A riveting collection of stories from one of gay erotica's new stars. Dipping into a variety of genres, Bowen crafts tales of lust unlike anything being published today.

KYLE STONE

HOT BAUDS 2
$6.50/479-8
Another collection of cyberfantasies—compiled by the inimitable Kyle Stone. After the success of the original Hot Bauds, Stone conducted another heated search through the world's randiest bulletin boards, resulting in one of the most scalding follow-ups ever published. Here's all the scandalous stuff you've heard so much about—sexy, shameless, and eminently user-friendly.

FIRE & ICE
$5.95/297-3
A collection of stories from the author of the infamous adventures of PB 500. Randy, powerful, and just plain bad, Stone's characters always promise one thing: enough hot action to burn away your desire for anyone else....

HOT BAUDS
$5.95/285-X
The author of Fantasy Board and The Initiation of PB 500 combed cyberspace for the hottest fantasies of the world's horniest hackers. Stone has assembled the first collection of the raunchy erotica so many gay men cruise the Information Superhighway for.

FANTASY BOARD
$4.95/212-4
The author of the scalding sci-fi adventures of PB 500 explores the more foreseeable future—through the intertwined lives (and private parts) of a collection of randy computer hackers. On the Lambda Gate BBS, every hot and horny male is in search of a little virtual satisfaction!

THE CITADEL
$4.95/198-5
The sequel to The Initiation of PB 500. Having proven himself worthy of his stunning master, Micah—now known only as '500'—will face new challenges and hardships after his entry into the forbidding Citadel. Only his master knows what awaits—and whether Micah will again distinguish himself as the perfect instrument of pleasure....

THE INITIATION OF PB 500
$4.95/141-1
He is a stranger on their planet, unschooled in their language, and ignorant of their customs. But this man, Micah—now known only by his number—will soon be trained in every last detail of erotic personal service. And, once nurtured and transformed into the perfect physical specimen, he must begin proving himself worthy of the master who has chosen him....

RITUALS
$4.95/168-3
Via a computer bulletin board, a young man finds himself drawn into a series of sexual rites that transform him into the willing slave of a mysterious stranger. Gradually, all vestiges of his former life are thrown off, and he learns to live for his Master's touch....

MASQUERADE BOOKS

ROBERT BAHR
SEX SHOW
$4.95/225-6
Luscious dancing boys. Brazen, explicit acts. Unending stimulation. Take a seat, and get very comfortable, because the curtain's going up on a show no discriminating appetite can afford to miss.

JASON FURY
THE ROPE ABOVE, THE BED BELOW
$4.95/269-8
The irresistible Jason Fury returns—this time, telling the tale of a vicious murderer preying upon New York's go-go boys. In order to solve this mystery and save lives, each studly suspect must lay bare his soul—and more!
ERIC'S BODY
$4.95/151-9
Fury's sexiest tales are collected in book form for the first time. Follow the irresistible Jason through sexual adventures unlike any you have ever read....

LARS EIGHNER
WHISPERED IN THE DARK
$5.95/286-8
A volume demonstrating Eighner's unique combination of strengths: poetic descriptive power, an unfailing ear for dialogue, and a finely tuned feeling for the nuances of male passion.
AMERICAN PRELUDE
$4.95/170-5
Eighner is widely recognized as one of our best, most exciting gay writers. He is also one of gay erotica's true masters—and American Prelude shows why. Wonderfully written, blisteringly hot tales of all-American lust.
B.M.O.C.
$4.95/3077-6
In a college town known as "the Athens of the Southwest," studs of every stripe are up all night—studying, naturally. Relive university life the way it was supposed to be, with a cast of handsome honor students majoring in Human Homosexuality.

DAVID LAURENTS, EDITOR
SOUTHERN COMFORT
$6.50/466-6
Editor David Laurents now unleashes a collection of tales focusing on the American South—reflecting not only Southern literary tradition, but the many contributions the region has made to the iconography of the American Male.

WANDERLUST: HOMOEROTIC TALES OF TRAVEL
$5.95/395-3
A volume dedicated to the special pleasures of faraw⟨ places. Gay men have always had a special interest travel—and not only for the scenic vistas. Wanderlu⟨ celebrates the freedom of the open road, and the allure ⟨ men who stray from the beaten path....
THE BADBOY BOOK OF EROTIC POETRY
$5.95/382-1
Over fifty of today's best poets. Erotic poetry has long bee⟨ the problem child of the literary world—highly creati⟨ and provocative, but somehow too frank to be "literature.⟨ The Badboy Book of Erotic Poetry restores eros to its rig⟨ ful place of honor in contemporary gay writing.

AARON TRAVIS
BIG SHOTS
$5.95/448-8
Two fierce tales in one electrifying volume. In Beirut, Trav⟨ tells the story of ultimate military power and erotic subj⟨ gation; Kip, Travis' hypersexed and sinister take on fil⟨ noir, appears in unexpurgated form for the first time—including the final, overwhelming chapter.
EXPOSED
$4.95/126-8
A volume of shorter Travis tales, each providing a uniq⟨ glimpse of the horny gay male in his natural environmen⟨ Cops, college jocks, ancient Romans—even Sherlo⟨ Holmes and his loyal Watson—cruise these pages, fre⟨ from the throbbing pen of one of our hottest authors.
BEAST OF BURDEN
$4.95/105-5
Five ferocious tales from this contemporary maste⟨ Innocents surrender to the brutal sexual mastery of the⟨ superiors, as taboos are shattered and replaced with th⟨ unwritten rules of masculine conquest. Intense, extrem⟨ —and totally Travis.
IN THE BLOOD
$5.95/283-3
Written when Travis had just begun to explore the tr⟨ power of the erotic imagination, these stories laid th⟨ groundwork for later masterpieces. Among the mar⟨ rewarding rarities included in this special volume: "In th⟨ Blood"—a heart-pounding descent into sexual vampirism⟨
THE FLESH FABLES
$4.95/243-4
One of Travis' best collections. The Flesh Fables include⟨ "Blue Light," his most famous story, as well as oth⟨ masterpieces that established him as the erotic writer ⟨ watch. And watch carefully, because Travis always buries⟨ surprise somewhere beneath his scorching detail....
SLAVES OF THE EMPIRE
$4.95/3054-7
"A wonderful mythic tale. Set against the backdrop ⟨ the exotic and powerful Roman Empire, this wonde⟨ fully written novel explores the timeless questions ⟨ light and dark in male sexuality. The locale may b⟨ the ancient world, but these are the slaves an⟨ masters of our time...."
—John Prest⟨

MASQUERADE BOOKS

BOB VICKERY

SKIN DEEP
$4.95/265-5
So many varied beauties no one will go away unsatisfied. No tantalizing morsel of manflesh is overlooked—or left unexplored! Beauty may be only skin deep, but a handful of beautiful skin is a tempting proposition.

JR

FRENCH QUARTER NIGHTS
$5.95/337-6
Sensual snapshots of the many places where men get down and dirty—from the steamy French Quarter to the steam room at the old Everard baths. These are nights you'll wish would go on forever....

TOM BACCHUS

RAHM
$5.95/315-5
The imagination of Tom Bacchus brings to life an extraordinary assortment of characters, from the Father of Us All to the cowpoke next door, the early gay literati to rude, queercore mosh rats. No one is better than Bacchus at staking out sexual territory with a swagger and a sly grin.

BONE
$4.95/177-2
Queer musings from the pen of one of today's hottest young talents. A fresh outlook on fleshly indulgence yields more than a few pleasant surprises. Horny Tom Bacchus maps out the tricking ground of a new generation.

KEY LINCOLN

SUBMISSION HOLDS
$4.95/266-3
A bright young talent unleashes his first collection of gay erotica. From tough to tender, the men between these covers stop at nothing to get what they want. These sweat-soaked tales show just how bad boys can really get.

CALDWELL/EIGHNER

QSFX2
$5.95/278-7
The wickedest, wildest, other-worldliest yarns from two master storytellers—Clay Caldwell and Lars Eighner. Both eroticists take a trip to the furthest reaches of the sexual imagination, sending back ten stories proving that as much as things change, one thing will always remain the same....

CLAY CALDWELL

JOCK STUDS
$6.50/472-0
A collection of Caldwell's scalding tales of pumped bodies and raging libidos. Swimmers, runners, football players... whatever your sport might be, there's a man waiting for you in these pages. Waiting to peel off that uniform and claim his reward for a game well-played....

ASK OL' BUDDY

$5.95/346-5
Set in the underground SM world, Caldwell takes you on a journey of discovery—where men initiate one another into the secrets of the rawest sexual realm of all. And when each stud's initiation is complete, he takes his places among the masters—eager to take part in the training of another hungry soul...

STUD SHORTS
$5.95/320-1
"If anything, Caldwell's charm is more powerful, his nostalgia more poignant, the horniness he captures more sweetly, achingly acute than ever."
—Aaron Travis
A new collection of this legend's latest sex-fiction. With his customary candor, Caldwell tells all about cops, cadets, truckers, farmboys (and many more) in these dirty jewels.

TAILPIPE TRUCKER
$5.95/296-5
Trucker porn! In prose as free and unvarnished as a cross-country highway, Caldwell tells the truth about Trog and Curly—two men hot for the feeling of sweaty manflesh. Together, they pick up—and turn out—a couple of thrill-seeking punks.

SERVICE, STUD
$5.95/336-8
Another look at the gay future. The setting is the Los Angeles of a distant future. Here the all-male populace is divided between the served and the servants—guaranteeing the erotic satisfaction of all involved.

QUEERS LIKE US
$4.95/262-0
"Caldwell at his most charming." —Aaron Travis
For years the name Clay Caldwell has been synonymous with the hottest, most finely crafted gay tales available. Queers Like Us is one of his best: the story of a randy mailman's trek through a landscape of willing, available studs.

ALL-STUD
$4.95/104-7
This classic, sex-soaked tale takes place under the watchful eye of Number Ten: an omniscient figure who has decreed unabashed promiscuity as the law of his all-male land. One stud, however, takes it upon himself to challenge the social order, daring to fall in love.

CLAY CALDWELL AND AARON TRAVIS

TAG TEAM STUDS
$6.50/465-8
Thrilling tales from these two legendary eroticists. The wrestling world will never seem the same, once you've made your way through this assortment of sweaty, virile studs. But you'd better be wary—should one catch you off guard, you just might spend the rest of the night pinned to the mat....

MASQUERADE BOOKS

DEREK ADAMS

PRISONER OF DESIRE
$6.50/439-9
Scalding fiction from one of Badboy's most popular authors. The creator of horny P.I. Miles Diamond returns with this volume bursting with red-blooded, sweat-soaked excursions through the modern gay libido.

THE MARK OF THE WOLF
$5.95/361-9
The past comes back to haunt one well-off stud, whose unslakeable thirsts lead him into the arms of many men—and the midst of a perilous mystery.

MY DOUBLE LIFE
$5.95/314-7
Every man leads a double life, dividing his hours between the mundanities of the day and the outrageous pursuits of the night. The creator of sexy P.I. Miles Diamond shines a little light on the wicked things men do when no one's looking.

HEAT WAVE
$4.95/159-4
"His body was draped in baggy clothes, but there was hardly any doubt that they covered anything less than perfection.... His slacks were cinched tight around a narrow waist, and the rise of flesh pushing against the thin fabric promised a firm, melon-shaped ass...."

MILES DIAMOND AND THE DEMON OF DEATH
$4.95/251-5
Derek Adams' gay gumshoe returns for further adventures. Miles always finds himself in the stickiest situations—with any stud whose path he crosses! His adventures with "The Demon of Death" promise another carnal carnival.

THE ADVENTURES OF MILES DIAMOND
$4.95/118-7
Derek Adams' take on the classic American archetype of the hardboiled private eye. "The Case of the Missing Twin" promises to be a most rewarding case, packed as it is with randy studs. Miles sets about uncovering all as he tracks down the elusive and delectable Daniel Travis.

KELVIN BELIELE

IF THE SHOE FITS
$4.95/223-X
An essential and winning volume of tales exploring a world where randy boys can't help but do what comes naturally—as often as possible! Sweaty male bodies grapple in pleasure, proving the old adage: if the shoe fits, one might as well slip right in....

JAMES MEDLEY

THE REVOLUTIONARY & OTHER STORIES
$6.50/417-8
Billy, the son of the station chief of the American Embassy in Guatemala, is kidnapped and held for ransom. Frightened at first, Billy gradually develops an unimaginably close relationship with Juan, the revolutionary assigned to guard him.

HUCK AND BILLY
$4.95/245-0
Young love is always the sweetest, always the most sorrowful. Young lust, on the other hand, knows no bounds—and is often the hottest of one's life! Huck and Billy explore the desires that course through their young male bodies, determined to plumb the lusty depths of passion.

FLEDERMAUS

FLEDERFICTION:
STORIES OF MEN AND TORTURE
$5.95/355-4
Fifteen blistering paeans to men and their suffering. Fledermaus unleashes his most thrilling tales of punishment in this special volume designed with Badboy readers in mind.

VICTOR TERRY

MASTERS
$6.50/418-6
A powerhouse volume of boot-wearing, whip-wielding, bone-crunching bruisers who've got what it takes to make a grown man grovel. Between these covers lurk the most demanding of men—the imperious few to whom so many humbly offer themselves....

SM/SD
$6.50/406-2
Set around a South Dakota town called Prairie, these tales offer compelling evidence that the real rough stuff can still be found where men roam free of the restraints of "polite" society—and take what they want despite all rules.

WHiPs
$4.95/254-X
Cruising for a hot man? You'd better be, because one way or another, these WHiPs—officers of the Wyoming Highway Patrol—are gonna pull you over for a little impromptu interrogation....

MAX EXANDER

DEEDS OF THE NIGHT:
TALES OF EROS AND PASSION
$5.95/348-1
MAXimum porn! Exander's a writer who's seen it all—and is more than happy to describe every inch of it in pulsating detail. A whirlwind tour of the hypermasculine libido.

LEATHERSEX
$4.95/210-8
Hard-hitting tales from merciless Max Exander. This time he focuses on the leatherclad lust that draws together only the most willing and talented of tops and bottoms—for an all-out orgy of limitless surrender and control....

MANSEX
$4.95/160-8
"Mark was the classic leatherman: a huge, dark stud in chaps, with a big black moustache, hairy chest and enormous muscles. Exactly the kind of men Todd liked—strong, hunky, masculine, ready to take control...."

MASQUERADE BOOKS

TOM CAFFREY

TALES FROM THE MEN'S ROOM
$5.95/364-3

From shameless cops on the beat to shy studs on stage, Caffrey explores male lust at its most elemental and arousing. And if there's a lesson to be learned, it's that the Men's Room is less a place than a state of mind—one that every man finds himself in, day after day....

HITTING HOME
$4.95/222-1

Titillating and compelling, the stories in *Hitting Home* make a strong case for there being only one thing on a man's mind.

TORSTEN BARRING

GUY TRAYNOR
$6.50/414-3

Some call Guy Traynor a theatrical genius; others say he was a madman. All anyone knows for certain is that his productions were the result of blood, sweat and tears. Never have artists suffered so much for their craft!

PRISONERS OF TORQUEMADA
$5.95/252-3

Another volume sure to push you over the edge. How cruel is the "therapy" practiced at Casa Torquemada? Barring is just the writer to evoke such steamy sexual malevolence.

SHADOWMAN
$4.95/178-0

From spoiled Southern aristocrats to randy youths sowing wild oats at the local picture show, Barring's imagination works overtime in these vignettes of homolust—past, present and future.

PETER THORNWELL
$4.95/149-7

Follow the exploits of Peter Thornwell as he goes from misspent youth to scandalous stardom, all thanks to an insatiable libido and love for the lash.

THE SWITCH
$4.95/3061-X

Sometimes a man needs a good whipping, and *The Switch* certainly makes a case! Packed with hot studs and unrelenting passions.

BERT McKENZIE

FRINGE BENEFITS
$5.95/354-6

From the pen of a widely published short story writer comes a volume of highly immodest tales. Not afraid of getting down and dirty, McKenzie produces some of today's most visceral sextales.

SONNY FORD

REUNION IN FLORENCE
$4.95/3070-9

Follow Adrian and Tristan on a sexual odyssey that takes in all ports known to ancient man. From lustful turks to insatiable Mamluks, these two have much more than their hands full!

ROGER HARMAN

FIRST PERSON
$4.95/179-9

A highly personal collection. Each story takes the form of a confessional—told by men who've got plenty to confess! From the "first time ever" to firsts of different kinds, *First Person* tells truths too hot to be purely fiction.

J. A. GUERRA, ED.

SLOW BURN
$4.95/3042-3

Welcome to the Body Shoppe! Torsos get lean and hard, pecs widen, and stomachs ripple in these sexy stories of the power and perils of physical perfection.

DAVE KINNICK

SORRY I ASKED
$4.95/3090-3

Unexpurgated interviews with gay porn's rank and file. Get personal with the men behind (and under) the "stars," and discover the hot truth about the porn business.

SEAN MARTIN

SCRAPBOOK
$4.95/224-8

From the creator of Doc and Raider comes this hot collection of life's horniest moments—all involving studs sure to set your pulse racing! A brilliantly sexy volume.

CARO SOLES & STAN TAL, EDITORS

BIZARRE DREAMS
$4.95/187-X

An anthology of stirring voices dedicated to exploring the dark side of human fantasy. *Bizarre Dreams* brings together the most talented practitioners of "dark fantasy," the most forbidden sexual realm of all.

CHRISTOPHER MORGAN

STEAM GAUGE
$6.50/473-9

This volume abounds in manly men doing what they do best—to, with, or for any hot stud who crosses their paths. Frequently published to acclaim in the gay press, Christopher Morgan puts a fresh, contemporary spin on the very oldest of urges.

THE SPORTSMEN
$5.95/385-6

A collection of super-hot stories dedicated to the all-American athlete. Here are enough tales of carnal grand slams, sexy interceptions and highly personal bests to satisfy the hungers of the most ardent sports fan. These writers know just the type of guys that make up every red-blooded male's starting line-up....

MUSCLE BOUND
$4.95/3028-8

In the New York City bodybuilding scene, country boy Tommy joins forces with sexy Will Rodriguez in a battle of wits and biceps at the hottest gym in town, where the weak are bound and crushed by iron-pumping gods.

MASQUERADE BOOKS

MICHAEL LOWENTHAL, ED.
THE BADBOY EROTIC LIBRARY VOLUME I
$4.95/190-X
Excerpts from *A Secret Life, Imre, Sins of the Cities of the Plain, Teleny* and others demonstrate the uncanny gift for portraying sex between men that led to many of these titles being banned upon publication.
THE BADBOY EROTIC LIBRARY VOLUME II
$4.95/211-6
This time, selections are taken from *Mike and Me* and *Muscle Bound, Men at Work, Badboy Fantasies,* and *Slowburn.*

ERIC BOYD
MIKE AND ME
$5.95/419-4
Mike joined the gym squad to bulk up on muscle. Little did he know he'd be turning on every sexy muscle jock in Minnesota! Hard bodies collide in a series of workouts designed to generate a whole lot more than rips and cuts.
MIKE AND THE MARINES
$6.50/497-6
Mike takes on America's most elite corps of studs—running into more than a few good men! Join in on the never-ending sexual escapades of this singularly lustful platoon!

ANONYMOUS
A SECRET LIFE
$4.95/3017-2
Meet Master Charles: only eighteen, and quite innocent, until his arrival at the Sir Percival's Royal Academy, where the daily lessons are supplemented with a crash course in pure, sweet sexual heat!
SINS OF THE CITIES OF THE PLAIN
$5.95/322-8
indulge yourself in the scorching memoirs of young man-about-town Jack Saul. With his shocking dalliances with the lords and "ladies" of British high society, Jack's positively sinful escapades grow wilder with every chapter!
IMRE
$4.95/3019-9
What dark secrets, what fiery passions lay hidden behind strikingly beautiful Lieutenant Imre's emerald eyes? An extraordinary lost classic of fantasy, obsession, gay erotic desire, and romance in a small European town on the eve of WWI.
TELENY
$4.95/3020-2
Often attributed to Oscar Wilde. A yung man dedicates himself to a succession of forbidden pleasures, but instead finds love and tragedy when he becomes embroiled in a cult devoted to fulfilling only the very darkest of fantasies.

HARD CANDY

KEVIN KILLIAN
ARCTIC SUMMER
$6.95/514-X
Acclaimed author Kevin Killian's latest novel examines the many secrets lying beneath the placid exterior of America in the '50s. With the story of Liam Reilly—a young gay man of considerable means and numerous secrets—Killian exposes the contradictions of the American Dream.

STAN LEVENTHAL
BARBIE IN BONDAGE
$6.95/415-1
Widely regarded as one of the most clear-eyed interpreters of big city gay male life, Leventhal here provides a series of explorations of love and desire between men.
SKYDIVING ON CHRISTOPHER STREET
$6.95/287-6
"Positively addictive."   —Dennis Cooper
Aside from a hateful job, a hateful apartment, a hateful world and an increasingly hateful lover, life seems, well, all right for the protagonist of Stan Leventhal's latest novel. Having already lost most of his friends to AIDS, how could things get any worse? An insightful tale of contemporary urban gay life.

PATRICK MOORE
IOWA
$6.95/423-2
"Moore is the Tennessee Williams of the nineties—profound intimacy freed in a compelling narrative."
                    —Karen Finley
"Fresh and shiny and relevant to our time. *Iowa* is full of terrific characters etched in acid-sharp prose, soaked through with just enough ambivalence to make it thoroughly romantic."   —Felice Picano
A stunning novel about one gay man's journey into adulthood, and the roads that bring him home again.

PAUL T. ROGERS
SAUL'S BOOK
$7.95/462-3
Winner of the Editors' Book Award
"Exudes an almost narcotic power.... A masterpiece."   —*Village Voice Literary Supplement*
"A first novel of considerable power... Sinbad the Sailor, thanks to the sympathetic imagination of Paul T. Rogers, speaks to us all." —*New York Times Book Review*
The story of a Times Square hustler called Sinbad the Sailor and Saul, a brilliant, self-destructive, alcoholic, thoroughly dominating character who may be the only love Sinbad will ever know. A stunning first novel—and an eerie epitaph for the author, who died tragically in the very milieu he portrayed in his fiction.

MASQUERADE BOOKS

WALTER R. HOLLAND
THE MARCH
$6.95/429-1
A moving testament to the power of friendship during even the worst of times. Beginning on a hot summer night in 1980, The March revolves around a circle of young gay men, and the many others their lives touch. Over time, each character changes in unexpected ways; lives and loves come together and fall apart, as society itself is horribly altered by the onslaught of AIDS.

RED JORDAN AROBATEAU
LUCY AND MICKEY
$6.95/311-2
The story of Mickey—an uncompromising butch—and her long affair with Lucy, the femme she loves.
"A necessary reminder to all who blissfully—some may say ignorantly—ride the wave of lesbian chic into the mainstream."
—Heather Findlay
DIRTY PICTURES
$5.95/345-7
"Red Jordan Arobateau is the Thomas Wolfe of lesbian literature… She's a natural—raw talent that is seething, passionate, hard, remarkable."
—Lillian Faderman, editor of Chloe Plus Olivia
Dirty Pictures is the story of a lonely butch tending bar—and the femme she finally calls her own.

DONALD VINING
A GAY DIARY
$8.95/451-8
Donald Vining's Diary portrays a long-vanished age and the lifestyle of a gay generation all too frequently forgotten.
"A Gay Diary is, unquestionably, the richest historical document of gay male life in the United States that I have ever encountered…. It illuminates a critical period in gay male American history."
—Body Politic

LARS EIGHNER
GAY COSMOS
$6.95/236-1
A title sure to appeal not only to Eighner's gay fans, but the many converts who first encountered his moving nonfiction work. Praised by the press, Gay Cosmos is an important contribution to the area of Gay and Lesbian Studies.

FELICE PICANO
THE LURE
$6.95/398-8
"The subject matter, plus the authenticity of Picano's research are, combined, explosive. Felice Picano is one hell of a writer."
—Stephen King
After witnessing a brutal murder, Noel is recruited by the police, to assist as a lure for the killer. Undercover, he moves deep into the freneticism of Manhattan's gay highlife—where he gradually becomes aware of the darker forces at work in his life. In addition to the mystery behind his mission, he begins to recognize changes: in his relationships with the men around him, in himself…

AMBIDEXTROUS
$6.95/275-2
"Makes us remember what it feels like to be a child…"
—The Advocate
Picano's first "memoir in the form of a novel" tells all: home life, school face-offs, the ingenuous sophistications of his first sexual steps. In three years' time, he's had his first gay fling—and is on his way to becoming the widely praised writer he is today.
MEN WHO LOVED ME
$6.95/274-4
"Zesty…spiked with adventure and romance…a distinguished and humorous portrait of a vanished age."
—Publishers Weekly
In 1966, Picano abandoned New York, determined to find true love in Europe. Upon returning, he plunges into the city's thriving gay community of the 1970s.

WILLIAM TALSMAN
THE GAUDY IMAGE
$6.95/263-9
"To read The Gaudy Image now…it is to see firsthand the very issues of identity and positionality with which gay men were struggling in the decades before Stonewall. For what Talsman is dealing with…is the very question of how we conceive ourselves gay."
—from the introduction by Michael Bronski

ROSEBUD

THE ROSEBUD READER
$5.95/319-8
Rosebud has contributed greatly to the burgeoning genre of lesbian erotica—to the point that our authors are among the hottest and most closely watched names in lesbian and gay publishing. Here are the finest moments from Rosebud's contemporary classics.

LESLIE CAMERON
WHISPER OF FANS
$6.50/542-5
"Just looking into her eyes, she felt that she knew a lot about this woman. She could see strength, boldness, a fresh sense of aliveness that rocked her to the core. In turn she felt open, revealed under the woman's gaze—all her secrets already told. No need of shame or artifice…." A fresh tale of passion between women, from one of lesbian erotica's up-and-coming authors.

RACHEL PEREZ
ODD WOMEN
$6.50/526-3
These women are sexy, smart, tough—some even say odd. But who cares, when their combined ass-ets are so sweet! An assortment of Sapphic sirens proves once and for all that comely ladies come best in pairs. One of our best-selling girl/girl titles.

MASQUERADE BOOKS

RANDY TUROFF

LUST NEVER SLEEPS
$6.50/475-5
A rich volume of highly erotic, powerfully real fiction from the editor of *Lesbian Words*. Randy Turoff depicts a circle of modern women connected through the bonds of love, friendship, ambition, and lust with accuracy and compassion. Moving, tough, yet undeniably true, Turoff's stories create a stirring portrait of contemporary lesbian life.

RED JORDAN AROBATEAU

ROUGH TRADE
$6.50/470-4
Famous for her unflinching portrayal of lower-class dyke life and love, Arobateau outdoes herself with these tales of butch/femme affairs and unrelenting passions. Unapologetic and distinctly non-homogenized, *Rough Trade* is a must for all fans of challenging lesbian literature.

BOYS NIGHT OUT
$6.50/463-1
A *Red*-hot volume of short fiction from this lesbian literary sensation. As always, Arobateau takes a good hard look at the lives of everyday women, noting well the struggles and triumphs each woman experiences.

ALISON TYLER

VENUS ONLINE
$6.50/521-2
Lovely Alexa spends her days in a boring bank job, saving her energies for her nocturnal pursuits. At night, Alexa goes online, living out virtual adventures that become more real with each session. Soon Alexa—aka Venus—feels her erotic imagination growing beyond anything she could have imagined.

DARK ROOM: AN ONLINE ADVENTURE
$6.50/455-0
Dani, a successful photographer, can't bring herself to face the death of her lover, Kate. Determined to keep the memory of her lover alive, Dani goes online under Kate's screen alias—and begins to uncover the truth behind the crime that has torn her world apart.

BLUE SKY SIDEWAYS & OTHER STORIES
$6.50/394-5
A variety of women, and their many breathtaking experiences with lovers, friends—and even the occasional sexy stranger. From blossoming young beauties to fearless vixens, Tyler finds the sexy pleasures of everyday life.

DIAL "L" FOR LOVELESS
$5.95/386-4
Meet Katrina Loveless—a private eye talented enough to give Sam Spade a run for his money. In her first case, Katrina investigates a murder implicating a host of society's darlings. Loveless untangles the mess—while working herself into a variety of highly compromising knots with the many lovelies who cross her path!

THE VIRGIN

$5.95/379-1
Veronica answers a personal ad in the "Women Seeking Women" category—and discovers a whole sensual world she never knew existed! And she never dreamed she'd be prized as a virgin all over again, by someone who would deflower her with a passion no man could ever show....

K. T. BUTLER

TOOLS OF THE TRADE
$5.95/420-8
A sparkling mix of lesbian erotica and humor. An encounter with ice cream, cappuccino and chocolate cake; an affair with a complete stranger; a pair of faulty handcuffs; and love on a drafting table. Seventeen tales.

LOVECHILD

GAG
$5.95/369-4
From New York's poetry scene comes this explosive volume of work from one of the bravest, most cutting young writers you'll ever encounter. The poems in *Gag* take on American hypocrisy with uncommon energy, and announce Lovechild as a writer of unforgettable rage.

ELIZABETH OLIVER

PAGAN DREAMS
$5.95/295-7
Cassidy and Samantha plan a vacation at a secluded bed-and-breakfast, hoping for a little personal time alone. Their hostess, however, has different plans. The lovers are plunged into a world of dungeons and pagan rites, as Anastasia steals Samantha for her own.

SUSAN ANDERS

CITY OF WOMEN
$5.95/375-9
Stories dedicated to women and the passions that draw them together. Designed strictly for the sensual pleasure of women, these tales are set to ignite flames of passion from coast to coast.

PINK CHAMPAGNE
$5.95/282-5
Tasty, torrid tales of butch/femme couplings. Tough as nails or soft as silk, these women seek out their antitheses, intent on working out the details of their own personal theory of difference.

ANONYMOUS

LAVENDER ROSE
$4.95/208-6
A thrilling collection of some of the earliest lesbian writings. From the writings of Sappho, Queen of the island Lesbos, to the turn-of-the-century *Black Book of Lesbianism*; from *Tips to Maidens* to *Crimson Hairs*, a recent lesbian saga—here are the great but little-known lesbian writings and revelations.

MASQUERADE BOOKS

A CIRCLE OF FRIENDS
$4.95/250-7
The story of a remarkable group of women. The women pair off to explore all the possibilities of lesbian passion, until finally it seems that there is nothing—and no one—they have not dabbled in.

BAD HABITS
$5.95/446-1
What does one do with a poorly trained slave? Break her of her bad habits, of course! The story of the ultimate finishing school, *Bad Habits* was an immediate favorite with women nationwide, and remains an incredible bestseller.
"Talk about passing the wet test!... If you like hot, lesbian erotica, run—don't walk—and pick up a copy of *Bad Habits.*"   —*Lambda Book Report*

ANNABELLE BARKER
MOROCCO
$6.50/541-7
A luscious young woman stands to inherit a fortune—if she can only withstand the ministrations of her cruel guardian until her twentieth birthday. With two months left, Lila makes a bold bid for freedom, only to find that liberty has its own excruciating and delicious price....

A.L. REINE
DISTANT LOVE & OTHER STORIES
$4.95/3056-3
In the title story, Leah Michaels and her lover, Ranelle, have had four years of blissful, smoldering passion together. When Ranelle is out of town, Leah records an audio "Valentine:" a cassette filled with erotic reminiscences....

A RICHARD KASAK BOOK

SIMON LEVAY
ALBRICK'S GOLD
$20.95/518-2/Hardcover
From the man behind the controversial "gay brain" studies comes a chilling tale of medical experimentation run amok. LeVay—a lightning rod for controversy since the publication of *The Sexual Brain*—has fashioned a classic medical thriller from today's cutting-edge science.

SHAR REDNOUR, EDITOR
VIRGIN TERRITORY 2
$12.95/506-9
The follow-up volume to the groundbreaking *Virgin Territory* includes many essays inspired by the earlier volume's success. Focusing on the many "firsts" of a woman's erotic life, *Virgin Territory 2* provides one of the sole outlets for serious discussion of the myriad possibilities available to and chosen by many contemporary lesbians. Some of today's best writers 'fess up about the thrill of the first time.

VIRGIN TERRITORY
$12.95/457-7
An anthology of writing by women about their first-time erotic experiences with other women. From the ecstasies of awakening dykes to the sometimes awkward pleasures of sexual experimentation on the edge, each of these true stories reveals a different, radical perspective on one of the most traditional subjects around: virginity.

MICHAEL FORD, EDITOR
ONCE UPON A TIME:
EROTIC FAIRY TALES FOR WOMEN
$12.95/449-6
How relevant to contemporary lesbians are the lessons of these age-old tales? Some of the biggest names in contemporary lesbian literature retell their favorite fairy tales, adding their own surprising—and sexy—twists. *Once Upon a Time* is sure to be one of contemporary lesbian literature's classic collections.

HAPPILY EVER AFTER:
EROTIC FAIRY TALES FOR MEN
$12.95/450-X
A hefty volume of bedtime stories Mother Goose never thought to write down. Adapting some of childhood's most beloved tales for the adult gay reader, the contributors to *Happily Ever After* dig up the subtext of these hitherto "innocent" diversions—adding some surprises of their own along the way. Some of contemporary gay literature's biggest names are included in this special volume.

MICHAEL BRONSKI, EDITOR
TAKING LIBERTIES: GAY MEN'S ESSAYS
ON POLITICS, CULTURE AND SEX
$12.95/456-9
"Offers undeniable proof of a heady, sophisticated, diverse new culture of gay intellectual debate. I cannot recommend it too highly."—Christopher Bram
A collection of some of the most divergent views on the state of contemporary gay male culture published in recent years. Michael Bronski here presents some of the community's foremost essayists weighing in on such slippery topics as outing, masculine identity, pornography, the pedophile movement, political strategy—and much more.

FLASHPOINT: GAY MALE SEXUAL WRITING
$12.95/424-0
A collection of some of the most provocative testaments to gay eros. Michael Bronski presents over twenty of the genre's best writers, exploring areas such as Enlightenment, True Life Adventures and more. Accompanied by Bronski's insightful analysis, each story illustrates the many approaches to sexuality used by today's gay writers. *Flashpoint* is sure to be one of the most talked about and influential volumes ever dedicated to the exploration of gay sexuality. Includes work by Christopher Bram, Samuel Delany, Aaron Travis, and many others.

HEATHER FINDLAY, EDITOR
A MOVEMENT OF EROS:
25 YEARS OF LESBIAN EROTICA
$12.95/421-6

One of the most scintillating overviews of lesbian erotic writing ever published. Heather Findlay has assembled a roster of stellar talents, each represented by their best work. Tracing the course of the genre from its pre-Stonewall roots to its current renaissance, Findlay examines each piece, placing it within the context of lesbian community and politics.

CHARLES HENRI FORD & PARKER TYLER
THE YOUNG AND EVIL
$12.95/431-3

"*The Young and Evil* creates [its] generation as *This Side of Paradise* by Fitzgerald created his generation." —Gertrude Stein

Originally published in 1933, *The Young and Evil* was an immediate sensation due to its unprecedented portrayal of young gay artists living in New York's notorious Greenwich Village. From drag balls to bohemian flats, these characters followed love and art wherever it led them—with a frankness that had the novel banned for many years.

BARRY HOFFMAN, EDITOR
THE BEST OF GAUNTLET
$12.95/202-7

Gauntlet has, with its semi-annual issues, always publishing the widest possible range of opinions, in the interest of challenging public opinion. The most provocative articles have been gathered by editor-in-chief Barry Hoffman, to make *The Best of Gauntlet* a riveting exploration of American society's limits.

MICHAEL ROWE
WRITING BELOW THE BELT:
CONVERSATIONS WITH EROTIC AUTHORS
$19.95/363-5

"An in-depth and enlightening tour of society's love/hate relationship with sex, morality, and censorship." —James White Review

Journalist Michael Rowe interviewed the best erotic writers and presents the collected wisdom in *Writing Below the Belt*. Rowe speaks frankly with cult favorites such as Pat Califia, crossover success stories like John Preston, and up-and-comers Michael Lowenthal and Will Leber. A chronicle of the insights of this genre's most renowned practitioners.

LARRY TOWNSEND
ASK LARRY
$12.95/289-2

One of the leather community's most respected scribes here presents the best of his advice to leathermen. Starting just before the onslaught of AIDS, Townsend wrote the "Leather Notebook" column for *Drummer* magazine. Now, readers can avail themselves of Townsend's collected wisdom, as well as the author's contemporary commentary—a careful consideration of the way life has changed in the AIDS era. No man worth his leathers can afford to miss this volume of sage advice.

MICHAEL LASSELL
THE HARD WAY
$12.95/231-0

"Lassell is a master of the necessary word. In an age of tepid and whining verse, his bawdy and bittersweet songs are like a plunge in cold champagne." —Paul Monette

The first collection of renowned gay writer Michael Lassell's poetry, fiction and essays. As much a chronicle of post-Stonewall gay life as a compendium of a remarkable writer's work.

AMARANTHA KNIGHT, EDITOR
LOVE BITES
$12.95/234-5

A volume of tales dedicated to legend's sexiest demon—the Vampire. Not only the finest collection of erotic horror available—but a virtual who's who of promising new talent. A must-read for fans of both the horror and erotic genres.

RANDY TUROFF, EDITOR
LESBIAN WORDS: STATE OF THE ART
$10.95/340-6

"This is a terrific book that should be on every thinking lesbian's bookshelf." —Nisa Donnelly

One of the widest assortments of lesbian nonfiction writing in one revealing volume. Dorothy Allison, Jewelle Gomez, Judy Grahn, Eileen Myles, Robin Podolsky and many others are represented by some of their best work, looking at not only the current fashionability the media has brought to the lesbian "image," but considerations of the lesbian past via historical inquiry and personal recollections. A must for all interested in the state of the lesbian community.

ASSOTTO SAINT
SPELLS OF A VOODOO DOLL
$12.95/393-7

"Angelic and brazen." —Jewelle Gomez

A fierce, spellbinding collection of the poetry, lyrics, essays and performance texts of Assotto Saint—one of the most important voices in the renaissance of black gay writing. Saint, aka Yves François Lubin, was the editor of two seminal anthologies: 1991 Lambda Literary Book Award winner, *The Road Before Us: 100 Gay Black Poets* and *Here to Dare: 10 Gay Black Poets*. He was also the author of two books of poetry, *Stations* and *Wishing for Wings*.

WILLIAM CARNEY
THE REAL THING
$10.95/280-9

"Carney gives us a good look at the mores and lifestyle of the first generation of gay leathermen. A chilling mystery/romance novel as well." —Pat Califia

With a new introduction by Michael Bronski. First published in 1968, this uncompromising story of American leathermen received instant acclaim. Out of print even while its legend grew, *The Real Thing* returns from exile more than twenty-five years after its initial release, detailing the attitudes and practices of an earlier generation of leathermen.

MASQUERADE BOOKS

EURYDICE

F/32
$10.95/350-3

"It's wonderful to see a woman...celebrating her body and her sexuality by creating a fabulous and funny tale."
—Kathy Acker

With the story of Ela, Eurydice won the National Fiction competition sponsored by Fiction Collective Two and Illinois State University. A funny, disturbing quest for unity, *F/32* prompted Frederic Tuten to proclaim "almost any page... redeems us from the anemic writing and banalities we have endured in the past decade...."

CHEA VILLANUEVA

JESSIE'S SONG
$9.95/235-3

"It conjures up the strobe-light confusion and excitement of urban dyke life.... Read about these dykes and you'll love them."
—Rebecca Ripley

Based largely upon her own experience, Villanueva's work is remarkable for its frankness, and delightful in its iconoclasm. Unconcerned with political correctness, this writer has helped expand the boundaries of "serious" lesbian writing.

SAMUEL R. DELANY
THE MOTION OF LIGHT IN WATER
$12.95/133-0

"A very moving, intensely fascinating literary biography from an extraordinary writer....The artist as a young man and a memorable picture of an age."—William Gibson

Award-winning author Samuel R. Delany's autobiography covers the early years of one of science fiction's most important voices. *The Motion of Light in Water* follows Delany from his early marriage to the poet Marilyn Hacker, through the publication of his first, groundbreaking work.

THE MAD MAN
$23.95/193-4/hardcover

Delany's fascinating examination of human desire. For his thesis, graduate student John Marr researches the life and work of the brilliant Timothy Hasler: a philosopher whose career was cut tragically short over a decade earlier. Marr soon begins to believe that Hasler's death might hold some key to his own life as a gay man in the age of AIDS.

"What Delany has done here is take the ideas of the Marquis de Sade one step further, by filtering extreme and obsessive sexual behavior through the sieve of post-modern experience...."
—Lambda Book Report

"Delany develops an insightful dichotomy between [his protagonist's] two worlds: the one of cerebral philosophy and dry academia, the other of heedless, 'impersonal' obsessive sexual extremism. When these worlds finally collide ... the novel achieves a surprisingly satisfying resolution...."
—Publishers Weekly

FELICE PICANO
DRYLAND'S END
$12.95/279-5

The science fiction debut of the highly acclaimed author of *Men Who Loved Me* and *Like People in History*. Set five thousand years in the future, *Dryland's End* takes place in a fabulous techno-empire ruled by intelligent, powerful women. While the Matriarchy has ruled for over two thousand years and altered human society—But is now unraveling. Military rivalries, religious fanaticism and economic competition threaten to destroy the mighty empire.

ROBERT PATRICK
TEMPLE SLAVE
$12.95/191-8

"You must read this book." —Quentin Crisp

"This is nothing less than the secret history of the most theatrical of theaters, the most bohemian of Americans and the most knowing of queens.... *Temple Slave* is also one of the best ways to learn what it was like to be fabulous, gay, theatrical and loved in a time at once more and less dangerous to gay life than our own."
—Genre

The story of Greenwich Village and the beginnings of gay theater—told with the dazzling wit and stylistic derring-do for which Robert Patrick is justly famous.

GUILLERMO BOSCH
RAIN
$12.95/232-9

"Rain is a trip..." —Timothy Leary

An adult fairy tale, *Rain* takes place in a time when the mysteries of Eros are played out against a background of uncommon deprivation. The tale begins on the 1,537th day of drought—when one man comes to know the true depths of thirst. In a quest to sate his hunger for some knowledge of the wide world, he is taken through a series of extraordinary, unearthly encounters that promise to change not only his life, but the course of civilization around him.

LAURA ANTONIOU, EDITOR
LOOKING FOR MR. PRESTON
$23.95/288-4

Edited by Laura Antoniou, *Looking for Mr. Preston* includes work by Lars Eighner, Pat Califia, Michael Bronski, Joan Nestle, and others who contributed interviews, essays and personal reminiscences of John Preston—a man whose career spanned the gay publishing industry. Preston was the author of over twenty books, and edited many more. Ten percent of the proceeds from sale of this book will go to the AIDS Project of Southern Maine, for which Preston served as President of the Board.

MASQUERADE BOOKS

RUSS KICK
OUTPOSTS: A CATALOG OF RARE AND DISTURBING ALTERNATIVE INFORMATION
$18.95/0202-8

A huge, authoritative guide to some of the most bizarre publications available today! Rather than simply summarize the plethora of opinions crowding the American scene, Kick has tracked down and compiled reviews of work penned by political extremists, conspiracy theorists, hallucinogenic pathfinders, sexual explorers, and others. Each review is followed by ordering information for the many readers sure to want these publications for themselves. An essential reference in this age of rapidly proliferating information systems and increasingly extreme political and cultural perspectives. An indispensable guide to every book and magazine you're afraid you might have missed.

CECILIA TAN, EDITOR
SM VISIONS: THE BEST OF CIRCLET PRESS
$10.95/339-2

"Fabulous books! There's nothing else like them."
—Susie Bright,
Best American Erotica and Herotica 3

Circlet Press, devoted exclusively to the erotic science fiction and fantasy genre, is now represented by the best of its very best: *SM Visions*—sure to be one of the most thrilling and eye-opening rides through the erotic imagination ever published.

LUCY TAYLOR
UNNATURAL ACTS
$12.95/181-0

"A topnotch collection..." —Science Fiction Chronicle
Unnatural Acts plunges deep into the dark side of the psyche and brings to life a disturbing vision of erotic horror. Unrelenting angels and hungry gods play with souls and bodies in Taylor's murky cosmos: where heaven and hell are merely differences of perspective; where redemption and damnation lie behind the same shocking acts.

PAT CALIFIA
SENSUOUS MAGIC
$12.95/458-5

"*Sensuous Magic* is clear, succinct and engaging even for the reader for whom S/M isn't the sexual behavior of choice.... When she is writing about the dynamics of sex and the technical aspects of it, Califia is the Dr. Ruth of the alternative sexuality set...." —Lambda Book Report

"Pat Califia's *Sensuous Magic* is a friendly, non-threatening, helpful guide and resource... She captures the power of what it means to enter forbidden terrain, and to do so safely with someone else, and to explore the healing potential, spiritual aspects and the depth of S/M."
—Bay Area Reporter

"Don't take a dangerous trip into the unknown—buy this book and know where you're going!"
—SKIN TWO

DAVID MELTZER
THE AGENCY TRILOGY
$12.95/216-7

"...'The Agency' is clearly Meltzer's paradigm of society; a mindless machine of which we are all 'agents,' including those whom the machine supposedly serves...." —Norman Spinrad

The Agency explores issues of erotic dominance and submission with an immediacy and frankness previously unheard of in American literature, and presents a vision of an America consumed and dehumanized by a lust for power. All three volumes—*The Agency, The Agent, How Many Blocks in the Pile?*—are included in this one special volume, available only from Richard Kasak Books.

MICHAEL PERKINS
THE GOOD PARTS: AN UNCENSORED GUIDE TO LITERARY SEXUALITY
$12.95/186-1

Michael Perkins, one of America's only critics to regularly scrutinize sexual literature, presents this unprecedented survey of sex as seen/written about in the pages of over 100 major fiction and nonfiction volumes from the past twenty years.
COMING UP: THE WORLD'S BEST EROTIC WRITING
$12.95/370-8

Author and critic Michael Perkins has scoured the field of erotic writing to produce this anthology sure to challenge the limits of even the most seasoned reader. Perkins here presents the cream of the current crop.

TIM WOODWARD, EDITOR
THE BEST OF SKIN TWO
$12.95/130-6

Skin Two specializes in provocative essays by the finest writers working in the "radical sex" scene. Collected here are the articles and interviews that established the magazine's reputation. Including interviews with cult figures Tim Burton, Clive Barker and Jean Paul Gaultier.

MICHAEL LOWENTHAL, EDITOR
THE BEST OF THE BADBOYS
$12.95/233-7

The very best of the leading Badboys is collected here, in this testament to the artistry that has catapulted these "outlaw" authors to bestselling status. John Preston, Aaron Travis, Larry Townsend, and others are here represented by their most provocative writing.

CARO SOLES, EDITOR
MELTDOWN! AN ANTHOLOGY OF EROTIC SCIENCE FICTION AND DARK FANTASY FOR GAY MEN
$12.95/203-5

Meltdown! contains the very best examples of the increasingly popular sub-genre of erotic sci-fi/dark fantasy: stories meant to shock and delight, to send a shiver down the spine and start a fire down below.

MASQUERADE BOOKS

JOHN PRESTON
MY LIFE AS A PORNOGRAPHER AND OTHER INDECENT ACTS
$12.95/135-7
A collection of renowned author and social critic John Preston's essays, focusing on his work as an erotic writer and proponent of gay rights.

"...essential and enlightening... [My Life as a Pornographer] is a bridge from the sexually liberated 1970s to the more cautious 1990s, and Preston has walked much of that way as a standard-bearer to the cause for equal rights...." —Library Journal

"My Life as a Pornographer...is not pornography, but rather reflections upon the writing and production of it. In a deeply sex-phobic world, Preston has never shied away from a vision of the redemptive potential of the erotic drive. Better than perhaps anyone in our community, Preston knows how physical joy can bridge differences and make us well."
—Lambda Book Report

LARS EIGHNER
ELEMENTS OF AROUSAL
$12.95/230-2
A guideline for success with one of publishing's best kept secrets: the novice-friendly field of gay erotic writing. Eighner details his craft, providing the reader with sure advice. Because that's what Elements of Arousal is all about: the application and honing of the writer's craft, which brought Eighner fame with not only the steamy Bayou Boy, but the illuminating Travels with Lizbeth.

STAN TAL, EDITOR
BIZARRE SEX AND OTHER CRIMES OF PASSION
$12.95/213-2
From the pages of Bizarre Sex. Over twenty small masterpieces of erotic shock make this one of the year's most unexpectedly alluring anthologies. This incredible volume, edited by Stan Tal, includes such masters of erotic horror and fantasy as Edward Lee, Lucy Taylor and Nancy Kilpatrick.

MARCO VASSI
A DRIVING PASSION
$12.95/134-9
Marco Vassi was famous not only for his groundbreaking writing, but for the many lectures he gave regarding sexuality and the complex erotic philosophy he had spent much of his life working out. A Driving Passion collects the wit and insight Vassi brought to these lectures, and distills the philosophy that made him an underground sensation.

THE EROTIC COMEDIES
$12.95/136-5
Short stories designed to shock and transform attitudes about sex and sexuality, The Erotic Comedies is both entertaining and challenging—and garnered Vassi some of the most lavish praise of his career. Also includes his groundbreaking writings on the Erotic Experience.

"The comparison to [Henry] Miller is high praise indeed.... But reading Vassi's work, the analogy holds—for he shares with Miller an unabashed joy in sensuality, and a questing after experience that is the root of all great literature, erotic or otherwise.... Vassi was, by all accounts, a fearless explorer, someone who jumped headfirst into the world of sex, and wrote about what he found...."
—David L. Ulin, The Los Angeles Reader

THE SALINE SOLUTION
$12.95/180-2
"I've always read Marco's work with interest and I have the highest opinion not only of his talent but his intellectual boldness." —Norman Mailer

The story of one couple's spiritual crises during an age of extraordinary freedom. While renowned for his sexual philosophy, Vassi also experienced success in with fiction; The Saline Solution was one of the high points of his career, while still addressing the issue of sexuality.

THE STONED APOCALYPSE
$12.95/132-2
"...Marco Vassi is our champion sexual energist."
—VLS

During his lifetime, Marco Vassi was hailed as America's premier erotic writer. The Stoned Apocalypse is Vassi's autobiography, financed by his other groundbreaking erotic writing and rife with Vassi's insight into the American character and libido. One of the most vital portraits of "the 60s," this volume is a fitting testament to the writer's talents, and the sexual imagination of his generation.
"The most striking figure in present-day American e rotic literature. Alone among modern erotic writers, Vassi is working out a philosophy of sexuality."
—Michael Perkins, The Secret Record

ORDERING IS EASY

MC/VISA orders can be placed by calling our toll-free number
PHONE 800-375-2356/FAX 212-986-7355/E-MAIL masqbks@aol.com
or mail this coupon to:
MASQUERADE DIRECT
DEPT. BMMQ27 801 2ND AVE., NY, NY 10017

BUY ANY FOUR BOOKS AND CHOOSE ONE ADDITIONAL BOOK, OF EQUAL OR LESSER VALUE, AS YOUR FREE GIFT.

QTY.	TITLE	NO.	PRICE
			FREE
			FREE

WE NEVER SELL, GIVE OR TRADE ANY CUSTOMER'S NAME.

SUBTOTAL _____

POSTAGE and HANDLING _____

TOTAL _____

In the U.S., please add $1.50 for the first book and 75¢ for each additional book; in Canada, add $2.00 for the first book and $1.25 for each additional book. Foreign countries: add $4.00 for the first book and $2.00 for each additional book. No C.O.D. orders. Please make all checks payable to Masquerade Books. Payable in U.S. currency only. New York state residents add 8.25% sales tax. Please allow 4-6 weeks for delivery.

NAME _____

ADDRESS _____

CITY _____ STATE _____ ZIP _____

TEL( ) _____

E-MAIL _____

PAYMENT: ☐ CHECK   ☐ MONEY ORDER   ☐ VISA   ☐ MC

CARD NO _____ EXP. DATE _____

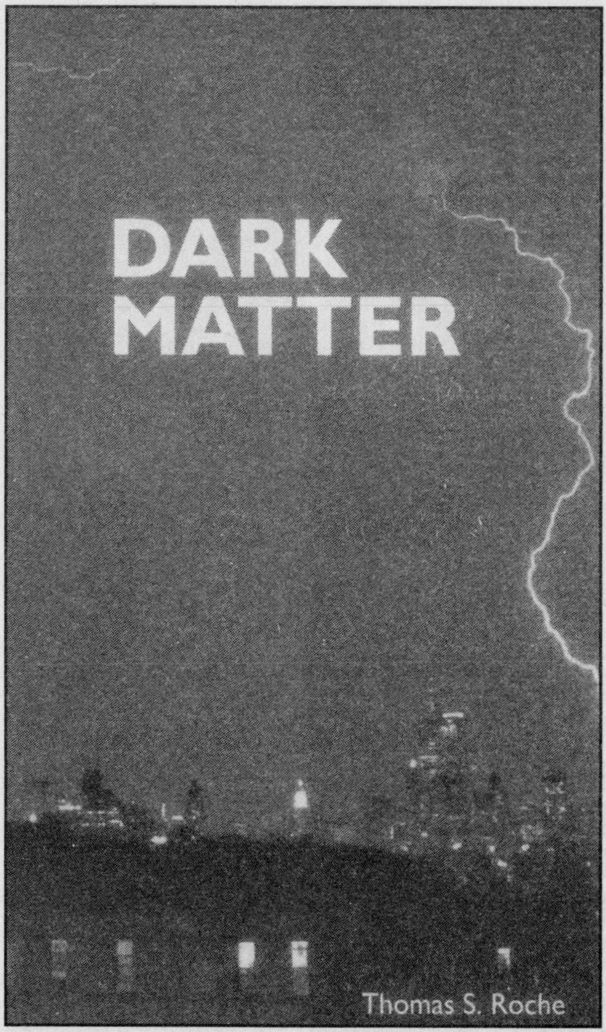
DARK
MATTER
Thomas S. Roche

PRIVATE PLEASURES

DON WINSLOW

MASQUERADE

THE ARCHITECTURE OF DESIRE

M. ORLANDO

"It wraps you in lush sensuality, then carries you along on an exhilarating ride crackling with sexual heat. Sophisticated erotica at its very best."

—Don Winslow

CINDERELLA

"A wildly decadent and completely original erotic fariy tale."
—Dr. Pascale Solange

ANONYMOUS

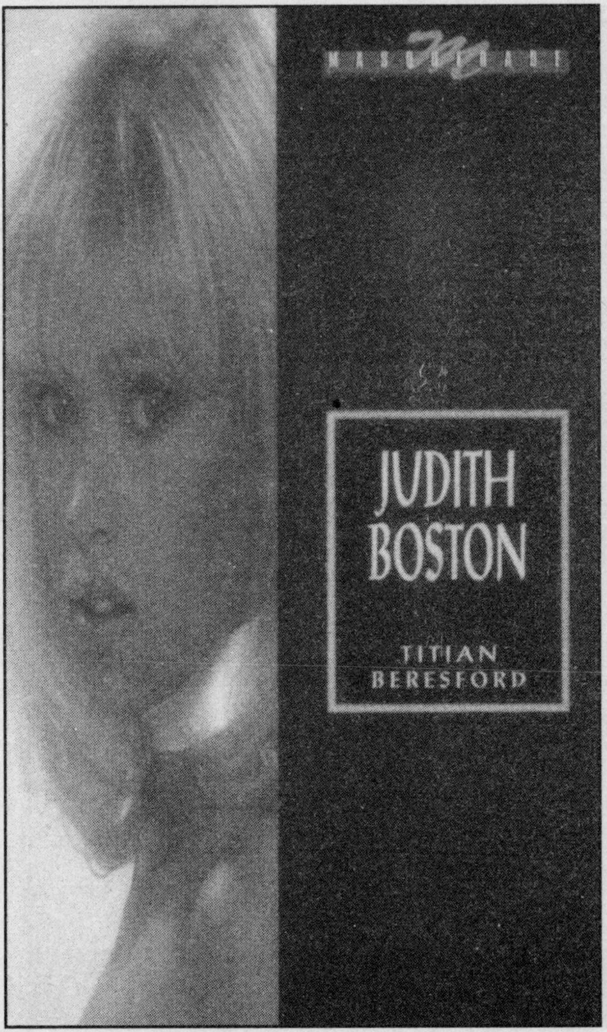
JUDITH
BOSTON
TITIAN
BERESFORD

MASQUERADE

KAMA HOURI & DEVA DASI

ATAULLAH
MARDAAN

Gynecocracy

VISCOUNT LADYWOOD

Three Volumes in One

MASQUERADE

THE PRISONER

PAUL LITTLE

ARCTIC SUMMER

KEVIN KILLIAN

SLAVE ISLAND

He created a
secret civilization
where females
served as love
slaves

$4.95 (CANADA $5.95) · MASQUERADE BOOKS

ANONYMOUS

M A S Q U E R A D E

The Many Pleasures of
IRONWOOD

D O N   W I N S L O W

MASQUERADE
SCIENCE FICTION

TARNSMAN OF GOR

INTRODUCTION BY CECILIA TAN

JOHN NORMAN

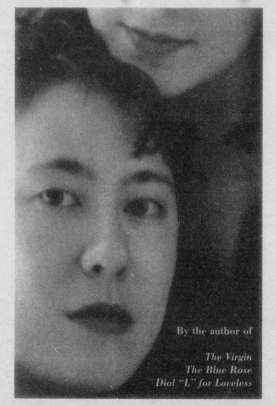

Blue Sky Sideways
& other stories

By the author of

The Virgin
The Blue Rose
Dial "L" for Loveless

A L I S O N   T Y L E R

SCIENCE FICTION

NOMADS
OF GOR

JOHN NORMAN